Annie's Quilted Mysteries™

CELTIC CHAINS

DONNA KELLY

Annie's®
AnniesFiction.com

Library of Congress-in-Publication Data
Celtic Chains / by Donna Kelly
p. cm.
I. Title
                              2014915169

AnniesFiction.com
(800) 282-6643
Annie's Quilted Mysteries
Series Creator: Shari Lohner
Series Editors: Shari Lohner, Janice Tate, and Ken Tate
Cover Illustration © iStockphoto LP

10 11 12 13 14 | Printed in China | 9 8 7 6 5 4 3

Death leaves a heartache no one can heal; love leaves a memory no one can steal.

—Irish proverb

one

"Your mom looks like she just won the lottery." Emma Cotton stepped back from the window of Cotton & Grace, the quilt design and restoration shop she owned with her best friend, Kelly Grace. Kelly watched a grinning Maeve Quigley motor across the street as fast as her short legs would carry her. "She has a death grip on that piece of paper she's waving."

"Uh-oh, I know that look," Kelly said as her mother stepped on the curb and crossed the sidewalk. "She has something up her sleeve."

They backed away from the door as Maeve tugged on the handle and pulled it open.

"And people say the luck of the Irish is a myth." Maeve breezed into the showroom and stuck the paper under Kelly's nose. "Well, here's proof it exists." Green eyes sparkled beneath Maeve's short, fiery hair, which looked even more blazing than usual under the sunbeams streaming through the windows.

"Oh, do tell!" Emma said, gesturing to the cluster of comfy chairs in the design alcove.

"This is an email from my cousin, Eamon Egan, my Uncle Connor's son. Kelly, you remember me telling you about my dad's brother, Connor, don't you? Eamon runs the family pub on the Connemara coast of Ireland." Maeve sat, then handed the paper to Kelly. "Guess who has a textile shop in the same town?"

Kelly's eyes scanned the paper. "Liam Gallagher. Unbelievable."

"Indeed," said Emma, a silent groan echoing in her head. The investigation into the death of their childhood friend Rose Peterson had already taken them all over the United States, not to mention across the pond to England. Lately, their sleuthing had resulted in more time out of the shop than in it, and flying made Emma edgy. Was she ready for another transatlantic flight?

Kelly passed the printed email to Emma. "I know what you're thinking. You'd rather not fly so far again so soon. But you did really well on the plane to England. Maybe if you take a light sedative like you did on that flight, you'll be able to sleep six hours again." She glanced at her mother and took a deep breath. "This time we'll have Mom's family—an entire clan of Egans—to help us while we're in Ireland."

"That's true," said Emma, her eyes on the email. "We can definitely use all the support we can get. It's just that planes—"

"Are the safest way to travel, even though it drives you nuts," Kelly finished for her. "We have no choice but to go to Ireland. We've ruled out all of the other male suspects."

This was true, and Emma was forced to admit Kelly was right. They couldn't stop now, even if it meant a seven-hour flight in cramped quarters. After fifteen years of wondering what had happened to Rose the night before she was found dead at the bottom of the stairs at Hawthorne College, they were finally close to solving the mystery. They'd ruled out nine of the twelve students who'd been in Rose's Visual Studies in Textile Design class by collecting DNA samples, having them analyzed at a private lab, and comparing the results to the two skin scrapings—one male, one female—discovered under Rose's fingernails. They only had three more to go. With Liam Gallagher being the only man untested, he was likely to be a positive match.

"We've come a long way since Dottie Faye discovered that ugly twelve-block quilt, haven't we?" Emma said, handing the paper back to Maeve.

Dottie Faye Sinclair, Emma's flamboyant aunt, had found the quilt tucked away in Emma's closet. The quilt had provided a suspect list for Rose's murder—even though the police in Mystic Harbor, Massachusetts, called it an accident. Each block had been created by a student from the class and signed on the back. Emma was confident the person responsible for Rose's death was on the class roll. Emma's life—and the lives of Kelly, Maeve, and Dottie Faye—hadn't been the same since the quilt had surfaced.

Maeve pulled a folded piece of paper from her purse and opened it, her eyes scanning what appeared to be a brochure. "You're going to Ireland, my homeland," she said in a dreamy voice Emma was surprised to hear.

Emma knew the story well. Maeve was just five years old when she immigrated to the United States with her parents and younger brother, Daniel. Although she was proud of her Irish heritage, she'd not been back to Ireland since she was a child. Daniel, however, had returned to attend Trinity College in Dublin forty years ago. He'd fallen in love, married, and stayed there to raise a family. Now he was a successful businessman as well as part owner of the pub.

The shop was quiet except for the soft hum of the air conditioner, and Emma thought of the whimsical adventures Rose had dreamed up for them when they were kids. They took magic carpet rides, danced with fairies, and sang for make-believe royalty. "I guess I didn't think much about traveling because Rose's imagination always took us so many great places," she said. "I never considered the possibility that I'd go out west, travel to England, or take a cruise."

"In a way, Rose got us to take real adventures," Kelly said.

"I'd give anything to have taken those trips *with* Rose instead of searching for her murderer," Emma said.

"Rose would approve of a trip to Ireland," Maeve said, then handed the brochure to Emma. "I think she'd be thrilled to see you stay in this castle bed-and-breakfast in Ireland. She always loved the idea of castles."

Looking over Emma's shoulder, Kelly sighed. "Mom's right, Rose would approve."

"And there will be plenty of Egans to help you. My dad's family is huge, lots of cousins." Maeve sounded wistful. "I wish I could go with you. But with our Kathleen off on one of her soul-searching trips to New Mexico, I guess I'll have to stay here to run the shop."

Emma didn't know what to say. With all of the time Maeve had put in at Cotton & Grace while Emma and Kelly took off, tracking down suspects, she certainly deserved to be included in the trip to Ireland. Kelly's sister, Kathleen, took care of the shop when she was in town and bunking in the tiny apartment upstairs, but she'd been out west for a while now. "We'd love for you to go with us, Maeve," Emma said. "We'll see what we can work out as far as the shop goes."

A trio of bells jangled as the door opened and Emma's Aunt Dottie Faye strolled in sporting a blue-and-white striped sailor top, skintight white jeans, red stilettos, and a red, white, and blue nautical cap perched atop her well-teased blond hair. Emma smiled at her swagger. Dottie Faye didn't look or act like she was in her mid-sixties.

"Well, don't y'all look cozy. Have I walked in on something?" Dottie Faye narrowed her eyes and patted the hat, presumably to straighten it, but probably to attract everyone's attention. "I have, haven't I? What sort of plot are you hatching?"

Kelly snickered, and she took a step away from Maeve and Emma. "We leave the plotting up to you, Dottie Faye. You're the best."

Emma waved a hand toward one of the comfy overstuffed chairs in the small, well-lit alcove she and Kelly used as their design studio. "Actually we *were* discussing the next step into our murder investigation," she said.

"Great! Where are we going?" Dottie Faye sat down and drummed her red, white, and blue lacquered nails on the chair arm. She was still celebrating Independence Day on the ninth of July. "I'm game. You know that."

Taking a deep breath, Emma chose her words carefully. "I'm happy to hear you say that, Dottie Faye, because we really need your help."

"Whatever you need, sugar pie. Just ask."

"Well, it turns out the next suspect on our list has a shop in Maeve's hometown in Ireland, and it would be a special treat for her to go back and see it with Kelly. And me." Emma sat back in her chair and slowly exhaled, waiting for the explosion.

Dottie Faye rolled her eyes. "If she must go, I suppose I can purchase an extra ticket so she can accompany us." She pointed to the brochure in Emma's hand. "Is that where we're going?"

Maeve squirmed in her seat across from Dottie Faye. "It's a castle bed-and-breakfast not too far from my cousin's house on the west coast of Ireland."

"So, let me see it." Dottie Faye plucked the brochure from Emma's hand and whistled as she gazed at the magnificent castle perched at the edge of the sea. "How romantic! I'll bet we can find Emma a brooding Irishman inside those ancient castle walls."

Ignoring the reference to her love life, Emma cleared her throat. "Dottie Faye, with Kathleen still away and Maeve taking the trip with us, Kelly and I need you to stay here and run the shop."

"It would be a big help." Kelly nodded. "Mom and I have always dreamed of taking a trip to Ireland together, but I'll enjoy it much more knowing the shop is in capable hands while we're gone."

Dottie Faye's drumming resumed, and Emma braced herself for a reaction. But her aunt took a deep breath and looked from one face to another without saying a word.

"Well," said Dottie Faye, her Southern accent turning the word into three syllables, "as I said, I'll do anything to help you get to the bottom of Rose's murder. And since I'm an experienced shop owner, having owned a hair salon and other businesses, I'm sure I'd run the place much better than just about anyone else I know." She sent a withering smile across the alcove. "So, I'll do it this time. But you'd better call me every day with updates."

Kelly jumped up and hugged Dottie Faye, whose eyes widened in surprise. "Oh, thank you, Dottie Faye! You don't know what this means to Mom and me. This is like a dream come true."

Dottie Faye pursed her lips and groaned.

"What is it?" Emma asked.

"I suppose you'll want me to feed that yellow-eyed devil cat you decided to adopt." Her aunt's nails resumed their drumming. "That creepy cat hates me as much as it loves destroying your curtains."

"Ichabod doesn't hate you. He's leery of people, that's all. You would be too, if you'd been poisoned once."

"Just because some sicko poisoned a scrawny black alley

cat doesn't mean you had to adopt it," said Dottie Faye. "You know I hate cats."

Emma quivered her lips with feigned emotion until Dottie Faye's face softened.

"Oh, all right. I'll feed the darned thing."

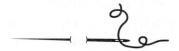

"And that's about it, Dottie Faye." Emma's index finger was still on the last item on the to-do list she'd written for her aunt to follow while she and Kelly were in Ireland. "I can't believe Kelly and Maeve pulled this trip together in two short weeks."

Dottie Faye sighed loudly. "I can't believe you're going without me. But you can count on me to take good care of Cotton & Grace—and the devil cat—while you're gone."

Placing the last of several new items on the display shelves—book covers in summer colors, a watermelon slice pincushion, an owl pillow, and several drawstring bags in various shapes and colors—Kelly crossed the shop to Emma and her aunt. "We'll bring you the brightest, coolest earrings and the most unusual Aran sweater we can find, I promise."

"Please don't get me one of those thick, bulky sweaters that would cover my curves." Dottie Faye rubbed her hands along her hips.

"We wouldn't do that," said Emma. "We'd have to go way too far to return it."

Kelly snickered and smiled broadly. "Thanks again, Dottie Faye."

"'Tain't nothing at all." Dottie Faye wrapped her arms around Kelly. "I couldn't love you more if you were my own niece."

"I don't know what we'd do without you, Dottie Faye," Kelly said, giving the older woman a quick squeeze before letting go and disappearing into the back office.

She emerged a minute later with a bunch of papers in hand as Maeve walked in the door. "Mom, your timing is impeccable. I printed out our itinerary and the airline tickets. We're really going to Ireland! I have one for each of us," she said, passing out the stapled packets. "There's even one for you, Dottie Faye, so you know how to reach us."

Emma flipped through the papers. "Everything's here. If you have your passports with you, I'll make a photocopy of them. I read it's good to have a copy in case the original gets lost or stolen."

"I put mine in my purse so I can't forget it tomorrow." Kelly rummaged through her purse, pulled out her passport, and handed it to Emma. "Mom, do you have yours?"

Fiddling with her purse strap, Maeve looked down and cleared her throat. "No, I don't have it with me." She shuffled her feet. When she looked up, her face almost matched her hair. "Emma, have you looked into exchanging currency?"

"Mom, are you trying to change the subject? Emma ordered us a few euros from the bank and picked them up yesterday. But you already knew that. What gives?"

"There's a little problem with my passport." Maeve's voice was barely audible.

"What kind of problem?" Kelly asked.

"I can't seem to find it."

"What?" Kelly's eyes widened. "Next to Emma, you're the most organized person I know."

"I've looked everywhere. It's not in the little safe where I keep all of my other important documents."

"I think a leprechaun took it," Dottie Faye said. "They're

supposed to be so mischievous and all. Maybe I'm supposed to go with you instead. I know where *my* passport is." Dottie Faye swept up her rhinestone-studded bag and pranced to the door. "If you're finished with me, I'm going to head home and get my passport!"

"We'll keep you posted, Dottie Faye." Emma waved. "And we'll see you just after lunch tomorrow. Don't worry about reopening the shop after the trip to the airport. Thanks for being our chauffeur."

"Anytime, sugar. I might be leaving my car in long-term parking." Dottie Faye closed the door behind her.

Maeve watched Dottie Faye cross the street. "She's right, you know. If I can't find my passport, I won't be able to leave with you tomorrow."

Kelly hugged her. "I'll come by the house after closing and help you look for it. It's got to be there somewhere."

"I'll come too," Emma said. "We've had a slow day. Maybe we'll close up a bit early."

Emma and Kelly stood side by side as Maeve left the shop. The ticking of the old grandfather clock mocked them with the sound of passing time. They had less than twenty-four hours to find that passport.

"Kelly, do you think we'll be able to make that flight tomorrow?" Emma asked.

"Yes," Kelly replied. "I'm not allowing myself to think any differently."

Emma closed her hands tighter around her copy of the itinerary and the two passports. "I sure hope your mom is right about the luck of the Irish."

two

Kelly rapped on Maeve's front door hard enough for the star-spangled bows on the wreath to shake. "I wonder why she's not answering the door. Her car's here, and I know she's waiting for us." She hesitated a moment before inserting a key into the lock.

As they walked through the door, Emma half expected to see Maeve's luggage neatly stacked by the front door. "It's not a good sign that your mom's bags aren't packed and waiting."

"Probably not." Kelly crossed the living room and peeked in the kitchen door. "Mom?"

No answer.

"Well, she's not in the kitchen." She joined Emma at the bottom of the steps and looked toward the landing at the top. "Mom!" Her voice was louder this time.

"I think we should check upstairs." Emma hoped they wouldn't find the sixty-eight-year-old woman sprawled on the floor beside a stepladder.

Nodding, Kelly led the way. She called again when they reached the landing.

A faint "I'm in here!" filtered down the hall past Kelly and Kathleen's old room and another across the hall that had been their brother's bedroom. Emma and Kelly trotted down the hallway to the master bedroom at the end.

They found Maeve sitting on the floor of her walk-in closet, surrounded by plastic storage boxes, her normally immaculate hair in disarray.

"Mom, you scared the daylights out of us. We thought you were hurt." Kelly stood with her hands on her hips.

"I didn't hear you." Maeve looked up at her daughter's frowning face. "I guess I was too preoccupied with that darned passport. I've looked everywhere—the fireproof safe where I keep important papers, my desk drawer, even the catchall drawer in the kitchen. I can't find it."

As Maeve reached her hands out to the nearby step stool and began to pull herself up, Emma placed a hand on her shoulder. "Don't get up. Why don't you keep looking in here while Kelly and I check other places? When did you last see your passport?"

Maeve bit her lower lip for a few seconds and shrugged. "It's been a while."

Emma and Kelly exchanged worried glances.

Maeve placed the lid on the container beside her and slid it on top of the others she'd presumably already searched. "Kelly, would you search through my dresser? And Emma, would you get my luggage out of the closet in Sean's old room and see if it could be in there?"

Kelly's eyebrows rose. "Mom, you're not packed yet? This isn't like you. Is everything OK?"

"Everything is fine. I've been preoccupied looking for my passport, but everything I want to pack, except for toiletries, is spread out on the bed in Sean's room." She waved the two younger women away. "Now get looking."

"Aye, aye, Captain!" Kelly saluted her mother and backed out of the closet with Emma in tow.

They didn't speak until they reached the hallway. Kelly put her hand on Emma's arm. "Do you think I should be worried about Mom? I've never seen her so addled."

They paused in the open doorway of Sean's old room and

stared at Maeve's travel clothes stacked in neat piles by garment type with accessories behind them. Each pair of shoes—low heels, sneakers, walking shoes, and slippers—was nestled in a clear plastic bag. A half-filled cosmetic case was open and leaning against pillows at the head of the bed. Ladies' clothing looked odd in a room filled with sports trophies, framed posters of Roger Clemens and Wade Boggs, and a display of military aircraft models.

Emma chuckled. "Not from what I see here. Despite the misplaced passport and her strange behavior in the closet, she seems pretty organized and ready to roll."

"That makes me feel better, thanks," Kelly said. "I'll yell if I find the passport."

As Kelly padded down the hall to Maeve's bedroom, Emma turned her attention to the closet in Sean's room. She found three different sizes of rolling luggage, two smaller cases nestled inside the largest bag. Assuming Maeve would take all three pieces to Ireland, Emma separated the suitcases and lined them up on the floor at the foot of the bed and opened each one. She'd completed searching the two larger cases without any luck when Kelly shouted from Maeve's bedroom.

Emma jumped up and hurried down the hallway to where Kelly was standing between the open drawers of the dresser and the side of the bed, waving a passport. "You'll never guess where I found it!" Kelly chortled as Emma crossed the room. "It was in Mom's sock drawer!"

Emma turned from Kelly to Maeve. "Your sock drawer? Why in the world would you put your passport in there?"

"Well, I …" Maeve stammered as her face darkened from pale white to pink to tomato red. "I guess I was a bit flustered after meeting a handsome widower on the train back from Montreal." She snatched her passport from Kelly's fingers.

"It's been a long time since I've had such an enjoyable time chatting with a man."

Kelly's eyes widened. "Wait! When did you go to Montreal?"

Maeve closed her eyes and sighed. "While you were chasing clues in England, Ellie Tallent talked me into taking a quick trip to visit her cousins. Your sister was here to watch the shop, so I decided to go."

Emma and Kelly looked at each other and erupted into a fit of laughter.

"And here we thought Dottie Faye was our most entertaining heartbreaker. Wait until she finds out you're her competition!" Emma chuckled. "Have you kept in touch with this gentleman?"

"Of course not. I mean, he's called a couple of times and left messages, but I haven't returned them. I could never replace Kelly's father," Maeve said.

"Aw, Mom, you should have a little fun," Kelly said.

Maeve waved her off. "And don't you dare tell Dottie Faye about this," she said. "I'll never hear the end of it."

Kelly snorted and reached into the drawer behind her, pulling a ball of meticulously rolled socks from the top dresser drawer and lobbing it at her mother. "I've got news for you, Mom; you're already not going to hear the end of it!"

Still blushing, Maeve brushed past Kelly to replace the socks in the drawer. "Now, if you'll excuse me, it's nearly seven o'clock and I have packing to do."

"Patrick's going to drop me off here after lunch tomorrow. Dottie Faye will pick up Emma first and will be by to get us around three o'clock," Kelly said. She hugged her mom goodbye.

Emma grinned. "As much as I detest flying, I might enjoy seeing you in action. Perhaps you'll meet a dashing stranger on the plane!"

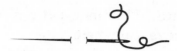

The shrieking, gossamer-clad woman was closing in as Emma ran down the endless maze of hallways in the great medieval castle. The eerie sound was getting louder, blocking the sounds of Emma's rapid breath and the clatter of her shoes on the stone floor. Soon the moaning pursuer would be close enough to grab a fistful of Emma's long blond hair. Why was this creature chasing her when all Emma wanted was to find the truth? Where was the staircase leading? Truth? Every heavy wooden door she tried was locked; passages went in circles.

Suddenly, the deafening noise stopped; silence filled the halls. As quickly as the ghostly woman disappeared, Emma's sobs filled the air. "Where are you Rose? I'm here."

"Emma. Wake up." Emma's eyes fluttered open to see the concern in Maeve's eyes. "You were dreaming. Everything's all right. We're about to land in Shannon. Shake the sleep out of your eyes and look out the window if you want to see the most gorgeous place in the world!"

Disoriented, Emma rubbed her eyes and sat up in her aisle seat. "We're here already? How long have I been sleeping?"

"Several hours, I'd say. You missed breakfast. We didn't want to wake you. It's just past daybreak, but there's enough sunlight to see the River Shannon," Maeve said. "Lean a bit this way. Can you see anything?"

Emma unfolded her long, slender legs and twisted in the seat as much as the safety belt would allow. Because they were making their descent to the airport, she wasn't allowed to unbuckle the belt, but she could get close enough to the window to make out a tree-lined body of water. "Wow, it really is as green as it looks in the movies!"

"Isn't it beautiful?" Emma had never heard Kelly so excited. "Mom, we're really here!"

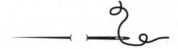

"No wonder the guy in the car rental place wished me luck after I told him I've never driven on the left-hand side of the road," Emma said. Her knuckles turned white as she gripped the steering wheel of the white minivan. "He suggested I practice in the parking lot before attempting to leave the airport and tackle the roundabouts. Maybe I should have listened."

While Emma had happened across similar traffic circles back home designed to ease congestion, these were anything but calm, and they did nothing to ease the strangeness of driving in the left lane in a vehicle with a steering wheel on its right side.

"You're doing fine," said Maeve. Emma could tell the woman had a death grip on the door handle.

"I thought you said the west of Ireland was sparsely populated," Emma said, mashing the accelerator in time to exit the roundabout before another car zoomed up and blocked her from getting out of the circle. "Wow, I hope that's the last one for a while. Boston rush hour has nothing over Irish roundabouts."

Emma concentrated on the road and traffic as Kelly navigated using her smartphone GPS from the backseat. Maeve divided her attention between the changing view and reading aloud from an Irish travel manual.

As the landscape became more rural, Emma relaxed and enjoyed the rolling green countryside that was becoming rockier with each kilometer. "This area is so unusual." She glanced at Maeve. "Where exactly are we?"

Kelly leaned forward. "It sort of looks like we're on the moon, doesn't it?"

"It's called the Burren," said Maeve. "Its name comes from the Irish word *boirreann*, which means a rocky place. It covers about 100 square miles." She flipped through several pages of the travel manual. "It says here the rock formations are bare carboniferous limestone. I guess I should know all of this, but I was only five when we moved to the States."

"I've seen the Burren in almost every Ireland calendar Patrick has given me each Christmas, but the photos can't do this justice." Kelly leaned closer to the window. "Look how little tufts of wildflowers shoot up between the rocks."

Traffic began to pick up on the road and Emma felt herself tensing as road signs appeared pointing toward Galway City. "The guy at the rental car place warned me about the treacherous roundabouts near the city. I feel safe in this minivan, but I wonder if a compact car wouldn't have been a better choice with these narrow, winding roads."

The van fell silent as Emma concentrated on staying on the proper side of the road and avoiding a collision. Kelly yawned and soon fell asleep while Maeve kept a keen eye out for traffic and roundabout exits. Soon after Emma had successfully navigated the worst of the roundabouts and finally steered the car northwest toward Clifden, the seaside town in County Clare near the village of Merrow where the castle bed-and-breakfast was located, Maeve suggested stopping to stretch their legs and allow Emma to relax.

A scenic overlook along Lough Corrib offered a safe place to pull off the road and enjoy a breathtaking view of Ireland's second-largest lake. Kelly woke as the van rolled to a stop on the small gravel parking area.

"You slept through Emma's daring drive around Galway

City," said Maeve. "She's now a pro at driving on the left side of the road and surviving roundabouts."

"I'm glad I missed the crazy traffic." Kelly slid the van door open and jumped onto the gravel. "But I'm happy I woke up for this."

Maeve didn't say a word as she walked to the grassy area sloping to the lake. She stared at the lake, her eyes drifting from the shore, to a small island, to the mountain backdrop.

Emma wasn't sure, but she thought perhaps she saw tears glinting in the older woman's eyes when she walked up beside her. Had Maeve ever cried in her presence? Emma couldn't think of a time, other than after Kelly's father died. Maeve had dreamed of returning to Ireland for a very long time.

"I feel it too, Mom," said Kelly, strolling to the other side of Maeve and placing an arm around her. "It's like I'm coming home to a place I've never been before."

Maeve nodded, her gaze transfixed on the horizon.

Emma stood back so mother and daughter could enjoy the moment. Kelly's dark brown hair looked almost auburn in the sunlight. Although petite herself, Kelly seemed to tower over her mother. Emma's heart swelled. She loved them both as much as if they were family.

"We should memorialize this moment," said Kelly, pulling her smartphone from her pants pocket. "Selfie time."

Kelly took a couple of photos with the three of them squished together and several of the pastoral view before Emma herded mother and daughter back to the van. "The sooner we get on the road, the faster we will get to the B and B and start working on finding Mr. Gallagher."

three

"Oh my goodness!" Emma pulled the van off the side of the narrow road as far as she could and put it in park. She pointed down the sloping pastureland to an imposing gray castle rising up from the deep green land by the sea. "I think that's our home for the next few days."

Kelly pressed her nose against the window and snickered. "I guess, since it's fit for a king, it'll do just fine."

"Rose finally got us to a castle," Emma said, putting the van into gear. "I wish she was here with us."

Maeve glanced back at Kelly before looking at Emma. "I have a feeling she knows we're here."

The two-lane road leading to the castle meandered through clusters of grazing sheep in the afternoon sun. What looked from afar like a low wall surrounding the perimeter of the castle was high enough to have kept marauders out in ancient times. Emma steered the car through the open wrought iron gates and drove around a massive circular drive. Maeve marveled at the large variety of sculpted hedges and colorful flowers in the center. Kelly was more interested in what the travel guide said about the availability of midday snacks at the castle.

Emma pulled the van behind a blue SUV and cut the engine.

Leaving their luggage in the van, Maeve, Emma, and Kelly stood in awe at the bottom of a steep flight of stone steps.

"Formal gardens, several turrets, a vine-covered wall, huge windows. All this place is missing is a drawbridge," said Kelly.

Maeve raised her eyebrows. "We can do without a drawbridge."

"But I can't do without food," said Kelly. She started up the stairs. "So, let's get checked in and explore the place."

When they reached the top step, two heavy wood doors opened as the three women crossed the entryway. A dashing, dark-haired man whose eyes matched his navy sport coat greeted them. "Welcome to Blayloch Castle. Will you be staying?"

Maeve nodded. "I'm Maeve Quigley. We have an open-ended reservation for three—my daughter, Kelly Grace; our friend, Emma Cotton; and me."

"My name is Kevan. I'll collect your bags while you check in. The reception desk is to your left, past the suit of armor. I'll meet you there."

"It may not have a drawbridge, but that's a pretty cool-looking suit of armor," Emma said, elbowing Kelly as Kevan walked away.

The streamlined registration didn't take long, and soon the trio were following the concierge up a steep flight of stairs and down a wide hallway lined with electric candelabras, sofas in rich red and gold, and slender rectangular tables. Every so often they'd pass a mounted game animal head, making Emma shiver. Their room door was below a boar's head, which Emma thought was a disturbing landmark.

Their escort unlocked the door and pushed it open to allow Maeve, Kelly, and Emma to enter the suite before her. Emma was pleasantly surprised to see a light, airy room featuring two big windows, light French provincial furniture, and a cheery yellow-and-periwinkle decor. Pretty nice, despite the boar's-head sentry.

"I hope you find everything to your satisfaction. Your

bags are divided between the two bedrooms according to your reservations," the concierge said. "If there's anything I can do for you, my name is Tara."

"The room is lovely." Emma's eyes swept around the room. "We'll definitely feel pampered here."

"Look." Kelly gazed longingly at the afternoon tea set up in the sitting area. "Three levels of tea cakes, cookies, and finger sandwiches."

"A Mrs. Sinclair ordered afternoon tea for you, as well as the fresh fruit bowl and basket of assorted Irish chocolates. She had the small refrigerator stocked with bottled water and assorted cheeses," Tara said. "Enjoy, and please ring if you need anything."

"Your Aunt Dottie Faye is really something." Kelly bounded over to the tea service as soon as the door closed. "I don't know where to start!"

Emma crossed the sitting area and pulled a bottle of water out of the refrigerator. "Why don't we start with tea? Maeve, maybe you can call your family and touch base with them so we can visit after we have a chance to freshen up and rest."

"And eat," Kelly said as she tucked in.

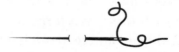

"There it is!" Maeve pointed her finger toward the left side of the windshield from the passenger side of the van. "On the other side of the roundabout."

Emma spotted "Gallagher's" written in cursive across the storefront of a salmon-colored building with large display windows. "Well, that was easy."

"Finding a parking place might be a little harder," said

Kelly. "I didn't expect to see so much traffic in a small fishing village like Merrow."

"You expected donkey carts, perhaps?" Maeve laughed. "I'll bet they have electricity here too."

"Very funny, Mom." Kelly joined in the laughter. "But isn't it beautiful? Look at the flower boxes. They're gorgeous."

Emma pulled into a parking place four doors down from the textile shop owned by Rose's former student.

They strolled past a bakery, where Kelly immediately stopped to drool over the day's specials on view in the window, and then they passed a glassworks studio and a dress store before they stood outside Liam Gallagher's shop. The window display featured a miniature bedroom filled with Gallagher products, including bed linens, draperies, quilts, blankets, throw pillows, and even several clothing items hung from hangers on an antique coat rack.

"He may run factories, but he still has an eye for design, that's for sure." Kelly opened the wood-and-glass door and held it for Maeve and Emma.

"Let's hope he has clues and a DNA sample for us," Emma whispered as she entered the shop.

A slender, raven-haired young woman stepped from behind the register counter. "Welcome to Gallagher's."

Emma walked forward and held out her hand. "I'm Emma Cotton." She retracted her hand when the clerk didn't extend her own, but she continued to introduce Maeve and Kelly. "We'd like to speak with Mr. Gallagher, please."

The woman's deep blue eyes narrowed. "I'm so sorry, but Mr. Gallagher isn't here right now, and I don't know when he will return. Are you friends of his?"

"Not exactly." Emma rooted around in her purse until she produced a business card. "Kelly and I own a quilt design business in the States near Boston. Mr. Gallagher attended college with a friend of ours years ago."

The clerk smiled and took the proffered card. "I'll give this to Mr. Gallagher should he return. He spends most of his time at the factory and offices in Dublin."

Emma clenched her teeth and slowly let out a breath. She felt Kelly squeeze her elbow. "I see. May I have the phone numbers, please?"

The clerk hesitated. "I can't give out the private numbers, but the factory and office numbers are on our website."

"Thank you." Kelly spoke before Emma could respond. "Our cellphone numbers are on the card, and we're staying at Blayloch Castle. We'd really like to speak with him while we're here."

"Enjoy your stay in Ireland." The clerk's voice was friendly again, but Emma had a feeling their message wouldn't make it to Liam Gallagher. Was he successful enough to be unreachable?

The three women were almost to the door when Maeve stopped and turned to the clerk. "One more thing. Would you please tell us how to find Egan's Pub from here?"

"Go left out of the shop and take the next left to Middleton Avenue to Market. Egan's is on the second block of Market Street."

Maeve grinned. "Thank you. You've been very helpful. Good day to you."

As soon as they were on the sidewalk, Kelly put her arm around Maeve. "That was brilliant, Mom."

"I was determined to get some sort of information from her. In this day and age of email, she didn't even offer to get a message to Mr. Gallagher." Maeve pulled a slip of paper from her pants pocket with the pub address. "I haven't seen most of my cousins since we were little kids."

Emma looked across the street and watched the boats at the marina bob in the bay, hoping their rhythmic motion would calm her. Maeve and Kelly were excited about seeing their family, but all Emma could think about was finding Liam Gallagher. She saw the looks of anticipation on their faces and knew that Dublin would have to wait until after the Egan family reunion. "On a positive note, at least the short visit to Gallagher's shop gives us more time with your family before jet lag takes its toll," she said.

The threesome walked to the end of the block, turned away from the bay, and headed down Middleton Avenue. Kelly had just pointed out the Market Street sign when several black-clad Gothic teenagers spilled out of the Sea Breeze Sweet Shop. The shopkeeper waved his broom at the teens while they nearly collided with the trio. Muttering obscenities through blackened lips, the youths took their teenage angst out on Maeve, Kelly, and Emma. Maeve stopped in her tracks and turned to the ruffians, her green eyes blazing. She took a sharp breath and started to open her mouth when Kelly linked one arm with her mother and the other with her friend. "Come on, Mom. This is not the time to get your Irish up."

Maeve threw a withering glance to the hooligans but didn't speak again until they crossed the road to Market Street. "Young people these days. I know its cooler here than it is back home, but it's not cold enough to be wearing full-length coats and gloves. It makes no sense."

Emma shrugged. "I guess teens in Ireland succumb to peer pressure just as easily as those in Boston or Mystic Harbor."

They found the stone walls of Egan's Pub nestled between a charming peach-and-white flower shop and a rather plain, but spotless, whitewashed meat market. Bright flowers in pink, purple, and yellow drew attention to the second- and third-floor window boxes. Over the heavy brown door, a light brown oval sign sporting a spotted salmon proclaimed Egan's was founded in 1803.

"Your family's been here a long time." Emma's eyes drifted from the sign to the door. "Are you ready to see them?"

"Yes." Maeve and Kelly spoke simultaneously.

They were barely inside the door when a tall, striking, middle-aged man came out from behind the polished wood bar lining one wall of the pub and strode across the floor. "As I live and breathe, it's my sister Maeve, although I would have sworn it was our mam walking in the door!"

A second later, Maeve was engulfed in the long arms of her brother, Daniel, whom she'd seen only a handful of times since he'd returned to Ireland in his mid-twenties. When Maeve raised her face from his shoulder, tears rested on her cheeks. "When did you get so tall?"

"It must be all of the rain here. I sprouted four inches after I moved back to Ireland for college. I can't believe it's been nearly forty years." Daniel turned to Kelly and wrapped her in a similar bear hug. "And you must be Kelly. Beautiful women run in the family."

A slight blush crept up Kelly's cheeks. His hair color, although tinged with silver, was exactly the same blend of brown and auburn. "You're not so bad yourself, Uncle Daniel. It must be our hair color."

Pulling away from her uncle, Kelly grabbed Emma's shirt sleeve and pulled her closer. "This is Emma, my closest friend in the world."

"It's nice to meet you." Emma held out her hand, but Daniel bypassed a handshake and gave her a hug too. "Maeve told us all about you in her emails. It seems like we know you already. I'm sorry my wife, Aileen, isn't here tonight. She had a previous engagement but will be here tomorrow to meet you. She sends her warmest welcome."

When Daniel let go of Emma, he gestured to a small alcove

adjacent to the bar. "Uncle Connor is waiting to meet you." He waved to a slightly younger man behind the bar. "Eamon, come join us when you can."

Connor Egan, the younger brother of Maeve's father, Frank Egan, stood to hug and kiss the cheek of each woman. In his eighties, Connor was tall with a shock of white hair and a deep voice. "Please sit." He remained standing until Maeve, Kelly, and Emma were all seated. "My son Eamon and his wife, Deirdre, will join us shortly with some fish and chips. My brother Owen called earlier; he's planning to visit in a day or two. He lives in Roscommon."

Before she knew it, Emma was caught up in Connor's stories of the Egan family, from the history of the pub to the fishermen of the family. After Eamon and Deirdre served dinner and joined the table, they talked about their son Brendan, who was making a name for himself throughout Ireland as a newspaper reporter. By the time a gigantic bread pudding was served, so many Egan relatives had filled the bustling pub that Emma couldn't keep track of them. Afternoon turned into evening, and she suddenly had an overwhelming desire to return to the quiet sanctuary of the bed-and-breakfast.

"I think your Emma has heard enough Egan family stories for the evening," Deirdre said.

"I'm a bit sleepy." Emma stifled another yawn. "I'd love to hear more after I've had a good night's sleep."

Deirdre looked at Eamon. "Jet lag," she said. "They all look bone-tired. Why don't you drive them back to the castle in their car? I'll follow in the truck. Plenty of family here to help with customers, if needed."

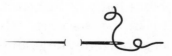

Emma tightened the sash on the cushy navy blue robe provided by the B and B before curling up beside Kelly on the sofa. "I think we should get a good night's sleep and leave for Dublin tomorrow after a leisurely breakfast."

"I hate to take Mom from her family so soon after reuniting with them." Kelly took a sip of hot herbal tea, replaced the dainty cup on the saucer, and set them on the coffee table. "Maybe she'd like to stay here and visit with them while we chase down Gallagher. By the way, I found the company website while you were changing. I stored the address and phone number for the factory and Dublin office on my phone."

Maeve's bedroom door opened and she appeared in her blue robe, making them a matching trio. "You two look serious. Or are you just tired?"

"Both. Sit with us a minute." Kelly nodded toward the fluffy floral chair. "We were talking about how happy you seemed with our relatives tonight. You've waited a long time to see them. Emma and I need to go to Dublin to chase down Gallagher, but there's no reason why you couldn't stay here."

The room fell silent while Maeve considered the suggestion. "I think I would rather do that. Are you sure you don't need me in Dublin?"

"We're just going to pay Gallagher a quick visit at his factory, get a DNA sample, and head right back here." Emma yawned. "Right now, we all need some sleep. Kelly and I can leave right after breakfast."

"Good plan." Kelly rose. "I want to indulge in one of those world-famous Irish breakfasts before we brave the big city."

They bid each other good night as Emma turned out the lamp and headed to her bedroom. Minutes later, she crawled into bed and felt herself melt into the mattress. But sleep wouldn't come. She thought about Maeve's big, demonstrative family and was overwhelmed by its sheer size and obvious close bond. Emma flipped onto her other side and fluffed the pillow before resting her head on it. She was trading a boisterous family in a quiet village for an unexpected trip to an unfamiliar metropolitan city. Would they find Gallagher in Dublin? She hoped so. The incessant traveling was getting tiresome—and fifteen years was much too long to wait for answers.

four

"Somehow I didn't expect Gallagher's factory to include a barbed-wire-topped gate with a guardhouse." Kelly leaned forward to read the "Do Not Enter" sign and red-lettered warning to stop at the gate.

Emma rapped her hand on the steering wheel. "We didn't come all this way to get derailed by a gate." She pulled up to the guardhouse and rolled down her window.

An older man dressed in a security guard's uniform walked to the window. His name tag identified him as M. Murphy. He wasn't carrying a gun. "Name?"

"I'm Emma Cotton and this is Kelly Grace. We're here to see Mr. Liam Gallagher."

Murphy pulled his glasses down by the bridge and peered over the lenses. "Are you, now? If you had an appointment, then you'd know his offices aren't at this location. So why are you really here? Miss Cotton, if that's your name."

"That's my name. I just want—"

"The shopkeeper at Gallagher's in Merrow said we could find Mr. Gallagher here." Kelly leaned toward the driver's side, smiled, and batted her eyelashes with almost as much gusto as Dottie Faye. "Mr. Gallagher went to college with a friend of ours in the States. We promised her we'd visit him while on holiday in Ireland. Can you please tell us how to find him?"

Emma rolled her window down farther and tilted her head closer to the guard. "How do we get to the Dublin office address?"

The guard put his hand on Emma's door and leaned down. "There's no need to be bothering Mr. Gallagher. He's a busy man. Leave him alone." He straightened up and stalked back to the guardhouse before Emma or Kelly could say anything else.

Kelly frowned. "What should we do now?"

"Why don't you call Gallagher's Dublin office and see if you can make an appointment to see him this afternoon?" Emma replied, backing up and making a U-turn.

Nodding, Kelly selected Gallagher's number from her phone directory and leaned back in her seat. After a few seconds, she gave her name and asked for Liam Gallagher's office. "I'd like to make an appointment for this afternoon, please." She gave Emma a thumbs-up and then grimaced. "Does he have any time tomorrow? Nine o'clock?" Kelly looked at Emma, who responded with a nod. "Fantastic. We'll see him then. Thank you very much."

"I guess we're staying in Dublin tonight." Emma pulled the car off the road. "We need a game plan."

"I'll call Mom and let her know we will be staying overnight; then I suppose we should find a hotel." Kelly plucked Maeve's travel guide from the compartment between the seats. "Since we have some extra time in Dublin, I'd really love to do some sightseeing."

"I'll peek at the map of Dublin in the travel guide and find a route into the city while you call your mom." Emma took the book from Kelly and perused the city map. She chose a route taking them into the St. Stephen's Green area, remembering that Kelly had mentioned wanting to see it. Back on the road, she headed for the city.

"Mom didn't mind us staying in Dublin at all. In fact, she suggested we stay at the Shelbourne because it played a large role in the Irish Civil War. She said to enjoy ourselves."

Kelly looked at Emma. "Where are we heading?"

"St. Stephen's Green, because I've heard you talk about it over the years." Emma grinned. "And it happens to be across the street from the Shelbourne Hotel."

Kelly looked up the hotel's address in the guide and entered it into the GPS. "As frustrating as it is to not be able to see Gallagher today, I'm glad we have a chance to see some of Dublin."

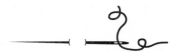

Kelly stood beside the imposing statue of Irish rebel Robert Emmett on St. Stephen's Green and smiled while Emma snapped a photo with her tiny point-and-shoot camera. Then she closed her eyes and stood as quiet and still as the statue. Emma was about to ask if she was OK when Kelly opened her eyes and slowly looked around in all directions. "The Irish Republican Army drilled here to prepare for the 1916 rebellion against English rule. Some of the men were only teenagers. Earlier it had been a place for executions and even the location of a leper colony. It's so beautiful and peaceful here now. I just can't picture it being used for such grisly purposes."

Emma took a photo of the foliage across the pond with ducks in the foreground. "As gorgeous as this is, we need to move along if we're going to see the rest of the places on your list."

The pair headed up Grafton Street toward Trinity College, where they saw the world-famous library and the medieval *Book of Kells*. They were still talking about the magnificence of the place as they crossed the River Liffey on the O'Connell Bridge.

"The *Book of Kells* was really something. I've never seen anything quite like it." Emma stopped to take another photo while crossing the bridge. "How can something written over 1,200 years ago still have such vibrant colors?"

Kelly pulled a granola bar from her bag. "I've always been amazed at the color on some of the colonial quilts we restore. But the *Book of Kells* is a great-grandma compared to them."

"You know, my stomach is rumbling. I'm surprised you took this long to pull out a snack. Let's find somewhere to get lunch on the other side of the bridge."

Stopping at a small pub a block up O'Connell Street, Emma had to admit she was glad to sit down in a padded booth by the window, but she crinkled her nose at the menu of "pub grub." "I really just want a salad."

Kelly nodded toward the plates carried by a redheaded server as she whisked by their booth. "Oh, you'll come to love pub grub. It's the tourist thing to do, so we may as well indulge while we're spending the day walking."

Kelly had a point about the walking. "OK, but that looks like more fried food than I've eaten in the last decade."

After ordering two fish-and-chips platters, Emma and Kelly planned their route back to the car to include seeing the statues of noted historical figures and the General Post Office—the building was the headquarters for the men and women who participated in the Easter Rising in 1916—on O'Connell Street before heading back to St. Stephen's Green via the Grafton Bridge into Temple Bar.

"This looks fantastic!" Kelly said, gazing at the battered fish, and rubbed her hands together in anticipation. Then she looked at Emma. "Thanks for humoring me with the sight-seeing. I know we should be working on the investigation."

Emma speared the fish with her fork and tried not to cringe at the grease she knew was hidden under the crunchy layer. "This is the trip you and Maeve have been hoping for.

It's fun seeing your eyes light up when you see places you've only heard about."

"We'll plan our next move as we cross the bridge into Temple Bar." Kelly slid a perfectly fried chip into her mouth and groaned. "These are the best. Ever."

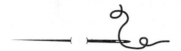

Back in the west of Ireland, Maeve pressed the hand brake on the bright pink bicycle as she coasted downhill toward the village in search of the perfect place to walk on the beach. She was anxious to feel the sand beneath her feet just as her fishermen ancestors had a hundred years before.

She waved at a passing car. What must they think of her—a mature woman with blazing red hair on a pink bike? Ma had never let her wear pink. She said it clashed with her hair. So she'd lived a lifetime avoiding pink. Perhaps it was time for a change. Perhaps.

The road veered toward the sea, and soon Maeve came across a gravel road cutting a wavy ribbon through a deep green pasture to the beach. She might need to walk the bike back to the blacktop, but she didn't care. Something told her this was the right way to go. The ruts were bumpy, and it made her feel impish. Knowing there wasn't a human being within earshot, she opened her mouth and let out an "Ahhhhhhh," giggling when it made the same odd vibration as it had when she was a child doing the same thing in her own backyard.

Never once taking her gaze from the water, she stowed her bike between a tuft of grass and a chair-like rock formation just paces from the sandy beach. The sun shone down between billowy white clouds. The sea's almost-tropical green-blue tint surprised her. Tears welled in her eyes, and she let them roll down her cheeks. She'd read of Americans visiting Ireland and feeling emotional as if they were returning home, but she'd always thought it was a bit of amusing drivel. Now here she was, doing the same thing.

Wiping her tears, she stood on the sand and inhaled deeply before taking a step in the direction of the village. Was she getting soft? Images of seeing her brother Daniel and meeting more of the family the night before flashed through her mind. Her Uncle Connor looked so much like her father that it was spooky. Dad had always missed the family he'd left behind, but he had taken becoming an American citizen very seriously. Never once did he mention moving back to his homeland.

Maeve strolled slowly, looking first in one direction and then in another, trying to see everything at one time. Occasionally she spied a cottage tucked among the green slopes at the sandy edge and wondered about the families who lived so close to the sea. Were their lives so different from hers, having been raised in a small New England fishing town herself?

Lost in thought, she nearly panicked when the biggest dog she'd ever seen kicked sand on her as he ran to the water. He was having so much fun frolicking in the water that she couldn't help but stop and watch. By the time he bounded onto the beach, his wiry fur was stuck together in clumps. The beast must have seen her watching, because suddenly he loped straight toward her.

"Don't worry. Fionn won't hurt you." Maeve whirled around to see an old man approaching her at a gait faster than she'd expect from a man of his age. A tan Donegal hat sat atop his ruddy, rectangular face. Steel-blue eyes danced beneath bushy gray eyebrows.

Maeve soon discovered the dog might not hurt her, but the giant beast didn't mind shaking off his coat and spraying her with water. She laughed and said as much to the man who watched her with amusement. "I'm Maeve. I just arrived here yesterday from the States."

"My friends call me Mick." He shook the hand Maeve had offered. "Do you have family here, Maeve-from-the-States?"

She nodded. "My father was Frank Egan. He left Ireland as a young man, but his brothers are still here, along with a small army of Egans."

"Egan, as in Egan's Pub?" Mick looked down the beach in the direction of the village for a moment before throwing a large stick for Fionn to chase. "Lots of Egans here."

"Yes, those are my Egans."

The four-legged giant loped back and dropped the stick at Mick's feet. "That's enough, Fionn. Time for tea." The old man swept the cap off his head. "Would you join us? My cottage is a stone's throw."

Maeve considered the invitation for a moment. Was it proper to go alone into the home of a man? Was it safe? Mick was a tall man, a bit stooped, and appeared to be in his late eighties and harmless. His lined face held a lifetime of stories. She wanted to hear at least one of them. "I think I'd enjoy that. Thank you."

The whitewashed cottage was simple and clean, with a low stone wall separating it from the beach in the front and the wild scrub grass in the back. Flanked on one side by a single window and two panes on the other, the door was low enough to almost require Mick to stoop as he entered behind Maeve.

"Please sit while I make us tea." He crossed the tiny room to the kitchen, which was little more than an alcove off the sitting area.

Maeve was impressed with the neat room and felt instantly at home. It was a man's room with a beige, no-frills slipcover on the sofa and a dark green afghan draped over the back. A dark green easy chair sat perpendicular to the sofa. Two small bookcases overflowing with books made up for the lack of a television. The two small windows didn't provide a scenic view of the beach, but a large painting on the far wall offered an impressionistic view of fishermen carrying their boat to the choppy sea.

"My great-niece makes the best pound cake in the whole of Ireland. I'm particular about who I share it with." Mick lowered a heavily laden tray to the table and poured the tea into two mugs. He removed two plates, each containing a fork and a slice of cake, and placed them on the table. The cream pitcher and sugar bowl remained on the tray. "Help yourself, and tell me about your family."

The next thing Maeve knew, she'd told Mick about her late husband, their three children, and even a little about Emma and Kelly's reason for visiting Ireland. "I've told you enough about me to bore you to tears. I want to hear about you."

"I'm a simple man. In my younger years I did some farming and a little carpentry." The old man hesitated a second. He opened his mouth to continue but was interrupted by shouting and what sounded like tomatoes splattering on the front walls of the house.

"Excuse me," Mick said. He retrieved a rifle leaning between the wall and a bookcase, and flung open the door. "Away with you! Leave me be."

Maeve ran to a small window to the right of the front door and peered through the glass, watching with dismay as two teenagers hurled handfuls of mud toward the cottage. They looked familiar.

Mick fired a shot into the air, stepped back inside, and slammed the door.

Maeve cringed and backed away from the window. "I've never thought much of using guns to solve problems."

"Some people won't listen to anything but a gun." Mick returned the rifle to its place.

"Maybe." Maeve's heart was still doing double-time. "Why were they harassing you?"

"This business started several months ago when these teenagers were congregated outside the hardware store. I tried to go through them and accidentally brushed up against their leader. He accused me of disrespecting him and shoved me into the door of the building."

Maeve nodded. "I recognize them. We had a similar run-in with them outside the candy store on our first day here."

"Try to avoid them if you can. Now they show up here every couple of weeks and throw mud at the side of the cottage."

"Have you called the police?"

Mick smiled. "We call them the Garda here. And no, I didn't. I think the hoodlums are harmless, and I try to stay away from most people."

Maeve drained her mug. "I never have been like most people."

"Indeed," Mick said.

Maeve stood up and held out her hand. "It's time for me to get back to the B and B. My daughter and her friend should be back from Dublin soon. Thank you for the tea. It was lovely."

Closing both hands around Maeve's, Mick squeezed lightly. "Thank *you* for your company."

He whistled. "Fionn—here, boy!"

Mick put a gnarly hand on the dog's head and looked at

Maeve. "I want you to take Fionn with you for protection. He will come home on his own."

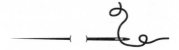

"I think I just crossed the line from tired to exhausted." Kelly shifted a bag of souvenir tea towels from one hand to the other. "But I'm glad we took the time to cross the Ha'penny Bridge. It's another one of the landmarks I just had to see." She looked at Emma. "Thanks for indulging my love of Irish history."

By the time they hit the Temple Bar area, Emma was feeling what hours of walking felt like on top of leftover jet lag. As she watched young men and women in their twenties and thirties hop from one trendy store or restaurant to another, she actually felt her age for the first time. Kelly's excitement was finally waning after their long day, and they made their way back to the Shelbourne.

five

"**M**r. Gallagher has been called away unexpectedly. He won't be here for the foreseeable future." The young receptionist was über-professional but not much help. "When he returns, you will be contacted."

After treating themselves to a luxurious night and breakfast at the historic Shelbourne Hotel, Emma and Kelly had arrived at Gallagher's office at 8:45 a.m. Emma was getting fidgety. "Is there a number or email address where he can be reached?"

The receptionist shook her head. "He will be unreachable."

Emma dug a business card from her purse and scribbled the name of the castle B and B on the back. "This is where we're staying. Please give this to him."

The receptionist tossed her jet-black curls and snatched the card from Emma's hand. She pursed her red lips and threw the card aside. "Now good day."

Kelly grabbed Emma's arm and tugged her away from the reception desk with a terse "thank you" as she propelled Emma toward the door.

"It won't do us any good if you get us thrown in jail or out of the country." Kelly let go of Emma's arm. "Are you going to behave?"

"I just don't understand the friction we've experienced in a country known for its hospitality."

"I don't get it either." Kelly shook her head. "I know we need to get back to Merrow, but do you mind if we tour the

Kilmainham Gaol before we leave? It's a grisly place—the rebel leaders from the 1916 Easter Rising faced the firing squad there—but it is an important part of history."

Emma peered at her watch. It wasn't even nine thirty yet. They had plenty of time. "Sure, we can do that."

They slowly walked three blocks back to the van while Kelly read aloud information about the jail. The van was in sight when Emma stopped and shivered before glancing back over her shoulder. "I just had the creepiest feeling, like someone was following us."

"After all of the crazy things we've endured since we started investigating Rose's murder, I think we've both gotten more skittish," Kelly said. "We haven't even talked to our suspect this time, so why would anyone be following us?"

"I don't know. I've felt strange since we pulled up at the factory gate yesterday."

"Yeats didn't call Ireland 'A Terrible Beauty' for nothing." Kelly studied the buildings and people around them for a moment. "It's a gorgeous country, but for centuries, some awful things happened here during its quest for freedom. Maybe that's what you're feeling—the ghosts of history."

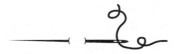

"Well, if I hadn't been creeped out before seeing Kilmainham Gaol, that place would have done it." Emma was glad to be steering the van toward Merrow.

"It's seen its share of tragedy, that's for sure. Dottie Faye would be conjuring all sorts of stories if she'd been with us." Kelly chuckled. "I sort of miss her amusing paranormal rambling."

"Me too." Emma felt a twinge of guilt at having to leave her aunt behind when she was the one largely paying for the trip.

As traffic waned and the landscape became more rural, Emma began to enjoy the ride. "Ireland really is beautiful." The road was hilly but fairly straight compared to what they'd seen, and there wasn't much traffic. "Want to take a turn at the wheel?" Emma asked Kelly. "Driving on the left side of the road is something everyone should try at least once."

Kelly studied the road ahead before glancing behind her. "Sure, I'm game. But I'm going to make you switch with me before we hit any of those crazy roundabouts."

The van coasted to a stop on the side of the road. Emma and Kelly switched seats, and soon they were on their way again. Sitting on the left side as a passenger felt strange to Emma, but she enjoyed the chance to relax. Their conversation lulled as Kelly concentrated on driving and Emma's eyelids became heavy.

"Emma, wake up." Emma fought to collect her thoughts as Kelly's voice became more insistent. "Emma! There's a car following us, and it's getting closer. Too close."

Emma jolted to attention as the van left the pavement and rumbled into pastureland, sending sheep scattering. Kelly hit the brakes, stopping just inches from a boulder, as a large black sedan disappeared over the crest of the next hill. "What just happened?"

"We were run off the road, and it was no accident. The car came up on us quickly, then cut us off." Kelly finally took a breath. "That rock is really, really close, isn't it?"

They exchanged looks and burst into nervous laughter. When they'd collected their wits, Emma took a small notebook and pen out of the console. "What do you remember about the car?"

"Not much. Black sedan. Tinted windows." Kelly squeezed her eyes shut in concentration. "And no license plate."

Emma scribbled the description in the notebook. "If anything else comes to you, just write it down. I'll drive now."

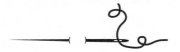

"Honestly, Kelly, I have no idea how you stay so slim," Emma said. "Can't you wait? We'll be back at the B and B in thirty minutes."

"That near miss made me hungry, and my granola bars are gone. I need a snack." Kelly's lap was filled with a wallet, brush, tissue packet, and map she'd pulled out of her purse in a desperate attempt to find food. "Let's just stop at the first pub we find for a quick bite, " she said as she returned her belongings to her bag.

"If we find one, I'll stop. But I can't say it looks promising."

The words were barely out of Emma's mouth when Kelly let out a yell and pointed to a small cluster of buildings off to the right. "Look! O'Riley's Family Pub."

"I hope they're open," Emma said as she steered the van into the parking lot.

O'Riley's was open, but its sole occupant was the bartender, a lanky man somewhat resembling a whooping crane in blue jeans. "I'm Paul," he greeted them. "Come sit at the bar and keep me company."

Kelly and Emma did as he suggested.

Kelly looked at the large clock hanging over the pool table. It was midafternoon. "We're a little late for lunch. Can we still get a bite to eat?"

Paul handed them a menu. "Sure you can. My wife went

upstairs to put our daughter down for her nap, but she'll be happy to fix something up for you in a few minutes. What can I get you to drink?"

Kelly ordered coffee. Emma asked for water.

"Colleen has her famous Irish stew on the stove, if you're interested. She'll also fix a Caesar salad, even though it's not on the menu," Paul said as he gave them their drinks.

They ordered one of each, and Paul disappeared into the back.

"What's our next step?" Emma asked Kelly, feeling frustrated and a little shaken.

"I don't know." Kelly took a sip of coffee. "I'm beginning to think this Mr. Gallagher is a figment of someone's imagination."

"Which Mr. Gallagher would that be?" Paul appeared from the kitchen, startling them. "Gallaghers are on every street in Ireland," he said as he placed a napkin and silverware in front of each of them.

Emma looked in his eyes. How much should they tell him? "The elusive Liam Gallagher who owns Gallagher Textiles."

The door to the kitchen cracked, and a blonde emerged. "Paul, your food's up."

"I'll be right back." He turned to the door. "Right-o, Colleen."

Paul returned with a tray of food, including a salad that Emma was looking forward to after their fried lunch. "Where are you from?" Paul asked.

Kelly told him about Cotton & Grace in between shoveling in mouthfuls of stew. Emma repeated the same cover story she had told Gallagher's employees. As they got more engrossed in their meals, Paul chattered about growing up helping in the pub and taking it over from his parents a couple years ago.

When Kelly scraped her bowl clean, Paul produced the check. "It's been a pleasure, ladies. Liam Gallagher is a regular customer when he visits home. He grew up here too. He's about due for an appearance. Would you like me to call when he comes in?"

Not believing their luck, Emma handed him a business card while Kelly placed cash on the bar. "That would be great. Thanks. My cellphone number is on my card."

"I'm happy to do it. I'm glad you stopped in during the slow time so we had a chance to talk."

They said their goodbyes, then made their way outside, where Emma threw an arm around Kelly's shoulder "You know, sometimes I'm thankful for your voracious appetite."

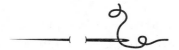

Rain pounded on the roof of Mick's tiny cottage, and the racket required Maeve to lean closer to hear the old man's raspy voice. She was enthralled with his recollection of passing through roadblocks during trips into Northern Ireland in the 1970s. His tales of guns, bombs, and police brutality made her shiver. "It was a different time then, especially for people living along the border."

Maeve knew the afternoon was fleeting, and she'd probably worn out her welcome, but she was fascinated by his stories of growing up in nearby Clifden and traveling through Ireland and Northern Ireland as a young carpenter's apprentice. It had been rude to drop in unannounced in the first place. She hadn't intended to visit, yet she'd still found herself knocking on his door on her way to explore the village. But Kelly and Emma were likely back from Dublin, and she should be returning to the B and B, even if it meant riding in the rain.

"I remember watching reports on television." Her father hadn't said much about the bombings. He would sit stone-faced and take in every word. "If they weren't broadcasting updates from the Vietnam War, they'd show clips from the aftermath of bombings in Ireland."

She collected their teacups and carried them to the kitchen. "Thank you for the tea and history. I need to get back now. I think the rain has almost stopped."

Mick took a towel from a kitchen drawer, then walked Maeve to her bike at the edge of the dunes. The wind lifted his gray hair as he wiped off the seat and handlebars. "Want to take Fionn with you?"

"Thank you, but I'll be OK on my own this time." Maeve grasped the handlebars and pushed up the kickstand with her foot. "I'd like to hear more stories, if you have time."

"I have time. Come back when you can. Fionn and I will be here." Mick waved his hand once. "Be careful."

The wind died and the air was eerie and still. Maeve picked up her pace when she heard voices and a rustling from the other side of the dunes. "Silly woman, it's just the wind." Her words were lost in the gust. She slid onto the bicycle seat as soon as she reached sand packed enough to withstand the weight, and pedaled as fast as her legs would go.

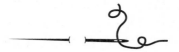

"Where have you been?" Kelly jumped up from the sofa as Maeve entered the suite. "It's nearly dark."

Emma finished pulling a needle through a quilt square and put it on the coffee table before patting the sofa beside her. "We've been worried about you in the storm. But you don't look soaked. Come sit. We ordered room service."

"I met the most interesting man." Maeve sank onto the sofa as Kelly sat on the chair.

"Oh really?" Kelly teased.

Maeve flushed. "He's old enough to be my father. But he did share what it was like growing up in a divided country."

She had just recounted her first meeting with Mick, including the mud-throwing teenagers and Mick defending his home with a rifle, when there was a knock at the door. "Room service."

The conversation ceased as a uniformed waiter wheeled in a linen-draped serving cart loaded with braised chicken, broiled veggies, and mashed potatoes.

"Tell me about Dublin," Maeve said. She paused as the waiter left the room. "Did you find Liam Gallagher?"

"Not exactly." Kelly said. "But we met someone who might be able to help us."

Kelly and Emma related their Dublin adventure to Maeve, describing their day from the time they arrived at the factory to the stop at O'Riley's Pub. They neglected to mention the black sedan running them off the road.

"Hopefully the bartender will phone you soon." Maeve covered her mouth as she yawned.

"I could have stayed in Dublin for a year and not soaked in all of the history." Kelly dove into the untouched bread pudding on the cart. "I felt an instant connection with Ireland as soon as our plane landed. I want to learn more about our family's history."

"I know how you feel." Maeve yawned again.

"I'm worn out," Emma said, taking a cue from Maeve. "Ready to call it a night?" She stood up, not waiting for an answer. "If we all get a good night's sleep, we can figure out our next step in the morning."

"That works for me," Kelly said. She rose and pulled Maeve to her feet. "I'm ready for another traditional Irish breakfast."

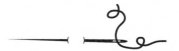

Emma woke with a start, her heart thumping and mind careening. Was that a thud coming from the sitting room? Was there an intruder in the suite, or had Emma had another nightmare? She crawled out of bed, reached for the bronze seal sculpture on the dresser, and groped her way to the bedroom door. Ear to the door, she listened. Yes, someone was definitely out there. Grasping the sculpture in one hand, she slowly turned the doorknob with the other.

Slipping through the doorway, Emma hesitated while her eyes adjusted to the shadows cast by the soft early morning light peering in through the heavy curtains. The intruder was bending over the sofa, and Emma heard the faint sound of a zipper. What was he stealing? Emma inched closer to the sofa and tightened her grip on the sculpture.

She lifted the bronze seal over her head and started to bring it down on the intruder's head when light filled the room.

"Dottie Faye! What on earth are you doing here?" Emma shouted as she stopped herself from clubbing her aunt with a seal.

SIX

"*How* did you get in here at this hour?" Emma asked as Maeve stood by the light switch, startled and confused.

Dottie Faye smiled in triumph and held up her pick and tension wrench. "Easy peasy. I picked the lock."

Kelly appeared in the doorway from her bedroom, rubbing her eyes. "What is going on?"

"I'll tell you what's going on. My niece just tried to kill me with a bronze sea mammal." Dottie Faye stood with her hands on her hips, blue eyes blazing under her blond bouffant.

Emma placed the statue on the end table. "Not that I'm not glad to see you, Dottie Faye, but what are you doing here? Who's minding the store?"

Dottie Faye sat on the sofa next to her bag. "That lovely young Kathleen returned from New Mexico just after you left. She was so rejuvenated from her yoga and meditation retreat that she practically begged me to join you in Ireland so she could run the shop for you."

"You left Kathleen in charge of the store. Again?" Kelly groaned.

"Now, Kelly Ann, your sister did quite well minding the store when we went to England, remember? She'll be fine." Dottie Faye yawned. "I'm so tired it feels like I didn't sleep a wink on the plane. Oh, that's right. I didn't! I was too busy chatting with this dashing gentleman from Kilmore. What a funny name for a city."

"He probably wanted to visit Kill-a-Dottie by the time the plane landed," Maeve whispered to Kelly.

Emma was too tired to deal with warring women. "I'm really glad to see you, Dottie Faye, but I'm exhausted. Let's catch up after you get some sleep. Maeve and Kelly are bunking together in one room. We share a bathroom connecting the two bedrooms. You and I can either share the queen bed in my room, or I can sleep on the sofa."

"Oh heavens, no, sweet pea. I crashed your party. It would be bad manners to take your room. I'll sleep on the sofa." Dottie Faye looked at the television perched in a converted armoire. "I like to watch TV before bed sometimes anyway."

"I'm going to say goodnight and go back to bed." Emma turned toward her room. "I have an extra cover and pillow you can use." Emma fetched the bedding for Dottie Faye and returned to her room. She let out a soft sigh as she slipped between the sheets.

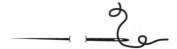

Emma opened the door to the sitting room to find Maeve and Kelly dressed for the day and watching the news on television. Dottie Faye was nowhere to be seen. "I had this wild dream that Dottie Faye broke into the suite, and I nearly clobbered her on the head with a sculpture. Remind me to not drink the high-octane tea before bedtime."

"You can't blame it on the tea, Emma." Maeve pointed the TV remote at the screen, and the news anchor disappeared. "Dottie Faye did make a grand entrance last night. But we have no idea where she is now."

"I'm sure she's trolling the halls of the castle looking for eligible bachelors," Kelly said. "I'm ready for breakfast. She'll find us in the dining room." Kelly stood up and bounded to the door. She giggled when she reached it. "Here's a sticky note from Dottie Faye. She's exploring the castle."

Dottie Faye's exploration had taken her as far as the dining room, and the women found her there, holding court.

"I've been exploring this castle for hours, and I've not seen a single ghost or fairy." Dottie Faye held the attention of guests at four different tables. "I guess the ghosts here in Ireland aren't as active as ours in Mississippi."

Emma, Kelly, and Maeve stood in the doorway, waiting for the host, who, like everyone else in the room, was staring at Dottie Faye. If it was not for her conversation, then certainly it was for her outfit. She'd donned a red wig pulled back in a green bow to match her blouse, which was paired with a red skirt and coordinating stilettos.

"Oh my stars," Maeve said. "She's dressed up like Maureen O'Hara in *The Quiet Man*."

Emma felt a twinge of embarrassment. "I suppose we should save her and interrupt."

She hesitated too long. Before Emma could speak, an older couple sitting next to Dottie Faye's table took over the situation.

"I beg your pardon, but it seems to me you'd do well to respect our fair country's folklore, especially banshees, harbingers of death, and the pooka." The man's Irish accent was thick but melodic. Dressed in khaki slacks, a light blue oxford cloth shirt, and a navy sport coat, he was a man of distinction. "You might not find them hospitable, if you did see one. Be careful what you wish for."

"Mr. and Mrs. Duncan, is everything all right here?" The host was clearly distressed at having lost control of the dining room.

"Everything would be just fine if some Americans would not

wax bombastic about cultures of which they are ignorant." Mr. Duncan smiled at the host. "We're almost done here, anyway."

Emma decided she couldn't wait any longer. "Dottie Faye. There you are." Emma took her aunt's arm. "We were worried when we woke and you were gone. We ordered tea, toast, and fruit to be sent to our beautiful suite."

Emma sent a pointed look to the host, who nodded and disappeared into the kitchen. She hoped an update on the strange incidents in Dublin would teach her aunt to choose her words more carefully.

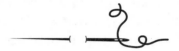

"Hallo!" Mick called and waved as Maeve emerged from the dunes onto the gravel surrounding his cottage. "I hoped you'd return."

She leaned her bicycle against the stone wall and removed a canvas bag from the handlebar. "And I'd hoped you'd welcome me." She held up the bag by its handles. "I brought tarts from the castle to have with our tea."

"Ah, you're just in time. I've put the kettle on." Mick took the bag as they walked to the cottage.

Inside, the old man told Maeve to sit down and relax, but she helped him prepare their tea instead. In short order, they were sitting on the sofa with a plate of tarts and two cups of tea on the table before them.

"Maeve, I'm glad you came back because I want to talk about your father. You might not like me too much when I'm done, but you need to know."

Something about his tone sent a shudder through her. "Go on," she said.

"I knew your dad better than I've led you to believe. We were boyos together in the village, and were raised listening to tales of the Irish Republican Brotherhood. We were taught to love our country and believe in a united Ireland."

Mick rose and shuffled to the bookcase. He removed a thick book from the middle shelf and a large square tin box from the top and placed them on the coffee table before sinking onto the sofa. "Your father, Frank, was two years older than I. His younger brother, Connor, and I are the same age. Their brother Owen was a year behind us. But Frank and I shared two fierce passions—the first was for fishing and the other was for our country."

"I remember Dad talking about Owen. I hope I get to meet him while I'm here." Memories of her father flashed through Maeve's mind like a montage. "Dad always did love to fish." Maeve picked at the tart she'd put on her plate but was too distracted to eat it. "I guess he didn't love Ireland enough to stay, and I never understood that."

A smile tugged at Mick's weathered lips. "There's only one thing he loved more than Ireland. His family—you, Daniel, and your mother, Bridgid."

Eyebrows raised, Maeve cocked her head. "I don't understand. Why did he leave a country he loved and believed in?"

Mick reached for the book and put it on his lap. He flipped through several pages of faded black-and-white photos until he came to a picture of a young man of about twenty-five with one arm around a stunning dark-haired woman holding a baby on one side and the hand of a little girl on the other. "This was taken just before I spoke to your father the last time. I've always regretted the words we exchanged that night."

Maeve felt a tug at her heart. Her mom and dad didn't stop looking at each other that way until the day he died of a heart attack at age seventy-two. "What happened?"

"To understand, you must have an idea of what the country was like at the time for lads like us, raised on the heroes of the 1916 Easter Rising, when the Irish fought for our independence—men like Cathal Brugha, Michael Collins, and Robert Emmett, who were totally committed to the cause."

If Maeve remembered her Irish history correctly, the Irish Free State had been formed by 1923, long before Mick or her father had been born. "What happened in 1951 to make Dad decide to leave Ireland?"

"Ireland was again in turmoil. The British Parliament had passed the Ireland Act of 1949, which decreed Northern Ireland would remain part of the United Kingdom unless the Parliament of Northern Ireland decided otherwise. With the British government controlling the Northern Ireland Parliament, it prevented a united Ireland." Fionn lumbered over to Mick, sat down, and placed his head on his owner's thigh. "This sparked a resurgence of the IRA violence. By 1951, Frank and I were in the thick of the fighting. Your dad—or 'da' as we say here—believed his family was in danger. He was probably right."

Mick flipped several pages of the photo album and stopped when he came to a photo of Maeve's father with two other young men. "We were mates, your da, Cormac O'Broin, and me." He pointed to a different face on the photo with each name. "We believed in the possibility of a united Ireland. We did whatever we were asked in the name of the country."

Maeve gasped.

Mick leaned forward and grabbed the box, prying off the lid as he leaned back onto the sofa. "For your dad, it all stopped when Cormac was killed."

He sifted through the pile of yellow newspaper clippings

until he pulled one from near the bottom of the box and handed it to Maeve.

Halfway through the article, Maeve's hands began shaking. "Cormac was planting a bomb in a neighborhood filled with children when it went off prematurely?"

"That was the end for Frank. Not only losing Cormac, but knowing the bomb had killed two children." Mick handed her another clipping: "IRA Operatives Assassinated." His eyes clouded. "But a fellow didn't just leave the IRA, and Frank was well aware of that. He couldn't just walk away."

He leaned forward, elbows resting on his knees and gnarled hands rubbing the sides of his face. "He trusted me enough to tell me his plans. I told him he was daft and a traitor to his country. Then I pulled my gun and told him he was dead to me."

Maeve sat in stunned silence. What could she say?

Mick rose again and disappeared into a room at the back of the cottage and returned with a pistol in his hand. "Frank never flinched. He threw his gun on the ground and walked away. This is his. I kept it all these years to remind me to not get too close to anyone again."

He ran his fingers down the barrel of the pistol. "As I grew older, I saw the wisdom in Frank's decision. I was in my mid-fifties when I went into the mountains and lived as a hermit. Twenty years later, I returned to Merrow as a bearded old man nobody recognized."

Mick opened the chamber, emptied the bullets into his hand, and placed them on the table in front of them. Holding the pistol by the barrel, Mick held it out to Maeve. "It hasn't been fired since I picked it off the spot where your dad threw it."

Maeve closed her eyes as her fingers wrapped around the handle of the gun, her heart racing while holding this link to her family's past. She thought of her father's youthful face in the old black-and-white photo and tried to imagine him holding the weapon the same way.

"Keep the gun. It's a piece of your history." Mick said. "It belongs in your family."

The father she knew had never owned a gun and had been insistent on the family not keeping one in the house. Shuddering, Maeve shook her head and handed the gun to her father's old friend. "Dad hated guns. He wouldn't want me to keep it."

"Understood." Mick returned the bullets to the chamber and laid the gun on the coffee table before picking up the photo album. "I want you to have this photo of Cormac, Frank, and me."

Mick stood up and handed her the photo. "I'm afraid my storytelling has tired me. But if you return tomorrow, I'll tell you about boyhood fishing trips and happier times."

"I'd love to hear them." Maeve stood on her toes and hugged him. "Thank you for telling me the truth."

She could still feel the weight of the gun in her hand as she walked her bike down the path to the beach.

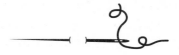

Maeve stood next to her bike at the edge of the water and tried to make sense of her father's past. Guns, bombs, and a secret brotherhood were words she couldn't associate with the kind, peace-loving man who'd raised his children to serve the community and help others. How could she possibly explain this to Kelly when she didn't understand it herself? She pointed her bike toward the village and pedaled.

Soon she realized she was headed to Egan's Pub. She needed some answers, and Uncle Connor might have them. She was hopeful when she leaned her bicycle against the planter outside the pub and tugged on the door. Egan's was quiet, and she found Connor at his usual corner with a man she didn't remember meeting.

"Hello, Uncle Connor. I'm glad to see you." Maeve squeezed her uncle's arm.

"Maeve, your timing is perfect. Your Uncle Owen, my youngest brother by a year, just came in from Roscommon." Connor Egan looked across the table. "Owen, meet Maeve Quigley, Frank's daughter."

Owen Egan stood and hugged Maeve, then invited her to join them.

Connor nodded. "You look like you have something on your mind."

"I do." Maeve sat with her uncles. "I met the most interesting man on the beach. He told me he'd been in the IRA with my dad. Is it true? Was Dad in the IRA?"

The brothers exchanged a look. Connor spoke first. "Yes, it's true."

Owen cleared his throat and took a sip of water. "What was this man's name?"

"Mick." Maeve's voice was small. "He didn't give me a last name. He lives in a tiny cottage on the beach."

"Frank worked with many operatives, and Mick is a common nickname for Michael," Connor said. "What did he tell you?"

The men sat silently as Maeve recounted her visits with the old hermit, Mick. Her eyes were filled with tears when she stopped. "I don't know why Dad didn't tell me."

"Frank had to put the past behind him. It was the only

way he could leave the IRA and protect his wife and children." Tears glistened at the edge of Connor's eyes. "You, your ma, and your brother Daniel were more important than anything to him, even his country. He left Ireland and the rest of the family to keep you safe."

Maeve let Connor's words sink in before she spoke. "Mick seems like such a good man, and he truly was hurt when Dad left Ireland. My father was such a mild-mannered soul. I can't understand the killing."

Owen cleared his throat. "Maeve, Ireland was different back then. Your father and this Mick were caught up in the passion and believed they could make a difference in their country. They wanted to carry the legacy of those who'd fought to free Ireland from Britain's rule."

She was swept back in time as her uncles told her about the side of her father she never knew. When she pushed up the kickstand of her bike to head to the bed-and-breakfast two hours later, Maeve was still trying to wrap her head around her father's past.

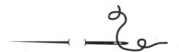

Emma sighed as her head sank into the cushy pillow on her bed at the B and B. The afternoon of shopping with Dottie Faye and Kelly was fun. Her aunt had made sure they all purchased a piece of jewelry made with local Connemara marble and at least one outfit. Emma was sure they'd graced the door of every clothing, jewelry, and china shop in the village.

She was a bit concerned about Maeve, who'd been silent and sullen after her visit with the old man she'd met on the beach. Kelly couldn't get her to talk about it. Even Dottie Faye seemed concerned about Maeve's odd behavior.

Emma felt a bit guilty as she burrowed down into her room's luxurious bed linens. It wasn't long, though, before Emma felt her eyes shut and all her cares evaporate.

A distant wailing pierced Emma's sleep, and she struggled to get her bearings. What time was it? The clock on the dresser said it was 1 a.m. Was she dreaming about Rose again? But she didn't feel the heart-pounding fear of the other dreams. Before she was fully awake, she recognized the hysterical shrieking. *Dottie Faye!*

Barreling into the sitting room, Emma nearly collided with Maeve and Kelly. Dottie Faye was pacing in front of the door, now babbling. "It was the harbinger of death!" Dottie Faye grabbed Emma by the shoulders. "I've been visited by the banshee. My time here is short. I'm gonna die!"

seven

Emma looked at the huge breakfast before her and could have sworn she felt her arteries clogging. "What happened to my hazelnut yogurt and coffee?"

The young man who had just put the plate on the table turned a nice shade of pink to match the rose in the table's bud vase. "Is it not what you ordered?"

"Yes, it's what *I* ordered for you while you three were exploring the library." Dottie Faye answered for her. "You can't stay in an Irish castle and not eat traditional Irish food. It's like breakfasting in Mississippi but refusing to eat grits." She turned to the server. "Everything is fine and dandy. Except I'll want more of that delicious-looking brown bread, and I imagine Kelly will too."

Emma pressed a spongy-looking black circle with her fork and looked at the server. "What is this?"

His eyes twinkled with amusement. "That's black pudding, miss."

"It doesn't look much like pudding to me." Emma put her fork on her plate.

"That's because it isn't, really. It's actually a sausage made from pig's blood, onions, herbs, spices, and barley. No Irish breakfast is complete without it." He nodded. "I'll be back with your bread shortly."

As soon as he disappeared, Emma glared at Dottie Faye. "Irish bacon, fried eggs, baked beans, fried mushrooms, and tomatoes. You know me better than that."

"Just try it once. For me." Dottie Faye's dangling Connemara marble earrings swayed as she moved her head. "After all, I was nearly scared to death last night by that moaning crazy woman."

Kelly speared a bite of bacon. "You really should try this. It's quite good."

"Emma, black pudding takes some getting used to, but try the bacon." Maeve sliced off a piece of the pudding. "It tastes more like ham than the bacon in the States."

Emma was saved from the bacon when the server returned with two men in uniform. "My apologies. These men are with the Garda, the Irish police. They're here to speak with Mrs. Quigley."

"I'm Maeve Quigley." Maeve lifted her hand.

"I'm Inspector Bailey." The older man swept off his hat. "This is Garda Lowney. We'd like to ask you a few questions about your relationship with the recluse known as Mick. Perhaps there's a room where we can talk privately?"

The Garda and the women followed the server to an empty dining room off the terrace. When they sat down, the server excused himself.

Maeve cleared her throat. "I'm afraid I can't be much help to you. I just met Mick a few days ago. He said he knew my father when they were very young. What is this about?"

"The old man was found dead this morning by the woman who tidies up his place for him. It looks like foul play." The inspector glanced at his notebook, and then looked Maeve in the eye. "We received an anonymous tip indicating you may have been the last person to see him alive."

Maeve closed her eyes for a moment and seemed lost in thought. "I was just getting to know him. He was very kind." She described how she'd met Mick and Fionn on the beach and gave them as many details about their three visits as she could remember, omitting their discussion of the IRA and Mick's connection to her family. "He fixed me tea, and I took him tarts." She paused and looked at the inspector. "What happened to the dog, Fionn?"

The inspector closed his notepad. "He's at an animal shelter until we can locate the man's next of kin."

Garda Lowney, who hardly looked older than Kelly's eighteen-year-old son, Keith, placed a hand on Maeve's arm. "Mrs. Quigley, if you'll voluntarily provide a DNA sample and agree to be fingerprinted, we can rule you out as a suspect and you can continue on your holiday."

The room fell silent. Kelly tapped her fingers on the table. "Is my mother under arrest?"

"Not at all. She's a person of interest in the death. We'd hoped she could give us his full name." The inspector stared at Maeve. "Can you?"

Maeve shook her head. "He only gave me his first name. I … I never asked for his last name. If it will help, I'll gladly provide a DNA sample and fingerprints."

"That would be most helpful, Mrs. Quigley," the inspector said.

Emma jumped out of her seat. "I think Maeve should retain a lawyer before she goes around providing fingerprints and DNA for a possible murder investigation."

The color drained from Maeve's face. Even her lips were pale. "I don't need a lawyer. I have nothing to hide."

"I think Emma's right. Let me call Uncle Daniel," said Kelly, pulling out her phone and moving to an empty dining room for privacy.

Emma stared out of the large picture window and watched the sea roll relentlessly into the shore. It looked like they had two mysteries to solve. There was no way they could leave Ireland until they found Liam Gallagher and Maeve was cleared of Mick's murder.

The door opened, and the server entered the near-empty room. "I ordered you another breakfast—complimentary, of course. I hope everything is all right?"

"It will be," said Kelly, stepping into the doorway. "Daniel's calling his solicitor and he'll let us know what we should do."

The inspector stood up and pulled a card from his shirt pocket. "In that case, come by the front desk of the station later this morning. Good day."

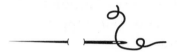

Emma was relieved to find hazelnut yogurt, a small bowl of fresh fruit, and a steaming cup of coffee at her place when they returned to the formal dining room. Kelly and Dottie Faye were equally pleased with the full Irish breakfast spread across the table.

"Emma, you just don't know what you're missing." Dottie Faye speared a bite of black pudding and dredged it in the fried egg before popping it in her mouth. "This black pudding is nearly as good as southern scrapple."

"I'll take your word for it, Dottie Faye." Emma was glad her aunt hadn't forced the stuff down her throat. She looked across the table at Maeve, who was now merely pushing food around her plate. Emma hoped the Irish police were faster at solving murders than the Mystic Harbor Police. "Maeve, I know all of this is a shock, but the police will find Mick's murderer. You have the truth on your side."

Dottie Faye's fork dropped to her plate with a clatter.

"Ah-ha! The banshee wasn't looking for *me* last night. It was looking for the hermit and visited the wrong place."

Even Maeve smiled at this. "I don't think you understand. Banshees are spirits. They don't make those kinds of mistakes."

The couple who had tangled previously with Dottie Faye seemed to be enjoying the conversation, particularly the husband. "You're dead on, madam. Banshees are serious business."

Emma wondered if Dottie Faye even noticed the twinkle in his eye. "Kelly, what does your smartphone thing say about banshees?"

Kelly tapped on the phone's screen a few moments. "It says here that the banshee is an Irish and Scottish mythological creature who begins to weep or screech when someone is about to die nearby," Kelly read. "Oh, now *here's* something I didn't know. Major families of Ireland—the O'Gradys, the O'Neills, the O'Briens, the O'Connors, and the Kavanaghs—are said to have banshees attached to them."

Emma chuckled. "I hate to burst your bubble, Dottie Faye, but our family doesn't have roots in Celtic culture. You must have been dreaming last night."

Dottie Faye started to protest when Kelly's cellphone rang.

"It's Daniel," Kelly said, looking at the phone screen before she answered.

Emma shushed Dottie Faye so she could hear Kelly's side of the conversation.

"I see." Kelly listened silently for a minute. "Does Mom need to go to the station?" She nodded. "We have a day trip planned to Galway City today. Will we still be able to go?" Kelly nodded again. "OK. I'll tell her, and we'll wait for a call from you or Mr. Rooney. Thanks for letting us know."

"What did he say?" Maeve asked when Kelly placed her phone on the table.

"Daniel said Mr. Rooney, his solicitor, will call the inspector, then he'll come by to get us soon to go to the police station. We can go to Galway City when we're done." Kelly took a sip of her coffee.

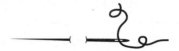

"This was a great idea." Kelly stared at the sign on Blake Castle and read its history of serving as a fifteenth-century town house for the Blake family and later a jail before becoming part of a hotel. She looked at Maeve. "I'm glad you insisted on some sightseeing to take our minds off our visitors this morning."

"I'd hate to let a misunderstanding get in the way of seeing as much of Ireland as we can." Maeve looked down Quay Street. "At least we weren't too long at the police station, and I wasn't treated horribly." Maeve looked down at her fingertips and rubbed at a remaining pit of ink from the fingerprinting.

"That inspector certainly wasn't too hard on the eyes," Dottie Faye said.

"Oh, look, there's the fish-and-chips bar listed in the travel guide." Kelly pointed up the street.

"Let's give it a try," Maeve said.

"And then we can come back for some Irish bling." Dottie Faye gestured toward the jeweler's sign claiming the shop to be "The Home of the Claddagh Ring."

After the morning Maeve had endured, Emma wasn't about to give her a hard time about food. "Fish and gems it is."

"The food must be super," Kelly said, scanning the crowded rows of long wooden tables and benches inside the restaurant. "I see a few spots at the end of that bench."

Emma couldn't believe the number of people crammed into the room. The owners had decorated the dining area with canoes, paddles, and fishing rods hung from the ceiling. But the chattering, munching diners didn't seem to notice them.

After placing their order at the window and taking a number, the quartet claimed the seats Kelly spied when they'd entered. Just down the table from them was a balding, rotund man sitting across from a skeletal blonde who turned out to be his wife. Emma felt a little claustrophobic and was about to suggest moving when she heard a snippet of the couple's conversation.

"It says here the cutthroat developer is buying up parcels along the Connemara coast near Blayloch Castle by intimidating the few landowners and tenants left." The man pointed to a photo on the folded newspaper beside his basket of fish. His accent told Emma he was a local.

His wife grimaced. "Developers are ruining this country. Everything has gotten so commercial. But this Bartley Foley is the worst. He needs to be stopped."

Maeve and Emma stared at each other with wide eyes. Emma decided they'd stay put. Had she heard the conversation correctly? Between the restaurant noise and the couple's thick Irish accent, Emma was having a difficult time understanding the couple's words.

"Excuse me, I couldn't help but overhear." Emma leaned closer to the man. "We're staying at Blayloch Castle, so I'm curious about this developer. What kind of intimidation does this Foley guy use?"

"He's been known to harass homeowners by turning them in for some small infraction, such as picking beach vegetation or building permit violations. I've also heard he's threatened to send his hard men out to give homeowners messages if less-violent methods don't work."

Maeve dropped the chip she had halfway to her mouth and looked at the woman beside her. "Do you think he's capable of murder?"

"I really couldn't say, but I wouldn't put anything past a man like him," said the skeletal woman.

The man handed Emma the newspaper. "We need to get back to our shop, but you're welcome to the newspaper."

Emma thanked them, then watched the couple walk out before folding the paper so it was a quarter of its size with the Foley story on the front.

Maeve tossed her silverware into her empty newspaper-lined fish basket. "Maybe we should discuss the article some-place a little quieter."

"Works for me."

The sun peeked out of the clouds as the four women strolled down Quay Street to the River Corrib. They found two side-by-side benches overlooking the water. Emma read the article aloud, although it didn't have much more informa-tion than their local tablemates had mentioned, while Kelly searched the Internet on her cellphone for information about Bartley Foley and his development company.

Kelly whistled. "No wonder those locals are so against Foley. According to these online articles, he's bought up several environmentally and historically valuable pieces of property to convert into commercial developments like resorts and golf courses. His tactics have been questioned in each one."

Foley's handsome smiling face staring from the paper unnerved Emma. "Could Foley have arranged Mick's murder to gain access to the land?"

"Maybe." Kelly scrolled through results of her Internet search. "I see lots of innuendo and flashy headlines, but no arrests." She stopped scrolling to read. "He's been sued several times for his business practices, but he's always come out on top."

"I just happened to pack a navy blue power suit with a strategically placed Dottie cam on the matching hat. I'll make an appointment with Mr. Foley and make a power play of my own." Dottie Faye's heels clicked on the sidewalk. "You can tell a lot about a man by the way he reacts to a powerful woman."

"I think there are better ways to go about this." Maeve interrupted Dottie Faye's grand scheme. "My nephew Brendan, Daniel's son, is a reporter with the *Western News Leader*. He might be able to give us some leads on Foley or at least tell us how to find more information about him."

Emma watched a pair of sea gulls warily approach, looking for a few tasty morsels.

"Earth to Emma." Kelly's voice crashed Emma's thoughts.

Emma jumped. "I was just watching the birds and thinking about how frustrating it is to scavenge for clues for two murders at one time again. But we won't be able to go home even if we determine whether or not Liam killed Rose—unless Mick's murderer is found. We should call Brendan."

eight

"Why are we on a windy beach before 7 a.m. when I should be curled up in that cushy bed at the castle?" Kelly clutched a paper cup between her hands. "It's barely light out here."

"Because the developer in question has been known to walk this stretch of beach at this hour when he's in town, supposedly surveying his ill-gotten property." All eyes turned to the sound of the lilting Irish brogue. "At least that's what my colleague who writes for the business section of the newspaper says."

Kelly wiped her hands on her jeans to dry the coffee that spilled when she jumped at the sound of his voice. "You must be Brendan. You have the Egan red hair. I'm Kelly."

She introduced Maeve, Emma, and Dottie Faye.

"Don't mind Kelly, she gets crabby when she's sleepy and hungry." Emma offered her hand to Brendan. "In this case, I fear she's both."

"Very funny." Kelly laughed. "But she's right, I could use some food with this coffee."

"There will be time for that later." Brendan pulled a photo from his shirt pocket and handed it to Kelly. "I took this from our photo archives."

Emma peered over Kelly's shoulder. Foley appeared to be in his fifties. His chin-length brown hair was combed back, revealing his widow's peak and framing his thin, smirking lips. "He looks more like a rock star than a developer."

"Those are some steely eyes." Kelly took a closer look before handing the photo back to Brendan.

"It was taken about six months ago when Foley was in the area closing the deal on a piece of waterfront property about a quarter mile down the beach." He pointed toward the village of Merrow.

Kelly looked in the direction Brendan indicated, closed her eyes a second, and faced the other way. "Mick's cottage is this way, right?"

"Yes." Brendan nodded. "Have you thought about what you'll say if you see him?"

Dottie Faye cleared her throat. "I took the liberty of bringing my tropical flower Dottie cam." Dottie Faye lightly patted the pink hibiscus with her left hand. "I'll just use my feminine wiles on him and see what happens."

"That's your plan?" Brendan looked at Maeve with raised eyebrows. "Maybe it would be best to follow the man first and see where he goes. We might get some answers without saying a word."

Emma saw Dottie Faye's lips purse. "Dottie Faye, let's try it his way. After all, Brendan *is* an investigative reporter. Your Dottie cam will come in handy to document where he goes."

Dottie Faye looked unconvinced. "I still think—"

"You'll have plenty of time to unleash your feminine wiles on the man once we learn a little more about him." Kelly drained the rest of her coffee and tossed the cup into the nearby trash basket.

They walked in a tight line down the beach as Brendan told them about the one time he'd met Foley during a political event several years before. "He was charismatic in front of the cameras, but I happened to walk in on a heated discussion between him and the campaigning politician. Foley threatened to destroy the man's career if he didn't support the project he was working on at the time."

Maeve stopped walking. "There's Mick's cottage." Her voice wavered. "I still can't believe he's gone."

"Is that Foley?" Dottie Faye tapped Emma's shoulder. "Look on the path just off the beach."

"Yes, I think so." Emma watched as Foley walked farther onto the beach and looked back at Mick's cottage.

"He sure didn't waste any time, the vulture," Maeve said through clenched teeth.

"He might recognize me from my photo on the newspaper website. I'll hide in the dunes." Brendan motioned the group forward. Emma was surprised by how close they were to Foley before he seemed to notice them.

"He doesn't look too amused, does he?" Emma said.

Kelly shook her head and inched forward. She stopped, her mouth dropping as Maeve ran ahead of them toward Foley.

"Excuse me, are you Bartley Foley?" she said, stopping several paces in front of him.

"Who are you?" Foley's chin-length brown hair blew in the breeze.

"I was a friend of the man who lived here." Maeve glanced at the cottage as Kelly and Emma caught up with her. "Did you know him?"

His thin lips curled into a sneer. "You could say that."

Before Maeve could reply, two gorilla-looking men in dark suits approached, pushing Brendan to stand in front of Foley.

"I recognize you. You're that political snoop for the *Western News Leader*. I'm not talking to the press. If you don't respect my privacy, then the newspaper will hear from my attorneys. Get out of here, all of you." Foley disappeared into the dunes.

The bald man to the left of Brendan lifted his coat to show a pistol. "Mr. Foley asked you nicely. We won't be so polite."

His nearly toothless partner grinned, and they released

Brendan. "We like being impolite. Now get out of here. And stay away from Mr. Foley."

Maeve took a deep breath and opened her mouth to speak, but Brendan linked his arm through hers and turned her around. "I think it's time for us to leave while we still can."

Brendan picked up the pace and didn't look back. He didn't slow down until they were close to where they'd met earlier. "We should be OK now. I don't intimidate easily, but those are guys you don't want to tangle with." He looked at Maeve. "You were about to tangle with them, weren't you?"

"So, what do you suggest as our next step?" Emma said before Maeve could respond. She didn't want to waste time spinning their wheels.

"I suggest you call that handsome inspector." Dottie Faye tried to calm her windblown hair—now a lopsided, teased, and sprayed mass—by flattening it with her hand. "Better yet, we can stop by the station on the way back to the B and B. He'd be a nice catch for you, Emma. You'll need to comb your hair, though. It's a mess."

"Mrs. Sinclair, I suggest you not call or visit the inspector. In fact, I don't think you should go back to the bed-and-breakfast yet, just in case you're being followed. Do a bit of sightseeing or shopping for a few hours. In the meantime, I'll see if our crime reporter has gotten any information about the murder. I'll also do more digging for information about Foley."

Kelly's face brightened. "I've always wanted to see the Cliffs of Moher. They look so haunting and majestic in photos."

Emma groaned to herself. Delays in clearing Maeve complicated their efforts to find Liam Gallagher. "We can go, but maybe we should spend some time trying to find out where Gallagher lives. We can't forget why we came to Ireland in the first place. Brendan, do you have any ideas?"

"You can try to access the Land Registry online, but I don't know exactly how that works." He didn't sound confident. "You might be able to do a search on his name. He may own property through various companies, but it's worth a try."

Kelly smiled. "I can search on my phone while you drive us to the Cliffs of Moher."

"Sounds like a good compromise. Brendan has a good point, we do need to be cautious and lay low awhile." Emma turned to Brendan. "Can you give us directions?"

He removed his reporter's notebook from his back pocket and scribbled a few lines before tearing off the sheet and handing it to Emma. "It's a beautiful drive, but the road is curvy and narrow. Take it slow and enjoy the view."

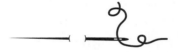

By the time Emma pulled the van into the Cliffs of Moher visitor center parking lot, everyone in the car was enchanted with the rugged Atlantic coast of Ireland. While Maeve and Dottie Faye searched for the restrooms, Kelly stood along the rail at the main observation area, her face to the wind, and slowly moved her head from one direction to the other to take in the view. Emma held back and watched her best friend soak in every nuance of the place.

Emma walked to Kelly's side and stood in silence for a moment before lightly touching the sleeve of Kelly's jacket. "Is it everything you expected?"

"Moher or less." Kelly grinned.

Emma laughed and put her hands on the guardrail as she looked down. "It *is* sort of magical here. Makes me want to believe in those fairies Rose was so sure existed." Emma was disappointed that Kelly hadn't found a listing for Gallagher's property on the Land Registry site, but she wasn't going to let it ruin her day. They would dig deeper and find out if he used a corporate name. "I'm glad I'm here to experience it with you."

"I'm glad you're here with me too." Kelly inhaled like she was trying to take in every bit of the salt air. "The cliffs rise up to 700 feet at the highest point and extend for almost five miles over the Atlantic Ocean. I can understand why so many poems and songs have been written about them."

How long had Kelly been talking of visiting Ireland? Ever since they'd met as kids. A sharp pang ran through Emma. She'd made this trip all about finding Rose's murderer and had ignored its importance to Maeve and Kelly. "Maybe this would be a good time for one of those selfies. We can memorialize your first look at the Cliffs of Moher."

Kelly took the photo with her smartphone and sent a copy to her kids, Keith and Julie, before strolling back to the underground exhibition center to find Dottie Faye and Maeve. "They've been together awhile now." Kelly opened the door to the center. "I hope they haven't wounded each other."

"Maybe they're plotting to find me a husband. Things get scary when those two start to cooperate." Emma stepped into the circular room.

Emma and Kelly drifted along themed exhibits lining the walls, stopping from time to time to read about the cliffs. They found Maeve and Dottie Faye in the center of the building, watching a film about the area's history.

Joining Maeve and Dottie Faye on the long row of wooden seating, Emma and Kelly were soon caught up in the story of the Cliffs of Moher. After the film, they headed to the bottom-floor café to satisfy the rumbling in Kelly's stomach while taking in a stellar view of the cliffs.

"What a rush it must be to stand right at the edge." Kelly's nose almost touched the window, her roast beef sandwich largely untouched on the plate behind her. "Can we do it?"

"I think this is the first time I've ever seen you more interested in scenery than food." Emma shuddered. "The view from here works fine for me. Being too close to the edge reminds me of looking out of an airplane window."

"Where's your sense of adventure?" Dottie Faye looked at her niece and shook her head. "I think we should walk around a bit outside before we head back to the B and B."

Maeve looked down at Dottie Faye's signature stilettos. "I have no idea how you walk in those things, much less on steep slopes."

"Years of practice." Dottie Faye recrossed her legs. "I'm more comfortable in these than in sneakers. I'll meet my Maker wearing fabulous shoes."

Kelly turned around in her chair and looked at her plate, the only one on the table with food left on it. She wolfed down the rest of her sandwich, then announced that she was ready to go.

When they emerged into the windy sunshine, Kelly's phone vibrated, signaling a new voice mail was waiting for her. She motioned for the group to stop as she punched in her password to retrieve the message. "It's from Brendan." Kelly covered one ear from the wind and seemed to strain to hear the message. "The authorities released a statement announcing they've discovered Mick's true identity," Kelly told the rest. "They're working on a couple of leads."

She snapped the phone shut and slipped it into her pocket. "Brendan said the inspector refused to release the old man's full name. He'll call us as soon as he has an update."

The women took the path to the Sea Stack viewing area

and O'Brien's Tower. Even Emma, enchanted with the cliffs, found herself inching closer to the edge than she'd ever imagined. Mesmerized by the sea mist and the waves crashing below, she stood alone, taking in the scene as the others headed toward the tower. She was starting on the path when two hands grabbed her from behind and forced her toward the edge of the cliff. Her screams were carried over the cliffs by the wind, but Emma had no intention of following them. Her arms pinned against her body by muscled biceps, her hands grasped for skin, clothing, jewelry, anything that might cause him to let go.

With the wind and her heartbeat roaring in her ears, Emma watched the cliff edge as her feet neared it. *God help me, please. Don't let me die before I find out what happened to Rose!*

nine

Emma lurched backward and the man's arms suddenly released her as she fell to the ground. Stunned when her cheek slammed into a rock, Emma sat up just in time to see Dottie Faye sprawled on the path lobbing a second stiletto at the back of a hulking man dressed in blue jeans and a black shirt.

When the shoe struck him on his head, Dottie Faye pumped her fist. "Take that, you monster!"

Emma was shaking and laughing at the same time. *God really does work in mysterious ways, doesn't He?*

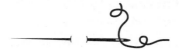

Emma thanked Kevan, the castle's host, but declined his offer of a wheelchair after he'd spotted her hobbling through the front door. She felt wimpy enough, agreeing to allow Kelly to drive home from the cliffs and use the valet service so Emma wouldn't have to walk from the car park.

"Let me escort you into the drawing room," he said. "I took the liberty of ordering you tea when I saw you arrive."

Emma started to reply, but Dottie Faye shushed her.

"Just let him spoil us." Dottie Faye, with one broken heel, walked unevenly across the stone floor. She looked at Kevan and brushed her hands across her throat. "We've just had a traumatic experience. Emma was accosted at the Cliffs of Moher and nearly plunged to her death. We could use a treat."

"Miss Cotton, are you all right?" Kevan asked, taking her arm and ushering her toward the drawing room. "There are beverages on the bar—hot tea, coffee, sodas, and mineral water. We'll have sandwiches, fruit, and sweets for you shortly."

He waited as the women found seats, Emma and Kelly on the sofa with Dottie Faye and Maeve in overstuffed chairs.

"Yes, I'm fine, really. I received first aid where I took the spill. Evidently, it's park policy to require visitors to seek first aid and file a formal report if there's an incident on-site." Emma was happy to see a small flame in the fireplace; the evening had turned chilly. She was equally glad to notice there were no other guests in the room.

Kelly's phone rang just as she stood to pour four cups of tea. "Hello? Yes, Inspector. Do you mind if I put you on speakerphone so my mother and friends can hear?"

"Yes, well … I'm calling to inform you that the deceased man known as Mick has been identified as the former IRA operative Hugh Slane. Mrs. Quigley, a background check has revealed your father's identity as a former IRA terrorist. We know Frank Egan had a falling-out with the IRA and immigrated to the United States when you were a child. I caution you to remain in this country until this case is solved. Do you understand?"

Maeve hesitated a split-second. "Yes, I understand. Is that all?"

They said their goodbyes, and Kelly disconnected the call with wide eyes. "Mom, why didn't you tell me about Grandpa?"

"I just found out from Mick, and I wanted to learn more." Maeve's lip quivered. "But I never had the chance."

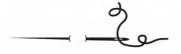

"Mmm, there's nothing like the perfect cup of coffee to start the day." Emma watched steam swirl from her mug and disappear. "The Irish may be known for their love of tea, but this coffee is the best."

After the previous day's excitement, they all decided to order room service for breakfast in hopes of starting the day on a more peaceful note.

"I don't know. This breakfast tea is some of the best I've ever tasted." Maeve added a splash of milk to her tea and leaned back in her chair.

Kelly spread jam on a scone and was just about to drop a dot of clotted cream onto it with a spoon when someone pounded on the door. She jumped and the cream plopped on the plate instead.

"I'll get it." Dottie Faye placed her Hollywood gossip magazine upside down to mark her place. "You never know when a gentleman caller will show up."

She pressed wrinkles from her pants before opening the door. "Why Inspector Bailey, come right on in here." Dottie Faye stood aside and winked at Emma as the man entered. "What can we do for you?"

He stepped to the left and approached Maeve. "We found your fingerprints on the grip of the weapon used to kill Hugh Slane." Inspector Bailey removed the handcuffs from his belt. "Maeve Quigley, you are under arrest for the murder of Hugh Slane."

Maeve looked confused. "I'm being arrested? All we did was have tea."

Bailey cuffed Maeve's hands together while explaining her rights. "You are not obliged to say anything unless you wish to do so, but anything you say may be taken down in writing and may be used in evidence."

Kelly leapt from her chair. "Mom, don't say anything until we get you a lawyer. We'll call Daniel and Brendan and ask them how to handle this."

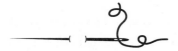

Two hours later, Deirdre placed a large basket of sliced brown bread next to a plate of cheese on the large table in the alcove of Egan's Pub. "Bread is good for the soul." A teapot was on one end and a coffee carafe on the other. "We're still waiting on Nessa and Orrin."

Connor, the eldest Egan, sat at the head of the table. He'd motioned for Kelly, Emma, and Dottie Faye to sit in the three seats to his right. Emma sat in front of the coffeepot between Kelly and Dottie Faye. There was enough food to feed a small army. How many Egans were going to be a part of this family meeting to decide how to handle Maeve's arrest? Emma pulled a pen and a small notepad from her purse to keep track of Kelly's family members and to take notes about Maeve's situation.

"Daniel's on the phone with our solicitor." Connor Egan's voice was strong with purpose despite his advanced age. "Have you spoken to Maeve since the arrest?"

Kelly shook her head. "No, we called you first. We didn't want to go to the station until we had more information and some sort of game plan."

Eamon and Deirdre added plates and silverware to the table, and then claimed seats across from Emma, leaving an empty chair next to Connor.

Emma looked around the table at Kelly's family. "We don't have a great track record with law enforcement in the United

States, so we thought it would be better to talk to you first."

At Connor's urging, Kelly and Emma told the story of Rose's death and their frustration with the Mystic Harbor Police Department. They'd just finished when Daniel joined them. Before he could say a word about the solicitor, Eamon's sister Nessa and her husband, Orrin Halloran, arrived.

Daniel spoke as soon as everyone was seated. "Unfortunately, I don't have any news. Irving was just going into a meeting with a barrister on a fraud case." He looked at Kelly. "He did say he'd have an associate do some checking and see exactly what charges were filed. Right now, the best thing to do is wait until we get some answers from Irving. However, you might want to consider calling the American consulate in Dublin and see what they can do for Maeve. They're not open today since it's Sunday, but I'd call first thing in the morning."

Nessa reached for a slice of bread. "I think you should leave the investigating up to the Gardaí and do some sightseeing. There's not much you can do now, is there?" She spread a pat of butter on the bread. "Go visit the craft shops in Spiddal; they have the finest Aran sweaters and fabrics. Then take the ferry across Galway Bay to Inishmore of the Aran Islands. I'd love to show you around."

"I have to say you're dead wrong, my love." Orrin Halloran smiled at his wife before addressing Kelly. "If you wait for the authorities to handle it, then Maeve will never be cleared. They won't look past her fingerprints to find the real killer."

Daniel shook his head. "I don't think we need to rush into anything. Let's wait until Irving calls back with a plan. My sister is a tough old bird. She'll be OK." He glanced down at his notes. "Brendan called last night and mentioned the developer you tangled with on the beach. I passed the information along to Irving. Did you tell the inspector about it?"

"No, we didn't." Kelly snagged a piece of cheese from the tray. "I didn't think about it, actually. We were all in shock when Mom was arrested. We're going to the jail when we leave here. Do you think we should report the incident?"

"I think it's best to keep it among us at the moment, at least until we hear from Irving," Daniel answered.

Emma nudged Kelly with her foot and nodded in agreement. She was glad Kelly understood her desire to keep silent. After all, the Mystic Harbor Police had done their part to slow the investigation into Rose's death. It was probably best to not mention their suspicions about Foley to Inspector Bailey—at least not yet.

Kelly looked around the table at her relatives. "Thank you all for your help. Now we really need to get to the station to see Mom, but we'll stop by after our visit."

ten

"They're allowing all of us to go in?" Dottie Faye put her lips closer to Emma's ear as they walked down the hall to the holding cell to see Maeve. "In all the TV cop shows, the only time they allow visitors in with the suspect is when they plan to eavesdrop for information to incriminate them."

Emma lowered her chin to signal she'd already thought of it. They'd gone through a security check and surrendered their purses at the front desk to be put in a locker during the visit. Kelly wouldn't be able to record the conversation on her phone, but at least they could talk to Maeve. Maybe they could help her remember something important. And maybe this was a way to get the cops to look at someone else as a suspect besides Maeve.

The Garda stopped in front of a door and hesitated until a buzzer sounded. "You have ten minutes."

Kelly hurried into the room and wrapped her arms around her mother. "How are you? I'm sorry we took so long to get here, but we stopped by the pub to get the family's advice on what to do next."

Emma grabbed Dottie Faye's arm to keep her from interrupting. Maeve looked tired and rumpled but calm as she and Kelly whispered greetings. Maeve never was one given to hysterics. Even so, how long could she hold up under this stress?

"Maeve, we're so glad to see you." Emma crossed the floor when Kelly waved them farther into the room. The fluorescent lights gave it a stark, foreboding atmosphere. "The Egan clan is lining up a solicitor for you. Hang in there."

Even Dottie Faye was affected by the surroundings and gave her rival a one-armed hug. "If we ask you a couple of questions about your visits with that Slane man, maybe it will jog your memory and help you recollect something important."

"That's not a bad idea," Maeve said. "Let's sit at the table, then fire away."

After a round of questions without any luck, the questions became more specific, and Maeve remembered a little more with each one. With some prodding, she remembered the group of hoodlums throwing mud at the cottage and described how Mick had run them off by firing a rifle shot into the air. "He hadn't seemed afraid, and it was like the youngsters were in the habit of harassing him." She closed her eyes in concentration. "I remember thinking I'd heard voices and rustling in the dunes when I left Mick's cottage after my second visit, but I never saw anyone. The wind had whipped up, and I figured I was just imagining things. I've already told you everything else."

Kelly looked at her mother. "Maybe this was all IRA related. Could the family of the guy who was killed years ago possibly be responsible for Mick's death? Maybe it's a vendetta."

A fluorescent light bulb flickered overhead and Emma felt her temples throb. "Why would they wait over fifty years for revenge? Why now? He's an old man."

Dottie Faye tapped the forefingers and thumbs of her hands together, and the clacking of acrylic nails broke the short silence in the tiny room. "Love triangle? Murders usually involve love triangles."

"I don't think so." Maeve shook her head. "The only

woman he mentioned was his great-niece who stopped by to visit with baked goods from time to time."

All four women flinched when the door squeaked open and the Garda entered the room. "Time's up. I'll walk you out. Mrs. Quigley, you'll remain here. Someone will be in to take you back to your cell."

Maeve hugged Kelly. When they separated, Maeve looked at all three women. "Please be careful. Stay safe."

Kelly looked back at her mom before she walked out the door, and the women filed out of the room behind the Garda. They ran into Inspector Bailey in the lobby.

"Good afternoon, Inspector." Emma led the entourage over to him. "I'm sure you know we just had a visit with Maeve Quigley. She told us a few more details about her visits with Hugh Slane."

He nodded and Emma had a feeling he already knew what they were about to tell him. She described Maeve's story about the local ruffians who had thrown objects at Slane's cottage, and Kelly filled him in about the family that might still blame the old man for Cormac O'Broins's death. Bailey made a show of making notes in his little book, but Emma noticed he didn't write down much of what they said.

Kelly fidgeted beside her. "Inspector, what's the next step? We can't just sit around sipping tea and eating scones while Mom languishes in jail."

"Obviously you've done enough, or Miss Cotton wouldn't have been attacked at the Cliffs of Moher. I don't know who you've rattled, but for your own safety, I suggest you stop playing investigator." Inspector Bailey looked each woman in the eye before continuing. "Do something fun where there aren't any cliffs."

Emma balled her hands into fists as a momentary desire

to slug him for being a condescending oaf surged through her. She came to her senses when Dottie Faye's elbow connected with her side

"Yes, we'll consider it," she managed to say between clenched teeth.

"Inspector, surely a strong, intelligent man such as yourself can understand our predicament." Dottie Faye batted her eyelashes and ran her fingers up his forearm. "We're in a foreign country, and our friend is being accused of a crime she didn't commit. You can't blame us for wanting to find answers. It would mean ever so much if you'd keep us informed of what's happening."

Bailey removed her hand from his shirt sleeve. "Stay out of the investigation and stop bothering fine upstanding Irishmen like Bartley Foley, or I'll be forced to detain you. I will find the ruffians your mother saw and look into their activities. Just remember what I said. You are tourists here. It would be in your best interest to act like it."

Emma flinched.

How did he know about their encounter with Foley?

eleven

"If I didn't know any better, I'd say I'm losing my touch." Dottie Faye pulled the station door shut behind her. "The inspector didn't even crack a smile, and I used my best lines too."

"It's not you, Dottie Faye." Emma frowned.

Kelly groaned. "I have to agree. I'd like to stop back by the pub and see if Uncle Daniel has any news."

"Good idea," Emma said. "Maybe we can ask about the young punks who were harassing Hugh Slane. Eamon and Deirdre might know who they are."

"Perhaps handsome young Brendan will drop in with some news of Foley." Dottie Faye grinned at Emma and ignored her scowl. "Well, you can't blame an adoring aunt for trying, Emma Jane."

The lunch rush was over, and most of the occupied seats in the pub were filled by members of the Egan family taking a break before preparing for the dinner hour. Emma, Kelly, and Dottie Faye found Connor holding court in the alcove.

"If it isn't our Kelly and company." Connor motioned them to the table where he was sharing a platter of *boxty*—potato pancakes—with Eamon and Deirdre. Eamon and Deirdre's son Michael was straightening up the bar. "Eamon, would you ask Michael to bring more for our guests? And some vegetable soup too."

Emma looked around the near-empty pub before pulling out her chair. She had never cared much for loud, crowded places. The quiet of midafternoon Egan's was cozy and inviting.

Framed faces of generations of Egan fishermen, musicians, farmers, and barkeeps graced the wall behind her. Several round game tables were lined up in front of the bar. Two had chess boards waiting for players to order pints and settle in for a lengthy match. An alcove on the far side of the pub held a snooker table, a pool table, and a dartboard. The tables and chairs were old and scarred but polished and as shiny as the mahogany bar. People, she could tell, came here to be part of a family.

Connor got down to business. "How is our Maeve? She's a strong woman, just like her own mother, God rest her soul."

Everyone waited as Kelly swallowed a bite of boxty and took a sip of the tea Eamon had put before her. "She seemed calm but concerned and tired."

Connor Egan listened silently as his great-niece described the visit to the Garda station. Every now and then, he'd take a spoonful of soup, but his eyes never left her face. When she stopped talking, the old man patted her hand. "It may seem bleak, but we'll get it figured out. As soon as Daniel hears back from Irving, we'll know what to do."

Emma felt Kelly nudge her foot. "Since we were warned to stay out of the investigation," Emma said, "I thought tomorrow might be a good time for us to take that trip to the Aran Islands with Nessa." She looked at Kelly with purpose. "It might be a bit of welcome distraction for you."

"Emma Jane, Maeve also told us something else." Dottie Faye pantomimed winding up and throwing an object at the wall, her collection of bangle bracelets jangling as they shook. "We were going to ask about the juvenile delinquents that had been harassing Mick—I mean, Mr. Slane. Remember?"

"Oh, is that what you were doing? Throwing fake mud globs?" Emma felt her face flush. "I guess this whole situation has all of us on edge, myself included." She looked at Eamon and Deirdre. "Have you had any problems with a pack of wild teenagers?"

"Ah, we know the group." Deirdre frowned. "Michael has had to run them out of here a time or two when they've hassled customers while playing pool."

Eamon bobbed his head. "They're constantly after mischief. You know, spray painting business signs, verbally accosting people, playing loud music. We've been the lucky ones. They've done nothing to the pub."

The door to Egan's opened and Nessa and Orrin entered with their preteen twins, John and Bridie. The youngsters waved a quick greeting and went directly to the pool table while their parents joined the family meeting.

"What's the story?" Nessa sat down in the chair Orrin pulled out for her at the far end of the table. "Did Irving ring?"

"He didn't," Eamon answered. "Daniel keeps checking back with Irving's office. He's at the bank right now. He should return soon. His property management company keeps him busy these days."

Customers began to filter into the pub, so Eamon and Deirdre excused themselves to take care of business. Emma was surprised to see a mix of patrons including a couple with two small children, several older businessmen in suits, a number of young adults sporting the latest fashions, and a pair of elderly gentleman who settled in to play chess.

Kelly yawned and Emma realized the stress of her mother's arrest was taking its toll on her friend. Maybe they should head back to the B and B. "Nessa, we need to be getting back to the castle in a few minutes, but are you still up for a trip to the Aran Islands tomorrow? I don't think there's much we can do at this point anyway."

"I am." Nessa stuck a fork in the last *boxty* patty on the platter and transferred it to her plate. "I'll come around to get you in the morning."

"We have a roomy minivan, and I'm getting the hang of this driving on the left side of the road." Emma wasn't good at sitting back and letting someone else do the driving. "How about we pick *you* up here?"

With the next morning's plans solidified, Emma, Kelly, and Dottie Faye stepped out of Egan's Pub and discovered they'd spent most of the afternoon with Maeve's family. They strolled down the street to the van and discussed their trip to the island. "Inisheer will be like stepping back in time. You'll love it," Kelly said. "We can cycle around the island and—"

She was silenced when the punks they'd seen on their first foray into the village spilled out of the alleyway and blocked their passage. *Maybe these are the same ones who had been harassing Mick*, Emma thought.

"Oi, it's the *Yanks*." The gang leader spit out the word as if spewing poison. "Have you found the leprechauns you Yanks always come searching for?"

Refusing to react to their aggressive behavior, Emma and Kelly simply stepped off the curb and ignored the black capes, gloves, and eyeliner as well as the slurs. They'd just taken a couple of steps into the street when Emma realized Dottie Faye wasn't with them. Emma wasn't sure if she should laugh or scream.

Her aunt was poised for action, her leopard-print-clad legs spread for balance and her left pointer finger aimed at the ruffians like a weapon. "You think you're so scary? You look utterly ridiculous in those vampire capes and black eye shadow. You should—"

The rest of her sentence evaporated as Emma and Kelly

pulled Dottie Faye across the intersection to a jewelry store while the juvenile delinquents roared with laughter in their wake. After Dottie Faye spent twenty minutes selecting a Celtic knot ring while lecturing Emma about standing up to bullies, the women made their way back to the van. Emma unlocked the doors with the remote, and as she started to slide into the driver's seat, she noticed a slip of paper under the windshield wiper. She grabbed it and got into the van before unfolding the paper.

Dottie Faye tapped Emma's shoulder. "What is it, sweet pea?"

"It's an unsigned note." Emma peered at the handwritten words and read them aloud. "If you want to see Maeve Quigley set free, take the ten o'clock ferry to Inisheer. We have information about the old man's murder. Contact will be made on the island. Keep the meeting secret, if you know what's good for you."

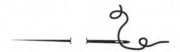

"You have a visitor." Kevan nodded to the seating area just past the front desk as Emma, Kelly, and Dotty Faye entered the B and B. "A Mr. Egan, although he did say you weren't expecting him."

All eyes followed Kevan's gaze. Kelly waved. "There are a lot of Egans around here. This one's my cousin Brendan. He's welcome to visit us anytime."

"Would you like refreshments during your visit? They can be served in the drawing room or the library, if you wish."

Dottie Faye shooed Emma and Kelly toward Brendan and hung back to answer Kevan. The last thing she heard before Dottie Faye was out of earshot was "Now aren't you just the sweetest?"

"Hallo!" Brendan first kissed Kelly's cheek, then did the same to Emma, sending a flush creeping up her face. Not one to use much makeup, Emma was glad she had listened to Dottie Faye and used a tad more foundation this morning to cover the scrape on her cheek.

"So what's the *craic*?" Brendan stepped back as Dottie Faye joined the group.

Dottie Faye put her hand on her hips. "Excuse me? Nobody here uses crack or any other street drug. Emma Jane is a health nut."

Brendan's snicker sounded oddly similar to Kelly's. "Dottie Faye, you're a gas! 'What's the *craic*?' means 'What's going on?'"

"Oh. I've heard it so much since we arrived in Ireland that I was beginning to wonder about the people here."

The laughter continued as they strolled into the library. Brendan looked at Emma. "How's your cheek? When I stopped by to see Ma and Da, they told me about what happened at the cliffs."

Emma brushed her fingers against the scrape. "It's feeling much better today." She crossed the room to the sideboard.

An array of cups and glasses, teapots and coffeepots, and bottled drinks were spread across an ornate Gothic walnut sideboard. Emma plucked a bottle of water from an ice bucket, eased herself down onto the brown leather sofa, and leaned against a burgundy and deep blue paisley pillow for extra cushioning. She was still a tad sore.

Brendan stood while Kelly and Dottie Faye assembled their coffee cups on a marble-topped table and settled into matching armchairs on either side of it. When the women were seated, he sat on the sofa with Emma.

Kelly was just finishing a dramatic retelling of Dottie Faye's excellent aim on the cliffs when a hostess wheeled in a tea cart laden with sandwiches, fruit, and an assortment of cookies. "They are certainly feeding us well in Ireland." Kelly plucked a crustless sandwich from the silver tray. "It almost makes up for some of the rude treatment we've received."

Brendan frowned. "Anything else happen?"

Emma explained their run-in with the hoodlums in the village, and she noticed Brendan was listening intently.

"That's some story." He grinned at Dottie Faye. "Fair play, Dottie Faye, fair play!"

Dottie Faye scowled. "I wasn't playing, young man. I meant business."

He laughed. "What I meant to say, as you Americans do, is way to go!"

"Kelly dear, I really like this cousin of yours." A mischievous glint flashed in Dottie Faye's eyes. She opened her mouth in a huge yawn and stared at Kelly. "I'm a little tired. Would you mind keeping me company while I wind down for the night?"

"Sure, Dottie Faye. Sounds like a good plan." Kelly drained her teacup. "I think I'll head up to the room too. You kids have fun."

Emma and Brendan said good night and watched the chattering pair of conspirators walk out of the library and close the double doors behind them.

"That was subtle." Brendan's lips lifted into a smile. "Does it happen often?"

Emma grinned too. "More than you know."

He shifted on the sofa, not only turning his body toward her but moving closer. "I'm glad they left. I've wanted to talk to you alone."

Emma noticed his eyes were the same shade of green as Maeve's. "Really?"

"Forgive me for asking this about my own aunt and your good friend, but is there any possibility Maeve could have killed Hugh Slane?" Brendan seemed to be staring a hole in her. "I've really just met her. I don't know her well enough to make a judgment, although I don't want to believe she's capable of murder."

Emma leaned away from him as far as she could without toppling over the arm of the sofa. "Are you asking as a nephew or a reporter?"

Brendan placed his hand on her shoulder for a brief second. "Nephew. I never mix news business with family matters. I'm only trying to help."

"Glad to hear it." Emma straightened her back and looked him in the eye. "Maeve may be a spitfire, but she's a woman of principles. She couldn't and wouldn't have killed Hugh Slane, especially since he'd been a link to her father's hidden past. Now that information is gone forever."

He nodded. "Makes sense. Da said you were here on some sort of business with Liam Gallagher. You have a quilt design business, right?"

"Design and restoration, yes." Emma hesitated, wondering how much she should tell a newspaper reporter about the real purpose of their trip. "But that's not why we're here."

Brendan stood and went to the sideboard to pour another cup of tea and fetch a second bottle of water for Emma. "So, why are you here? My gut tells me it's not just to meet Aunt Maeve's family."

Emma took the proffered water, unscrewed the cap, and took a swig before beginning the story she'd repeated so many times that she could now tell it without hesitation. Brendan listened without interrupting, taking a sip of tea from time to time.

Two cups of tea later, when she concluded with a blow-by-blow description of the events in Gallagher's Dublin office, Brendan whistled. "A famous actor, a fabric design guru, and a textile giant. You ladies certainly don't mind slaying dragons, do you?"

He sat motionless for a long minute. "Well?" Emma asked. "What are your thoughts?"

"So, you came to Ireland to solve one murder and landed in the middle of another one. I feel like I'm watching a Jim Sheridan film," Brendan said. "Foley has a bit of a reputation for being a bully who uses underhanded tactics, so I can see how he is a viable suspect in Hugh Slane's murder. But Gallagher is a local boy who built his company the honest way. I've not even heard rumors of shady dealings about him, although I've seen stranger things happen."

"I won't lie; it's been difficult trying to untangle two mysteries at the same time. The property search was a dead end. Gallagher's home must be under a different name. The lack of information is frustrating." Emma ran her finger through condensation on the water bottle and watched the water puddle against her finger. "Except for the warm welcome from your family, I've not seen much evidence of the Irish hospitality since arriving here."

"Don't give up on the Irish just yet. Everything will be better when Maeve is cleared." Brendan scooted to the edge of the sofa. "You look tired. I'm going leave you now." He stood up, and she followed suit. "I'm impressed with your dedication to your friends and your sleuthing abilities. It'll be fun watching you solve both of these mysteries."

twelve

The next morning, Emma stood at the rail on the sightseeing ferry, eyes closed, and inhaled the salt air. Inside the windbreaker's pocket, her fingers brushed against the note she'd found on the van's windshield the previous afternoon. She hoped they would get information to help set Maeve free.

"The sea has played a huge part in the history of Ireland, from the influence of foreign marauders to fishing industry folklore," Kelly said, playing her part well. Emma had shown Kelly the note immediately because they didn't keep secrets from each other. Nessa and Dottie Faye were blissfully unaware of the potential danger lurking on Inisheer.

"Indeed." Nessa took over the storytelling. "The *currach*, the boat fishermen used, was lightweight and made of a skeleton of thin, narrow pieces of wood covered with canvas and coated with tar. They were designed to survive the rough Atlantic waters. According to the legend, Aran fishermen refused to learn how to swim because they were sure to drown in any sea rough enough to sink a *currach*. Their reasoning was that it was better to drown quickly." She laughed. "Of course, the Egans are a hardheaded bunch, so most of them learned to swim just in case."

"I can vouch for the hardheadedness of the Egans," Emma joked, glancing at Kelly.

"Her mother's incessant desire to outdo me is further proof of the family flaw," Dottie Faye chimed in. "Not that she ever succeeds."

Nessa brushed her salt-and-pepper bangs out of her eyes, although it was fruitless in the wind. "What's with you and Maeve?"

"They're just two very competitive women." Kelly answered before Dottie Faye had a chance. "Neither one likes to be outshined by the other. Makes for some interesting times."

"I bet." Nessa pointed at the island, and the women watched as the boat nudged into the port and everyone gravitated toward the exit at the back of the boat. Emma scanned the dock but didn't see anyone who looked suspicious, although she knew from experience that both danger and help wore many faces.

"What do we do now?" Kelly's breath tickled Emma's ear.

Emma shrugged. "I guess we just get off the boat with everyone else and see what happens."

Kelly and Emma disembarked ahead of Nessa and Dottie Faye. They walked a few paces from the boat and let the other tourists pass as their land legs returned. But nobody approached them. Kelly pulled a folded sheet from her shoulder bag. "I printed this map at the B and B. Why don't we find a place on shore to sit and figure out what we want to see?"

Nessa mentioned a shipwreck, monastery ruins, and a castle as the women strolled to the end of the dock. "We could just walk around and see what draws you."

As soon as they stepped off the dock, a young man in brown trousers and a blue windbreaker greeted them. "Welcome to Inisheer Island. Enjoy your visit." He handed Kelly a folded brochure. "Be sure to check out the itinerary before you start your tour."

As Kelly took the brochure from his hands, Emma concentrated on remembering details of his appearance—dark hair, brown eyes, about 5 feet 9 inches, with an Irish lilt to his voice. No visible tattoos or piercings. He could be anyone in Ireland. He was maybe twenty-five years old.

His message delivered, the man trotted down the dock and hopped into a waiting motorboat. As the boat pulled away, Emma grabbed a notepad and pen from her purse and wrote down his description. "So, what are our instructions?"

Nessa crossed her arms. "Will someone please tell me what is going on?"

"Yes, please do." Dottie Faye put her hands on her hips. "Start talking, girls."

Emma pulled the note from her pocket and passed it to Nessa. "I received this yesterday morning. It promises us information to help free Maeve."

Nessa read the note aloud.

"And you believe that? Let me see this." Dottie Faye grabbed the note from Nessa's fingers. "I never took you two for gullible innocents. Do you really think you'll get anything more than trouble from these people, whoever they are?"

"At this point, we don't have anything to lose." Kelly looked at the brochure in her hand and then at Dottie Faye. "If you were in trouble, we'd do this for you too."

Nessa cleared her throat and pointed to a dot on the tour map. "Emma, are you up to cycling to the Teampall Chaomhain? We could hire a horse cart, but then we'd have to worry about the safety and interference of the driver."

"I can handle it." Emma looked at Dottie Faye's stiletto-clad feet. "But I'm not so sure Dottie Faye has the appropriate footwear. Those aren't exactly cycling shoes."

"What's wrong with my shoes? I think the rhinestones are gorgeous." Dottie Faye strutted a few paces, did a catwalk turn, and returned to the group.

"They're brill, really, but not for walking or biking around a hilly island." Nessa paused and looked around. "We know the people who wrote the note must be here somewhere. Why doesn't Dottie Faye check out the village while the rest of us go to the old church ruins and graveyard? We'll meet Dottie Faye back here when we get the next instruction."

Dottie Faye glared at Nessa while Emma and Kelly exchanged a knowing look. "The last time Dottie Faye was left behind, she showed up unannounced and scared us half to death," Kelly said. "Perhaps she should just give the bicycle a try."

"I think that's a *brill* idea." Dottie Faye flashed a triumphant grin at Nessa. "Lead the way to the bikes."

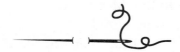

The sun burned off the clouds and bounced off the rhinestones of Dottie Faye's shoes as she pedaled her bicycle down the rutted path through the ancient graveyard to the ruins of Teampall Chaomhain, a tenth-century church.

"Wheeee. This is fun!"

Nessa steered her bike a little closer to Emma and Kelly. "Don't you think you should rein her in before she either wakes the dead or scares away the messenger?"

"You have a good point," Kelly snickered. "But you have to admit, once she realized she could pedal without breaking a heel, she really took off. Sure surprised me."

"Nothing about my aunt shocks me anymore," Emma said. She pressed the brake handle and brought her bike to a stop, then cupped her hands to her mouth. "Dottie Faye! Slow down and wait for us."

Just as Dottie Faye turned around to look back at Emma,

a man stepped out of the sunken ruins and into her path; she lost her balance and toppled off her bicycle. Emma, Kelly, and Nessa pedaled toward Dottie Faye as fast as they could.

"Are you OK?" Emma jumped off her bike and ran to her aunt while Kelly and Nessa pedaled closer to the ruins in search of the man.

Dottie Faye scooted away from the fallen bicycle and stood up, patting her hair. "Thank goodness for hair spray, or my do would have come undone."

The eerie quiet of the graveyard was broken by the sound of a motorbike revving and then sliding down the dirt road. A couple of minutes later, Kelly and Nessa walked their bikes back to Dottie Faye and Emma. "We looked around but didn't find a note or anything. I couldn't see his face. Suppose it was our guy?"

"Most likely." Emma sat next to Dottie Faye. "Maybe we should trade our bikes for a horse cart. We didn't want a driver around when the messenger tried to make contact, but we don't have to worry about that at the moment."

"I think we'd see more that way." Kelly leaned her bike on the low wall stretching nearby. "But I'd like to take a look around here first."

They descended into the ancient ruins. "I feel like I'm traveling back a thousand years." Kelly passed through one of several stone archways. "It makes me feel so small."

Emma understood what she was saying. "It's beautiful here, but so isolated, even now. I can't imagine living where it's so quiet."

Leading the way to the stairs, Nessa stopped on the bottom step and seemed lost in thought for a second. "Some people like living a quiet life, especially after great upheaval or a long, troublesome time."

"Like Mom's friend, Mick," said Kelly.

"Yes. My da said Hugh Slane wasn't always a hermit. Your da, Hugh Slane, and a lad named Cormac O'Broin were inseparable." Nessa led the group out of the ruins and through the cemetery as she told the story of the three friends who'd become passionate IRA operatives before they turned eighteen.

Every so often, Kelly would stop to take a photo, but Nessa's tale was largely uninterrupted. Even Dottie Faye, who had removed her shoes and tiptoed barefoot among the headstones, was captivated by her words. "The course of three families changed on the day Cormac O'Broin inadvertently set off that bomb. Your da chose immigration. Hugh became even more engrossed in the rebel cause until he was too old to be of use anymore."

"What happened to Cormac's family?" Kelly asked, pointing the group back to the bikes.

"No one in the family really knows." Nessa shook her head. "Apparently the O'Broins left Merrow because it hurt his parents too much to stay. Da says they probably never really got over the loss. I heard they may have moved to Kilkenny."

As they reached the edge of the cemetery, Emma looked back at the ruins buried under centuries of sand blowing over it on sea winds. When would they uncover the information they needed to free Maeve?

Having agreed to return the bicycles and hire a horse cart, the women retraced their route to pass the tiny airport and pristine beach. The pier had just come into sight when a man on a bicycle flagged them down with a wave. "I've a message for you." He braked his cycle, slowing long enough to hand a folded sheet of paper to Kelly before he picked up his speed and disappeared down a hill.

This time Emma didn't take time to study the messenger, although she could tell it was a different man. "What's it say?"

"It says to go to the *Aras Eanna* Arts Centre in four hours and wait for instructions." Kelly shoved the note into her shoulder bag. "This is getting ridiculous. What a cat-and-mouse game."

Dottie Faye frowned. "Kelly Ann, I don't want to say I told you so, but—"

"Then don't, please." Kelly started to pedal her bicycle. "Let's just get the horse cart."

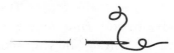

Seamus, the cart driver, was a rolling encyclopedia of Irish history and managed to divert the women's minds off Maeve and the new message long enough to share nearly a thousand years of history among the sloping green hills, miles of rock walls, serene lakes, and beaches. An avid storyteller, the lanky young man with a jovial laugh brought history to life as he introduced them to O'Brien's Castle, the ruins of a sixteenth-century three-story tower house; the pilgrimage site of Tobar Einne, the holy well of St. Enda, the patron saint of Aran; and the ruins of Cill Ghobnait, a small church dating back to the ninth or tenth century.

Emma was deep in thought as the horse cart rolled along the hills. She'd enjoyed watching Dottie Faye and Nessa get to know each other, but as the afternoon passed, she became concerned about whether they'd receive a message before the ferry stopped running at four o'clock. While Kelly seemed to be soaking in the Irish history, Emma knew her friend was worried about her mom. The beauty of this place was undeniable, but it would be even more so if Maeve were free, and if they could experience this place together.

After a small lunch at a café in the tiny village, Seamus dropped them off at the cultural arts center on the west side of the island. It consisted of two rectangular concrete buildings perched on a high spot overlooking the sea, and Emma and Kelly were thrilled to discover the center displayed both traditional and contemporary arts. After signing the guest book in the lobby, they found it also included a conference center, artist studio, gallery, exhibition center, coffee shop, and a small theater.

Emma looked at a map of the center. The place was bigger than it looked from outside. *How long will it take for us to connect with the next messenger?* She scanned the lobby, trying to decide where they should start.

"Excuse me, are you Emma Cotton?" Emma turned around to see a stylish young woman with close-cropped brown hair and dangling purple-and-blue glass earrings. Emma's pulse raced. Could this be the messenger?

"Yes, I'm Emma Cotton."

"My name is Alanna Morrison. I'm the director of the center. Your aunt just introduced herself in the gallery as she looked at the fiber art display." She held out her hand. "She mentioned you are in quilt design and restoration in the United States."

Emma smiled. "Yes, my friend and business partner, Kelly Grace, and I own Cotton & Grace in Mystic Harbor, Massachusetts. It's just outside Boston."

"Welcome to the Aran Cultural Arts Centre." Alanna handed Emma a brochure. "As luck would have it, we have a fiber art exhibit in the gallery, and tonight our quilting class meets in Studio B. We'd be honored if you'd consider spending the night on the island to take in the class, maybe provide some instruction. I can make arrangements for you at the inn, if you like."

Emma opened the brochure and glanced down to see if a note with instructions was attached or sprawled inside, but it contained only arts center information. "What a kind offer; thank you. I'll speak with my traveling companions and see what they want to do."

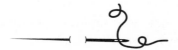

Emma pulled the deep yellow thread through the sunflower petal and felt her neck relax for the first time all day. She looked at the grinning jeans-clad blond teenager sitting beside her. "See, if you pull the thread gently, your stitches won't pucker the material."

Kelly sat nearby, dividing her attention between the girl's mother, Peggy, and a middle-aged bank executive named Ingrid, a quilter from Sweden who came to Inisheer specifically to see the arts center. "I'm starting to feel like a rock star with all of the attention we're getting, aren't you?" Kelly leaned in to talk to Emma. "It's been awhile since we've had an opportunity to instruct a class."

"It's definitely a nice way to unwind at the end of a busy day." Emma handed the sunflower quilt square back to the teen. "We really needed this."

Ten women—ranging in age from the sunflower girl, Siobhan, to Kitty, a weathered great-grandmother—sat around the two rectangular tables inside the classroom, each working on various stages of their quilts. They chatted about their projects, family, and how they were connected to the island. Some were Irish and simply taking a holiday, while others were tourists lured to Inisheer by its rich history or the art center's reputation.

"My mother's been waiting to return to Ireland since she

left at the age of five. I'd like to design and make a quilt for her to commemorate her reunion with our family." Kelly made the announcement to the whole group. "I've been thinking of creating a design based on the family crests of her family and my dad's. Any suggestions?"

"What a great idea. Maeve will love it," Emma said.

"I'm happy to hear you say that." Kelly grinned. "Because I'm banking on your help."

"You should consider using fabrics from Antonio Roman's latest collection. Have you seen them yet?" Kitty looked at Kelly. "They are absolutely gorgeous."

Emma and Kelly shared a glance and nodded at Kitty. They were well familiar with Rose's former student, Antonio Roman. "We've used Roman Original Fabrics. You're right, they're exquisite designs."

Ideas poured out of the group for nearly thirty minutes as work progressed on their individual projects. By the time Alanna came in to tell everyone the escort had arrived to return them to the inn, Kelly had written down about twenty ideas about family crests and seals, Irish symbols, flora and fauna, and folklore.

"Thank you for the suggestions. I wish I could incorporate them all." Kelly dug through her bag, pulled out several business cards, and handed one to each woman. "If you email me your contact information, I'll send you photos of the quilt so you can see how the design turned out. And definitely come see us if you're ever in Mystic Harbor."

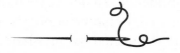

"Any word from the messenger?" Dottie Faye was sitting on the colorful quilt covering her bed and rubbing lotion on her feet when Emma and Kelly returned to the Islander Inn.

"Not a word." Kelly tossed her bag on the second double bed. "We were about to ask you the same thing."

"Nada." Dottie Faye capped the tiny lotion bottle provided by the inn and put it on the primitive nightstand. "But I found some new shoes at one of the shops, and we did meet some interesting people at the pub. I learned a couple of Irish step-dance moves."

"You should have seen your aunt on the dance floor," Nessa said. "Impressive, I tell you." Nessa closed the travel magazine she was reading. "We came back early, though. We had this strange feeling we were being followed, but nobody made contact. So, what's our next move?"

Emma plunked herself down in the other reading chair. "I guess we go back to the bed-and-breakfast tomorrow. There's no sense in staying here any longer."

"I second that." Kelly stretched out on her bed, her voice sounding tired. "I don't understand why we were sent on this wild goose chase, but I need to get back to Mom. I haven't heard from Daniel or his attorney all day."

"Now, Kelly Ann, before you go to sleep, I have something to help cheer you up." Dottie Faye reached for a bag leaning against the nightstand. "I bought us each a souvenir nightshirt from the gift shop next door. Now we don't have to sleep in our clothes."

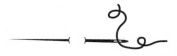

The next morning, Emma stood alone at the side of the ferry and watched as Inisheer faded into the distance. She tried to figure out why no one had made contact while they were on the island. What had been the purpose of the note?

Dottie Faye joined Emma and put her arm around her. "Everything's going to be OK. You know that, right?"

Emma returned her aunt's hug. "I'm glad you're here, Dottie Faye."

"Me too, sugar."

"Let's go find Nessa and Kelly. We need to decide what to do when we get back to the mainland." Emma took her camera from her bag and took a quick photo before turning to follow her aunt.

They were halfway across the stern when the boat suddenly slowed, the engine stopped, and an alarm sounded. When they reached the other side of the ferry, a crowd was lined up along the railing and crew members were trying to move people out of the way.

Dottie Faye tapped the shoulder of the man standing next to her. "What happened?"

"I think a woman jumped overboard." He stood on his toes. "But I can't really see anything."

"Emma! Dottie Faye!" Nessa was shouting and elbowing her way through the crowd with a woman wearing a black jacket sporting a ferry line company logo and the name Paulette McCoy. "Kelly was just thrown off the boat!"

thirteen

"What?" Emma froze. "Thrown? What happened?"

"We're trying to figure that out." The ferry representative motioned the three women to follow her up the stairs to the crew office on the upper deck. She didn't speak again until they were alone. "The captain is turning the boat around and a rescue boat is being deployed. We have every reason to believe she'll be OK."

Emma closed her eyes and whispered a quick prayer. "I'll hold you to that. She's my best friend."

"You were on the other side of the boat when Mrs. Grace went overboard?"

"Yes, my aunt and I were together." Emma paused to collect her thoughts. "We were on our way to find them when the alarm sounded."

Paulette McCoy took the names and contact information for all of them, but focused most on questioning Nessa.

"Tell me what happened." Paulette's pen was poised.

"We were standing near the railing, looking over at the water. We were discussing what to do when we reached the mainland." Nessa's voice was shaky, but she managed a slight smile. "Kelly was hungry and wanted to stop for tea on the way back to the bed-and-breakfast."

Paulette looked up when Nessa stopped talking. "Go on."

Nessa shook her head. "It happened so fast. One second we were talking, and the next, Kelly yelped. There was a big lad with his arms around her. He hoisted her over the barrier.

I said, 'Hey, you let go of her,' and I gave his arm a good tug. He dropped her and shook me off. Then I screamed."

"Tell me more about this big lad."

"He was wearing a dark jumpsuit like mechanics wear, and a dark ski mask. He pushed me and ran through the crowd toward the back of the boat. That's all I saw. At that point I was more concerned about Kelly than the man running away." Nessa's salt-and-pepper bangs fell into her eyes and she brushed them aside.

Paulette called the ferry captain and gave him the description of the culprit and asked if he had any information about Kelly. She held the radio close to her ear to hear the reply. "She's been spotted and appears to be alive. The lifeboat is being readied for launch. We have every reason to be optimistic."

Time crawled like a tortoise, and Emma felt useless sitting in the crew office. She resisted the urge to seek Paulette every five minutes, although the woman frequently returned to them with an update. When she couldn't sit any longer, she began pacing from one end of the office to the other. "I wish there was something we could do."

Emma was about to head out to find Paulette when the crew leader entered the office. "Mrs. Grace is on board. Shaken but coherent. A chopper is bringing paramedics. They'll be checking her. Come, I'll take you to her."

Emma, Dottie Faye, and Nessa followed Paulette to the lower cabin. Kelly was wrapped in a blanket, shivering, and finishing her statement to officials.

The investigator questioning Kelly looked up when the trio entered the lower cabin, nodded at them, and returned to the questioning. "Mrs. Grace, do you have any idea who would want to hurt you?"

She locked eyes with Emma before shaking her head. "No. I've not been in Ireland long enough to have enemies here."

Emma joined Dottie Faye and Nessa where they were sitting on a bench across the cabin. She was silent, but her brain was in overdrive. Who could have done this? Did Gallagher know they were on to him? What about the young punks Maeve had seen at Hugh Slane's cottage?

"I sure am glad to see you." Emma jumped up and hugged Kelly as soon as they were alone. "Do you feel up to telling us what happened?"

She nodded. "Nessa and I were standing by the rail, looking at the water and talking. The next thing I knew, I was lifted by a pair of steel arms. Suddenly, I was careening toward the water." Kelly shuddered. "Then I was alone. And cold. Watching the boat speed away."

"Do you remember anything about the guy?" Kelly had answered this for the officials, but maybe there was something she left out.

"He reeked of cigarette smoke," Kelly said.

A chill washed over Emma. She'd come close to losing a second friend to a nameless, faceless killer.

"Let's get one thing straight," Kelly said. "Mom's not going to find out about this. It will only make her worry, and she has enough on her mind. And don't even *think* about calling Patrick. He'd only feel helpless in the States and would hop on the first flight to Ireland, and there's no telling what he'd do to the person responsible for this if given the chance." She looked at Nessa. "We don't need another family member in jail."

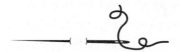

"Uh-oh. That's not a good sign." Emma pulled the van around the circular drive in front of the castle and slipped into the first parking space she found.

Kelly groaned from the backseat. "What now?"

"It appears the good inspector is here. Unless that's someone else's police car in the reserved parking spot," Emma said.

"Are you up for this?" Dottie Faye asked.

Worn out from her swim, Kelly had reclined her seat so far that Emma couldn't see her in the rearview mirror. "I just hope his visit is short and sweet. I have plans for a hot bath, a quick visit with Mom, and an early bedtime."

Stiff from falling so far from the boat into the icy water, Kelly took her time climbing out of the van and hobbling to the stairs of the castle. Emma and Dottie Faye linked arms with her on either side, and the trio took one step at the time until Kevan opened the front door.

"Mrs. Grace, are you OK?" Kevan's eyes filled with concern. "Do you need me to call a doctor?"

"I'll be OK." Kelly unlinked her arms from Emma and Dottie Faye and crossed the threshold. "It's nothing a nice hot bath and a good night of sleep won't cure."

When all three women were inside, he closed the main door behind them. "I'm afraid you have a visitor in the drawing room."

Emma sighed. "We figured as much when we saw the Garda car out front."

The walk to the drawing room seemed longer than usual. When they entered the room, a sullen Inspector Bailey was standing by the large window and gazing at the sea. Emma cleared her throat as she led Dottie Faye and Kelly into the room. "Good afternoon, Inspector. What can we do for you?"

"I have news." Inspector Bailey paused when he'd turned around far enough to see Kelly's damp, disheveled appearance. "What happened to you?"

The look on his face led Emma to believe he wasn't really

all that surprised. *Has he already heard about Kelly's mishap?*

Remembering Mystic Harbor Deputy Police Chief Tom Boyer's disdain for their investigation into Rose's murder, Emma shook her head slightly in hopes Kelly wouldn't say anything. She was relieved when Kelly gave an almost imperceptible nod in response.

Kelly shuffled her feet and raked her fingers through her tangled hair. "Well, this is embarrassing, but while we were on the ferry from Inisheer, I took an unplanned dip into the water."

"Inspector, you said you had news?" Emma hoped her question would refocus the inspector's attention.

"Yes, I looked into the band of ruffians Mrs. Quigley mentioned seeing at Hugh Slane's cottage, and they have an alibi." He removed a notepad from his shirt pocket and flipped a few pages. "A shopgirl in the village said they'd been hanging around outside the Village Book Corner, harassing her and the customers. She was very convincing."

"Does this mean those punks are off the hook?" Dottie Faye rolled her eyes. "Any guy who wears black lipstick and fingernail polish is liable to do anything."

"Yes. But we have reason to believe—"

"Inspector, my mother didn't do this," Kelly said.

Bailey held his hand up. "If you'll let me finish, I have more." He turned more pages in his notebook. "Remember the story about Cormac O'Broin?"

Emma nodded. She recalled the story well but didn't remember anyone actually telling the inspector about it. She opened her mouth to ask when it hit her; he must have been listening to their conversation with Maeve at the Garda station.

"Cormac O'Broin was a young man when the bomb he was planting exploded prematurely. We know his family still blames Hugh Slane and Frank Egan for his death." He glanced at his notes. "A couple members of O'Broin's family were spotted in the village recently. We're looking into that."

Emma noticed that Kelly looked pale and tired rather than encouraged by the news. "Thank you, Inspector. We appreciate the update. If we're finished here, we'd like to get cleaned up and have a brief visit with Kelly's mother before it gets too late. We're all quite tired."

"I'm finished here. For now. Spend time with relatives, do some sightseeing, and stay out of the investigation. Remember, the O'Broin family might be bent on avenging a death. If anyone related to Cormac O'Broin contacts you in any way, ring me up." He paused. "By the way, your mother's bail hearing was earlier this afternoon. They should be finishing up the paperwork soon. Did anyone contact you?"

"Mom has been released? That's fantastic!" Kelly smiled. "If anyone had tried to reach me earlier today, I wouldn't have gotten the call. My cellphone went into the water with me."

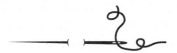

"I can't say I feel like a new woman, but the shower and clean clothes certainly helped." Kelly eased her body out of the van. "Remember, not a word about this to Mom."

"Kelly Ann, you don't think she'll notice how slowly you're moving?" Dottie Faye offered her arm to Kelly as the trio started up the steps. "But I'll keep my mouth shut. I promise."

As they reached the top, Emma stepped ahead and opened the door to the rather plain yellow boxy building and held it open. She watched Kelly's eyes drift to the second row of windows. Maeve was held in the back of the second floor and would be brought to a visitor's room on the first level.

The middle-aged Garda who greeted them in the lobby and confiscated their purses walked them down the long hallway to the holding room and entered it with them. He stood stone-faced at the door as Maeve hugged each of the women, even Dottie Faye. "Mr. Rooney arranged my bail, and Daniel paid it for me. They're finishing up the paperwork right now. Soon I'll be free!"

"That's great, Mom." Kelly hugged Maeve again.

"Daniel's been a godsend. He contacted the American Consulate yesterday morning, and by early afternoon, a representative was here to check on me and sort things out." Maeve sighed. "Things started moving after that. It wasn't long until the bail hearing was scheduled."

Emma looked at the Garda. "I guess we're going to have company this time."

"Sugar, we had company last time, we just couldn't see them," Dottie Faye said. "You go right ahead and talk. I'll take care of this."

She pranced over to the Garda, her purple stilettos clicking on the floor tiles with each step. "Hi there, handsome." She peered at his name tag. "Officer, I mean, Garda McMullen. You seem like a nice gentleman. Are you single?"

A faint pink tinge appeared on his face. "I am."

Dottie Faye batted her eyelashes more dramatically than ever, and Emma took advantage of her aunt's powers of distraction and scooted her chair as close to the table as possible. "Maeve, have they told you anything new at all?"

"Only that the gang of kids has an alibi. I get the feeling they aren't even looking seriously at Foley." Maeve looked at Kelly for a long moment. "You look tired, Kelly. Are you OK?"

"I'm pretty bushed. We took your suggestion to see Ireland. We spent the night on Inisheer. It was beautiful, but there was a lot of walking and bicycle riding."

Emma looked at her watch. She knew their time was limited. "Maeve, did Hugh Slane tell you anything about a man named O'Broin who'd been in the IRA with him and your dad in the late forties or early fifties?"

"Only that his given name was Cormac and they'd all grown up together in the village. He said they'd been mates until the bomb killed Cormac." Maeve closed her eyes, inhaled a breath, and held it a few seconds before exhaling. "He was going to tell me more about the good times during our next visit. Now I won't have a chance to hear the rest of the story."

"Maybe you will, Mom." Kelly leaned into the table. "Nessa told us the O'Broin family moved to Kilkenny shortly after Cormac died. Maybe we can find them."

"In fact, they may find us if we don't find them first." Emma glanced at Dottie Faye, who was still keeping Garda McMullen busy. "Inspector Bailey said members of the O'Broin family have been spotted in Merrow. Maybe they were here to settle the score. Sixty years is a long time for hatred to fester."

The door opened and Inspector Bailey entered the room with Irving Rooney. "You're free to go with some restrictions. You may not travel out of Galway County, and you must appear in court one week from today. Mr. Rooney has your paperwork with the details."

Emma, Kelly, and Maeve stood up.

Kelly shook Mr. Rooney's hand. "Thanks for everything."

Irving nodded. "We still have some challenges ahead, but we'll meet them head on." He turned to Maeve. "I'll call you tomorrow. We'll get started on planning your defense."

Kelly hugged her mom. "Let's get you back to the B and B for a proper bath."

fourteen

"I thought Maeve looked good this morning. It's amazing what a hot bath and a good night's sleep can do." Emma steered the van south on N59 as a sense of satisfaction flowed through her. She was getting accustomed to the narrow roads, driving on the left side, and the unfamiliar road-numbering system. "I'm glad she didn't ask specifics about where we were going."

"I imagine she was afraid what the answer would be." Dottie Faye's voice filtered from the backseat. "Some folks believe ignorance is bliss."

"Mom isn't usually one of them, but she's in a situation she's never experienced, so who knows? I'm glad she doesn't know our exact plans because now she can be honest with the inspector if he asks. I wish she could go to Kilkenny with us, but I'm thankful she's out of jail." Kelly pulled out her smartphone, which had dried out and was working again. "I'm trying to look up information about the O'Broins, but it seems we don't have service on this stretch of road. Or it might be acting up from the water damage. I hope not. I'd like to know who we're looking for."

"I have a surprise for you." Emma pointed to her bag sitting on the floorboard next to Kelly's feet. "Pull out the papers in the side pocket. I woke up early thinking about Nessa mentioning Cormac's son being an accountant, so I did some research on the O'Broins of Kilkenny. I printed the information at the guest business center before you woke up."

"Impressive." Dottie Faye clapped. "I admit, I've never

understood your love of waking with the chickens, but as peculiar as it is, I'm glad you woke up early today. So, what did you find?"

Kelly flipped through the papers. "Wow, she found listings for Michael O'Broin, Colm O'Broin, and Cormac O'Broin, a financial planner with a business address. I vote for the one with the business address. It's likely a public place, plus Cormac O'Broin is definitely a family name."

"Works for me. It'll take us about four hours to get there." Emma cut her eyes to Kelly. She hoped Kelly wouldn't mind foregoing the landmarks and making a beeline to Kilkenny.

"I'm all for driving straight through," Kelly said. "I've had enough walking and swimming for a while. Sitting in this van for several hours and taking in the view sounds good to me."

They left the windswept, rocky coast and headed inland to the rolling green fields, peaceful lakes, and crumbling, moss-covered ruins bathed in gentle sunshine. Stopping only once to stretch their limbs and get gas, the trio stepped back in time around two o'clock as they entered the walled city of Kilkenny, the medieval capital of Ireland.

"Mom's travel guide says the best thing to do is find a car park and ditch the wheels," Kelly said. "From the looks of these narrow streets, I think we should take that advice."

Emma peered at a street sign. "We're on Parliament Street, which appears to be the main drag. What's that address for Cormac O'Broin's office?"

"It's on Patrick Street. I think it's an offshoot of Parliament." Kelly ran her finger over the route in the travel guide. "But if we turn down this next street, there should be parking and we can walk back to Patrick."

Dottie Faye's head kept turning from side to side. "Look at all the shops. Jewelry, clothes, shoes. I think we can have some fun here."

"It looks like a shopper's paradise, for sure." Kelly turned around to look at Dottie Faye. "But shopping will have to wait until we find the O'Broins."

"Oh, you spoilsport." Dottie Faye sighed with dramatic flair. "But as soon as we find them, I get to choose where we celebrate with a little shopping spree."

Emma was relieved to find a parking place in an area called The Parade. She was accustomed to driving in the historic district of Salem, Massachusetts, but these streets were older and more uneven. They walked down Rose Inn Street to Parliament Street and, after a quick stop in a small café to relieve Kelly's hunger with coffee and a scone, found themselves on Patrick Street. While Kilkenny City oozed old-world charm, the signs on building facades advertised cutting-edge firms specializing in Internet consulting, business systems, real estate sales, and accounting services. O'Broin Financial Advisors was in a slate-blue building between P.J. O'Rourke, Solicitor and Johnston Engineering. With a wrought-iron railing leading up the four front steps and a brass plate across the bottom of the red door, O'Broin's office looked more like an upscale home than a business.

"I'm sure glad we took the time to freshen up at the café. I wouldn't want to go in here looking like a ragamuffin." Kelly reached for the brass door handle. "I guess we'll soon find out how deep this family wound goes."

Like the city, O'Broin's office was a blend of tradition and progress, with old architecture and contemporary decor. Original brick walls contrasted with a black spiral staircase to the second floor. The reception desk was a wavy piece of polished cherry topped with a layer of smoky glass. Large abstract paintings with bold colors contrasted with the old brick walls.

"How may I help you?" The receptionist looked up from her computer. "Have you an appointment?"

Kelly stepped closer to the desk. "My name is Kelly Grace. I'm here to see Mr. O'Broin."

The gatekeeper pulled her glasses down the bridge of her nose and raised her eyes over the lenses. "Do you have an appointment?"

"No, but please tell him Frank Egan's granddaughter is here to see him."

"I'm afraid that's out of the question unless you have an appointment. Now, if you'll excuse me." The receptionist pushed her chair from the desk and started to stand.

Stepping forward, Emma pulled a copy of the photo of the three IRA operatives Hugh Slane had given Maeve and slapped in onto the desktop. "Perhaps if you show him this, he'll see us."

The receptionist glared and snatched the photo. "This won't take long." She straightened her gray fitted jacket over the band of the matching above-the-knee skirt and disappeared up the spiral staircase, her deep purple heels clacking on the metal.

"You gave her the photo Hugh gave Mom? I don't think that was a good idea."

"Relax. Maeve gave the photo to Brendan to copy. He gave the original and several copies to me when he came to visit. The original is safe in our room at the B and B."

Dottie Faye wandered over to the large painting opposite the reception desk. She cocked her head one way and then turned it the other. "I don't get it. There are patches of red, orange, black, and yellow, but they make no sense. It looks like different colors of candles melted onto the canvas."

"But it made you think, didn't it?" The receptionist walked up beside Dottie Faye.

Dottie Faye gazed at the painting. "Yes, it did."

The receptionist turned to Kelly. "Mr. O'Broin is busy with a client. Is there a number where you can be reached?"

Kelly pulled a business card from her purse and wrote her cellphone number on the back. "We're only in Kilkenny for the day, but we'll be in the West of Ireland for a few more. I'd really like to see Mr. O'Broin before we head back to the States."

"I'll make sure he gets this." She pulled the card from Kelly's fingers. "Good day."

Leaving the office, Kelly closed the door to O'Broin Financial behind her. "She was a bit chilly."

"Maybe so, but she had fabulous taste in shoes." Dottie Faye looked across the street at the shoe store a few doors down the block. "We need some shopping therapy."

"I guess it wouldn't hurt to kill time before heading back to Merrow. Maybe Mr. O'Broin will finish with his client and give us a call." Kelly winked at Emma. "What do you say? Should we indulge a little? I'd also like to take a short walking tour."

"As long as we don't close the place down. Remember, we have a long drive back to the B and B."

"Yes ma'am." Dottie Faye grabbed Kelly's arm and stepped off the curb. "Let's get going before she changes her mind."

They dashed across Patrick Street as fast as Kelly could go and paused to catch their breath on the other side before walking to The Shoe Tree. Emma opened the door and held it for Dottie Faye and Kelly.

"Mrs. Grace! Please wait." A tall lean man in a navy blue business suit ran across the street waving a photo. He stepped onto the sidewalk and hurried toward them. "I'm Cormac O'Broin."

Kelly and Dottie Faye backed out of the store and joined

Emma and O'Broin on the sidewalk. Kelly held out her hand. "I'm Kelly Grace. These are my friends, Emma Cotton and Dottie Faye Sinclair. Thank you for coming to find us."

He brushed an unruly lock of red, wavy hair out of his eyes. "I'm somewhat curious to know why Frank Egan's granddaughter wants to see me."

Kelly looked at O'Broin without saying anything for a moment. "We brought my mother to visit her homeland. She wasn't feeling well this morning, so she stayed on the coast. We didn't know about the friendship between my grandfather, Hugh Slane, and your grandfather until we arrived in Merrow." Kelly looked Cormac O'Broin in the eye. "I was hoping to hear the rest of the story."

"I'm utterly gobsmacked." O'Broin began laughing, a slow chuckling growing into a deep guffaw. "It's interesting that Frank Egan's family wants to pay their respects five decades after he helped kill my grandfather."

"Now you listen here, fella. Kelly Ann doesn't deserve—" Dottie Faye's words were cut short when Emma grabbed her wrist.

"Let him finish, Dottie Faye." Emma's words were barely a whisper.

He stared at the photo and seemed lost in thought. "My da and granny might like to have a word with you though. I'll call him and ask. I can't talk any longer. I have an appointment."

Before Kelly could get another word out of her mouth, he turned his back and started across the street.

fifteen

"Emma Jane, one simply doesn't buy sensible shoes when indulging in shopping therapy." Dottie Faye frowned at Emma's feet. "You're supposed to splurge on exquisite suede leather pumps with some sort of embellishments like rhinestones or bows."

"I don't do rhinestones." Emma stuck a foot out to display her new walking shoe. "Well, these *are* leather, rather expensive, and comfortable for walking. Kelly did mention a walking tour. Which reminds me, if we're going to have time to finish an entire tour, then we'd best head to the tour office. The afternoon is flitting away."

"That works for me." Kelly put her new shoes back in the box. "I'll break in my shoes later."

After paying for their footwear, the trio followed directions to the tour headquarters, a narrow yellow building next to the Tourist Information Center. The walls of the tiny tour office were lined with old black-and-white photos of Kilkenny's historical landmarks: palatial homes, cathedrals, gardens, arched gateways, and castles. Emma recognized some of them from their trek down Parliament and High streets.

Halfway through the tour of historical highlights, the trio stood outside the stone walls of Kyteler's Inn, listening as Agnes, the tour guide swathed in period clothing, recounted the life of Dame Alice de Kyteler, a wheeler-dealer who had lived there centuries before. Dame Kyteler was accused of poisoning her four husbands and inheriting their wealth.

Dottie Faye was surprised to learn Dame Kyteler was involved in the world's first witch hunt, although it was her maid Petronella who was burned at the stake.

When she learned a statue of Dame Kyteler was in the cellar of what was now a restaurant and pub, Dottie Faye insisted they all troop through the establishment to see it.

"I might be forced to believe there are some places spookier than Mississippi's ghostly landmarks, because a maid taking the fall for a murderous witch is nothing to sneeze at." Dottie Faye stared at the haunting face of the long-haired money-changer.

Before the tour guide could reply, Kelly's cellphone chimed. After saying very few words, she ended the call. "We're to meet Cormac and Michael O'Broin in the gardens of Kilkenny Castle in an hour."

Agnes pulled a watch from its hiding place under her billowy dress sleeve. "We can make it through the rest of the tour, if we hurry." She smiled at Dottie Faye. "If we don't finish, I'll be happy to meet you tomorrow to do so."

"I know what you're thinking, Emma Jane," Dottie Faye said. "You want to get back to Merrow tonight. But I think we should check into a hotel, have our meeting at the castle, and finish our tour before we drive back to the coast tomorrow."

Emma held up her hands. "I'm just the chauffeur. It's Kelly's family, so it's her decision."

"I'll call Mom," Kelly said. "If she's doing OK, then maybe we should get a hotel room. I don't want to rush our meeting with Cormac O'Broin and his father."

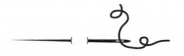

"I was charmed by the garden in the Kilkenny Hotel courtyard, but this is incredible." Emma looked at the fountain centerpiece and let her eyes drift from flower bed to sculptures to footpaths and the surrounding woods.

Kelly started down the path toward the center of the garden. "Mr. O'Broin said he'd meet us at the large fountain."

The trio had decided to stay after Kelly called her mom, who sounded relaxed and positive on the phone. Maeve had spent the first part of the day discussing her case with Irving Rooney. Then she had a visit at the B and B with her Uncle Owen; his daughter, Reagan; and granddaughter, Una.

Kelly stopped and looked across the garden. "Now I don't feel quite so guilty for not going back tonight. I don't want to rush our meeting with Cormac O'Broin. Whether or not someone in his family killed Hugh Slane, they might be able to tell me more about my grandfather's early life."

Emma had mixed emotions about staying in Kilkenny. "Dottie Faye, I'm sorry we're wasting your money by not staying in our room in Merrow. I didn't realize we'd spend so much time in other places."

Dottie Faye waved the comment away. "Sugar, don't you apologize for that."

Emma paused to scan the garden for Cormac O'Broin and his father. "Silly me, I thought we'd find Gallagher in the village, get the DNA sample, and solve Rose's murder within twenty-four hours."

"You can't be serious," Kelly snorted. "We've not had an investigation yet that hasn't taken us down multiple rabbit holes. Why would it be any different this time?"

"Is that them at the far edge of the fountain?" Dottie Faye pointed a bright red fingernail.

Kelly nodded and resumed descending the steps with

Emma and Dottie Faye on either side of her. "Everyone ready?"

"Ready." Emma and Dottie Faye spoke in unison.

Cormac and Michael O'Broin met them halfway around the fountain. "Thank you for meeting with us." Kelly extended her hand and smiled when the older man shook it. "I'm Kelly Grace and these are my friends Emma Cotton and Dottie Faye Sinclair."

"I tried to talk him out of coming here, but he'd have none of it," Cormac said. "Your grandfather caused our family a lot of hardship."

"That's enough, Cormac. These ladies didn't have anything more to do with my da's death than I did." The elder O'Broin was an older version of his son, tall and lean, although his red-brown wavy hair was now streaked with white. His eyes were the same shade of blue, but they sparkled in the late-afternoon sunlight. He strolled toward a pair of benches. "Let's sit." He stopped in front of one bench and held his hand out to offer Kelly the seat. "After you."

Emma and Dottie Faye sat on the next bench. Cormac chose to stand as if waiting to spring should Kelly suddenly thrust a dagger into his father's chest.

"He's a little wound-up, isn't he?" Dottie Faye said the words close to Emma's ear.

Emma shushed her. "We're just here to listen and protect Kelly if we need to."

Michael O'Broin watched his son but spoke to Kelly. "My son's a wee bit protective of me. I'll admit I'm both curious about Frank Egan's relationship with my family and resentful that he went on to have a happy life after my da died so young."

"I know very little about the relationship between my grandfather and your dad. My mother and siblings had no idea Grandpa had been in the IRA, much less an operative. It's a shock, actually. He never even told my mother, although my Uncle Daniel didn't seem too surprised. He moved back to Ireland years ago, so he heard stories from his relatives here."

Emma's attention bounced from the conversation between Kelly and Michael to Cormac's reaction to it. One minute, Cormac's eyes were wide with disbelief and another, his mouth was contorted in hatred. Could those be the eyes of a killer? In contrast, Michael's eyes didn't darken, even as the conversation became more intense. He never seemed anything other than pleasantly reserved.

"What were you told about my grandfather's friendship with your dad and a man named Hugh Slane?" Kelly took a deep breath. "My mother heard of it for the first time when she met Mr. Slane last week while walking the beach."

Now the older man's eyes darkened. "They were boyhood mates and did all of the usual things. Fishing, hunting, flirting with the lassies. Then, fueled by their fathers' stories of the 1916 uprising, they made a pact to stick together and join the IRA. At least that's the way I heard it." His eyes filled with tears, but he didn't wipe them away. "I don't even remember my da. I was only a baby when he was killed. Ma moved us to Kilkenny because it was too painful to remain where there were so many memories and the constant presence of the Egan and Slane families. Hatred for the Egans and Slanes nearly tore my family apart."

Kelly wrinkled her nose. "I don't understand the hatred and blame. I thought your father's death was an accident, that the bomb went off prematurely before it was in place."

"It did. But my da had been sick and didn't want to go out that night at all. Frank and Hugh, from what I was told, teased him about being a waster."

Cormac broke in, spitting out his words. "A waster is someone who's completely useless."

"If he'd stayed home, then he would have been around to see his son and grandchildren grow up." Kelly's words were barely audible. Emma looked at the darkening sky and realized the gardens would be closing soon. She knew they needed to get some answers. "Michael, does anyone in the Egan family ever visit the old village on the west coast?"

"Twice a year, on my father's birthday and on the anniversary of his death. Cormac and I take my ma to his grave in Merrow. Other than that, there's not much need for us to go visiting now. Nobody's left." Michael looked at his dad's namesake. "Last week was the 63rd anniversary of his death. Even at eighty-three years old, Ma never forgets. Neither does anyone else in the family."

Last week was the sixty-third anniversary of his death. The words rang through Emma's mind. This certainly gave credence to the reports the inspector had of the O'Broin family being spotted in the village around the time of Hugh Slane's death. While Michael seemed willing to make peace with the past, for some reason his son didn't. Could Cormac O'Broin's namesake have killed Hugh Slane?

Cormac O'Broin walked to his father and laid a hand on his shoulder. "The gardens are closing. We need to go."

"Indeed." Michael took Kelly's hand in his. "Talking was good for us, for our families. How long will you be in Kilkenny?"

"We plan to finish our walking tour in the morning and head back to Merrow soon after." Kelly squeezed his hand and released it. "Thank you for your time. And for your understanding."

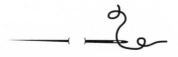

"There's been a change in plans," Kelly said the next morning as she climbed into the passenger side of their rental vehicle. "Michael O'Broin just called. His mother has invited us to tea. I took the liberty of accepting for us. I didn't think you or Dottie Faye would mind."

A few moments later, Dottie Faye came through the hotel doors and opened the sliding door of the van. "We're all checked out and good to go."

"I hope you don't mind missing the rest of the walking tour, Dottie Faye," Emma said, "but we've been invited to tea with Cormac O'Broin's widow."

Dottie Faye responded by pulling her Dottie cam flower from her bag and attaching it behind her ear. "Ready, willing, and able. Let's go."

They'd driven a block when Kelly's phone rang again. For several minutes, Kelly just listened and interjected an occasional "that's great" and "sounds like fun." Finally, she spoke. "Try to enjoy your day and thanks for letting us know where you'll be. We're going to look around a bit more today and head home this afternoon. We'll give you a full report tonight." She ended the call.

"Mom is in good hands today," Kelly said to Emma and Dottie Faye. "Daniel and his wife, Aileen, are picking her up so she can spend the day at their place in Clifden. They've invited friends in to meet her. She sounds upbeat, but I still want to get back to her as soon as possible."

Dottie Faye pulled a small camera from her sizable purse and aimed it out the back window. "I hate to break this to you, but I think we're being followed."

She videoed the scene behind them as Emma pulled in and out of alleys and side streets in an attempt to lose the tail. When Dottie Faye said the coast was clear, Emma circled around and pulled up in front of Rowena O'Broin's brick row house. Dottie Faye passed her camera to Kelly. "Does this car or person look familiar?"

"The video is too jumpy. I guess it's from the brick roads."

Emma pulled the keys from the ignition. "Let's go see what Mrs. O'Broin has to say."

As they approached the end of the walkway, the door opened before Kelly had a chance to knock. Michael O'Broin invited them to follow him down a hallway into a small sitting area where a tiny yet regal elderly woman sat in front of an unlit fireplace. Her fine gray hair was swept up into a bun, and a map of wrinkles ran from each cheekbone to her chin. A tray was set up with tea in a delicate floral pot and an assortment of cookies on a matching plate.

"Ma, this is Frank Egan's granddaughter, Kelly Grace, and her friends, Emma Cotton and Dottie Faye Sinclair." Michael might have inherited his father's unruly red hair, but his angular chin came from his mother.

Kelly sat in the matching wingback chair angled toward Mrs. O'Broin as Dottie Faye and Emma took seats on the antique sofa.

"Thank you for coming. It's been a long time since the Egan and O'Broin families have spoken." Mrs. O'Broin's chin shifted toward Michael. "Please serve our guests tea."

Michael did as instructed, his weathered hands pouring tea into dainty cups on equally fragile saucers and handing them to each of the guests. He refilled his mother's cup and settled in a leather chair opposite the sofa.

After a slow sip of tea, Kelly turned to Michael's mother. "Mrs. O'Broin, my mother and I just learned about my grandfather's connection with the Irish Republicans, particularly his friendship with your husband and Hugh Slane. We had never heard about this before. Mr. Slane told my mother the three were boyhood friends."

"They were. All three were very passionate young men. They loved their families, their country, and each other." Rowena O'Broin closed her eyes a moment. Emma wondered if she'd fallen asleep, but the old woman soon spoke. "Tell me about Frank. He disappeared just after my Cormac was killed. Some people said he killed Cormac and fled so we wouldn't do the same to him. Others called him a coward who failed his country and opted to immigrate to America. I didn't know who to believe. All I knew was that my husband was dead and the two mates who were supposed to stick with him were still alive and nowhere to be found."

Michael repositioned himself in his chair and cleared his throat, but he didn't comment.

"Mrs. O'Broin, all I know about what happened is hearsay, a story told by Hugh Slane to my mother." Kelly looked at the elderly woman and smiled. "I can tell you what she told me."

When Rowena O'Broin nodded, Kelly recounted the story Hugh Slane had told Maeve, that Cormac O'Broin's death had been an unavoidable accident that was the catalyst for Frank Egan's desire to leave the IRA. She also described Maeve's life after the age of five, growing up in New England with her parents, Frank and Brigid Egan, and her brother, Daniel, who'd returned to Ireland to attend Trinity College and never left.

"What did Frank do for a living?" Rowena asked.

"Granddad started out as a carpenter and eventually became a construction site manager before starting his own company. He died about twenty years ago, just about the time my daughter Julie was born. He had the reputation for being skilled and honest."

As Kelly told her grandparents' story, Emma's eyes and

mind began to wander. She knew Kelly's family story, except for the IRA part, as well as her own. Her eyes settled on a photo album entitled "Iona's Christening" sitting atop a stack of books on the accent table next to her chair. "What a lovely book. May I look at it?"

"That's the celebration book for the christening of my great-great-granddaughter Iona." The old woman's eyes lit up like fireflies. "The entire O'Broin clan attended the christening service and celebration here in Kilkenny. They came from all over Ireland."

Emma opened the first page of the album. "What a beautiful baby she is! I think she looks like you." Her eyes drifted down the page to the printed christening invitation and widened as she read the date and location.

Can this be true?

sixteen

"**K**elly, take a look at this adorable baby and the lovely invitation to her christening." Emma's heart felt like it was rapping on her ribcage as she held the album up for Kelly to see and tapped her finger on the invitation.

Kelly's jaw dropped and she pulled the photo album closer. Emma knew her friend had immediately seen that the christening was the same day as Hugh Slane's murder. Was it an alibi or a cover?

Realizing Kelly was reeling from the discovery, Emma kept talking. "The whole family. That must have been quite a hectic event with all of the cousins."

Rowena smiled for the first time. "You must not have a large family, Emma."

Dottie Faye's arm went around Emma's shoulders and pulled her close. "I'm pretty much it as far as Emma's family goes, except for her father who retired to Florida. But Kelly is like family to us, so our clan may not be quite as small as it seems. In fact, after meeting all the Egans on this trip, our family seems larger than ever."

"Family is so important." Rowena studied Kelly for a moment. "Thank you for sharing your memories of Frank. He doesn't sound anything like the monster I've imagined him to be all of these years."

"You mean you never really knew your husband's best friends?" Dottie Faye's dangling glass earrings smacked her cheek as she shook her head. "My dear Archibald didn't have many friends left near the end, but I knew all of them. They were fine southern gentlemen."

Rowena turned her head toward her son and she blinked before addressing Dottie Faye. "Ireland was different then. My Cormac had to keep his IRA dealings a secret, for his safety and my protection, although Hugh and Frank would show up at the flat from time to time." Her gaze drifted to Kelly. "I'd thought them as tight as brothers, until they left Cormac for dead when the bomb exploded."

"I wish my mother had been able to make the trip to Kilkenny so she could tell you the details of her visits with Mr. Slane. I've never met him." Kelly slid the photo album onto the coffee table. "He told Mom he and my grandfather tried to save Cormac after the explosion, but they could tell he'd been fatally wounded. In fact, Mr. Slane said Cormac himself had told his friends to run because the Garda was already on its way. They'd been forced to leave him."

When the older woman remained silent, Kelly continued. "Mrs. O'Broin, it was Cormac's death, and the death of the two children killed in the same explosion, that motivated my grandfather to leave his friends, family, and homeland to immigrate to the United States. He chose to put the violence behind him and create a new life where he wouldn't lose more loved ones the way he lost Cormac." When Kelly stopped talking, her eyes were moist and tears were freely flowing down Rowena O'Broin's cheeks. "Your husband's death probably saved my grandfather's life."

Silence settled on the room like fog on the Irish coastline. Emma didn't dare speak. Even Dottie Faye seemed to have no words at the moment. Kelly was like family to them, but this wasn't their story. The quiet wasn't theirs to pierce.

Michael claimed the silence, clearing his throat to disguise his emotions. His eyes were wet too. "As I told you before, Mrs. Grace, I wish I had memories of my father, but I was little more than a baby when he died. I never really knew him. It's always left me a little lost, I think."

Rowena's countenance changed, the tears ceased, and her jaw softened. "It's time to lay the past to rest. How can I reach Hugh?"

The question, coupled with the timing of the baby's christening celebration, told Emma what she needed to know. Rowena O'Broin and her son had no idea Hugh Slane was dead. Where would the investigation lead them now?

"Mrs. O'Broin, I have to tell you something." Kelly sat forward in her seat and balled her hands together in her lap. Her eyes swept around the room from Emma and Dottie Faye to Michael and finally settled on Rowena. "Hugh Slane was shot and killed several days ago, shortly after meeting my mother. The reason she didn't come to Kilkenny with us is because she's been falsely accused of Mr. Slane's murder."

Emma watched emotions wash across Rowena's face. She knew what regrets felt like, to want to do things differently but not have the chance. If she'd taken Rose's fears seriously, then maybe her friend would still be alive. Kelly had just closed the door on any hope the O'Broin family had of understanding what had happened between three very young men more than six decades ago.

Rowena opened her mouth to respond but closed it when the doorbell rang. Instead, her eyebrows arched in surprise. She gave a slight nod to Michael, who rose to answer the door.

When he returned, Inspector Bailey was at his side.

"Ma, this is Inspector Bailey from Merrow. Inspector, my mother, Rowena O'Broin." Michael waved his hand toward the other visitors. "From what you told me at the door, I believe you know Miss Cotton, Mrs. Sinclair, and Mrs. Grace from the United States."

"Indeed." Inspector Bailey crossed his arms. "Well, well. I knew the three Americans wouldn't stay out of my investigation. It took a long time for the Egan and O'Broin families to get their revenge on Hugh Slane, but you finally did it." He sneered at Kelly. "I never did buy your mother's story of coming to Ireland to visit relatives. You, all of you, seemed too tense."

Rowena and Michael started to protest at once but stopped when Dottie Faye jumped up from the sofa and shook her finger at the inspector. "So you were the one following us over here this morning."

"Dottie Faye, let's not make matters worse." Emma pulled the sleeve of Dottie Faye's blouse. "Please sit down."

"No, she can stay standing. You will return to the bed-and-breakfast in Merrow and stay there. I will arrest all three of you if you interfere with my investigation again." Inspector Bailey faced Michael O'Broin. "Will you please see these three women to the door?"

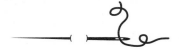

"A long, hot shower and a nice cushy robe are two of life's little blessings." Emma strolled into the sitting room of their castle suite with her head wrapped in a towel. She nestled against one sofa arm and watched Dottie Faye, who'd already showered and dressed in a flamboyant combination of magenta leggings and a long, black, rhinestone-studded T-shirt, as she emptied her polka-dotted tote bag. "What are you doing?"

"Oh sweet pea, all of this talk of murder and bombs is depressing. I'm treating myself to a quick shopping trip. That nice young man Kevan has hired a car to take me into the village." Dottie Faye tossed the contents of the tote—assorted magazines, hair accessories, and manicure supplies—into the plastic laundry bag provided by the B and B. "You and Kelly enjoy your relaxation time with Maeve. I'll see you later."

Dottie Faye slung her purse on one shoulder, grabbed the empty tote bag, and pranced to the door. She opened the door and looked back to blow a kiss.

"Where's she off to?" Kelly entered the sitting room just as the door closed behind Dottie Faye. "That woman is amazing. I hope I have half her energy when I'm her age. I have no desire to leave this place tonight."

"I'm with you, but I could be talked into exploring the castle a bit and ending our tour with tea in the drawing room." Emma unwound the towel from her head and dropped it on her lap. "You game?"

"I could be persuaded, but only if you put some clothes on first." Kelly snickered. "Really, I love the idea. We've spent so little time here. It will be nice to enjoy the amenities. Mom was napping when I showered and changed clothes. I'll see if she wants to go exploring with us."

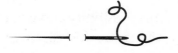

While Maeve continued napping, Emma and Kelly wandered the wide halls and stone staircases of the castle and marveled at the workmanship that had enabled the structure to survive since the Middle Ages. Standing at the top of the stairway in the second tower, Emma let her eyes follow the curve of the steps. The image of a crumpled Rose sprawled at the bottom of a different set of stairs flashed through her mind and sent a shiver down her spine. They'd been in Ireland well over a week but weren't any further along in their investigation of Rose's murder.

"Yoo-hoo. Emma?" Kelly's voice was close to Emma's ear. "Are you ready to go on downstairs?"

"What?" Emma struggled to collect her thoughts. "Oh— yes, let's go. I was just thinking about Rose and Liam Gallagher. We've sent emails and left messages at the shop in Merrow and the Dublin office. I don't know what else to do."

They started down the stairs.

"What I don't understand is why he has a factory and offices in Dublin and only one shop, and the one shop is in a small village like Merrow." Kelly stopped and looked at Emma. "Most of his lines are sold in upscale retail stores. Why would he have a small shop in Merrow? It doesn't fit the rest of his business model."

"I see what you're getting at." Emma turned to face Kelly. "Because this place means something to him. Maybe his family owns a piece of property here besides the textile shop. A family home, maybe?"

Emma nodded. "The guy at O'Riley's did say Gallagher was a regular."

They discussed this possibility and what to do next as they wandered through the castle and discovered two additional drawing rooms filled with oil paintings in gilded frames and other antique treasures, another library with floor-to-ceiling bookshelves, a billiard hall, a fitness room, an indoor lap pool, hot tub, and a solarium. The sun was just beginning to set over the bay as they stood at the French doors leading to a garden path.

"As much as I'd like to see the hedge maze, why don't we save the gardens for another day?" Kelly peered out the window then faced Emma. "Let's see what refreshments they have in the main drawing room and relax with the other guests for a while."

"Works for me."

As they walked the long hallway to the drawing room, Emma marveled at how modern comforts were added to the castle in such a way to make it luxurious yet still maintain the medieval ambiance. The drawing room was occupied, but by no means full. A man and his teenage son played chess at the game table. Across the room, a young couple studied the beverage offerings on the sideboard.

Emma and Kelly stood in front of the mahogany-and-marble serving table and surveyed the finger food options. Emma filled a plate with a pair of finger sandwiches and a fruit skewer while Kelly started with a selection of berry tarts and petit fours. They sat in the two chairs opposite the sofa, leaving it vacant for the young couple.

"This is exactly what we needed after the week we've had. No drama." Kelly popped the last bite of a tart into her mouth.

Emma took a swig of sparkling water. "It's nice to have time to collect our thoughts."

"Yes." Kelly shifted in her chair, pointing at the doorway. "Look, there's Mom."

They waved to Maeve, who took a seat on the sofa. "I thought I might find you in here."

"We explored for a while and came up with a new angle to find Liam Gallagher."

"Let me get myself a bite to eat, and you can tell me all about it."' Maeve stood. "I'll be right back."

Emma watched Maeve cross the room, pleased to see she was getting an appetite back.

"Do you mind terribly if we join you?" The accent sounded British.

Emma looked up to find the smiling young couple standing in front of the sofa, each with a wine glass in hand. "Please do. I'm Emma, and this is my friend and business partner, Kelly."

The young man blushed. "I'm Niall Browne and this is my lovely new bride, Adele. We were just married on Saturday."

"Congratulations!" Kelly lifted her ginger ale glass in a toast. "*Sláinte.*"

"Thank you." The bride and groom spoke in unison as they sat closely on one end of the sofa. Her voice had more of an Irish lilt.

"Did we hear you say you were looking for a Liam Gallagher, as in Gallagher Textiles?" The bride smiled. "He was friends with my father. They both grew up here in Merrow." She bit her lip. "Dad's gone now. I think Mr. Gallagher still owns his family's old house on Ram's Head Road. In fact, he was here for our wedding Friday night."

Emma groaned. "He was here at the castle on Friday?"

"While we were in Kilkenny." Kelly sighed. "We missed him."

"You missed who?" Maeve stood between Kelly's chair and the sofa.

"Liam Gallagher." Emma and Kelly spoke in unison.

"Oh dear. We'll find him." Maeve put her plate on the table and turned to get a chair.

Adele Browne patted the sofa beside her. "There's plenty of room on the sofa. We don't mind sharing."

Kelly introduced Maeve to the Brownes and explained their connection to Gallagher.

"Is he staying at the family's old home?" Maeve asked.

Adele shook her head. "I think he was driving back to Dublin this morning. Why do you need to see him?"

Emma's heart sank. Another dead end. "He knew a friend of ours when he was in college in the States through a study-abroad program. We wanted to talk to him. Do you have his cellphone number?"

"No, I'm sorry. I always contact him through his office. It's easier to reach him there. He's a workaholic."

"We haven't found it so easy," said Kelly.

Emma knew it was too dark outside to search for Gallagher's family home, so she let herself get drawn into the couple's vivid description of their wedding festivities. From time to time, Adele scurried from the sofa to the chairs to show Emma and Kelly photos from the fairy-tale wedding on her smartphone. The bride was just showing them the bouquet toss when a disheveled Dottie Faye came tearing through the door, waving her camera with one hand and dragging her tote bag in the other. Adele took one look at Dottie Faye's wild eyes and jumped out of her way, seeking refuge in her husband's arms.

"I was just attacked by the banshee again." Dottie Faye took a couple of gulps of air. "And I was quick enough to get a photo of her!"

Emma stood up and patted her aunt's shoulder. "Dottie Faye, sit down. Take a deep breath. I'm going to grab a chair from the game table."

The teenager and his father were already staring at Dottie Faye when Emma started to get a chair. The man carried it for her to the sitting area and returned to his son.

Emma scooted the chair closer to Dottie Faye. "Now, slowly, tell us what happened."

"The driver dropped me off out front. As I approached the entrance steps, the banshee came out of nowhere!" Dottie Faye punched a few buttons on her camera and held it out to

Emma. "See, there it is, the banshee. Just like the one in our suite. I didn't imagine it. And now I have proof!"

Emma pulled the camera closer. Sure enough, there was a blurry image of a spectral woman with long, serpentine locks and a flowing gossamer gown. She appeared to be levitating several feet off the ground.

"Emma, don't you see? The banshee really *was* looking for me. Maybe I'll be seeing my darling Archibald sooner than I thought."

A well-dressed older man and woman wandered into the room in the midst of Dottie Faye's dramatic declaration about imminently seeing her dead husband and froze mid-step. Emma vaguely remembered them from breakfast the morning after Dottie Faye's surprise arrival.

The newcomers looked at each other with wide eyes. "It isn't good for the banshee to visit twice." The man's voice trembled. "I'd be careful if I were you.

seventeen

"**Y**our idea of checking out Gallagher's village shop again was a good one, even if we didn't have any luck locating the man himself." Kelly tossed a bulging paper bag onto the sofa. "This fabric is perfect for the family quilt. Finding gorgeous fabric takes some of the sting out of not locating Gallagher at his house this morning."

Maeve sat on the sofa and pulled a piece of cloth from the bag. "Look at the quality of the weave and vibrant color. It's on par with Antonio Roman's designs."

Emma pulled a bottle of water from the mini-fridge. "I'm glad someone different was working at Gallagher's. It was nice of her to offer her worktable and scissors so we could cut some squares. I, for one, needed the distraction from my disappointment. I really thought we'd find him, or a relative, at the house."

"Me too." Kelly pulled more fabric out of the bag. "At least we were lucky enough to find a name on the mailbox. Maybe we can try again later."

"It'd be worth another try." Two days had passed since the trip to Kilkenny, and Emma was getting antsy. Maeve didn't have a court date. Brendan had no more information on Foley, and there'd been no word from the O'Broins. They were stuck in their investigation of Gallagher; Emma was beginning to believe he was a fictitious character. While his business dealings were well documented online, Emma and Kelly hadn't been able to find any concrete proof he existed in the flesh, unless one counted the comments from the bartender at O'Riley's Pub and the Brownes.

"What happened to Dottie Faye? I thought she was right behind us." Emma wondered if she should go looking for her aunt, given the strange things happening these days.

Kelly giggled. "I think she was distracted by that carload of businessmen checking in when we walked through the lobby. That woman has the most finely tuned man radar I've ever seen."

Despite the banshee appearance, Dottie Faye, who tended to create a social life wherever she went, seemed to be enjoying herself.

Kelly grabbed her smartphone from the coffee table and plopped onto the sofa next to Maeve. "I've missed three calls from Patrick. I've been dodging his calls because he'll worry about me when he finds out about all of this. Knowing his flair for playing the knight in shining armor, he might be motivated to book the next flight out of Boston."

Maeve chuckled. "Somehow I can't see Patrick surviving a trip that has Dottie Faye on the itinerary."

"I can't either. I'll tell him about your situation, but I'll keep it pretty bland." Kelly reached for her mother's hand and squeezed it. "It sure is good to hear you laugh."

While Kelly dialed Patrick's number and stepped into her bedroom, Emma carefully relocated the fresh flowers and Dottie Faye's gossip magazines from the coffee table to the desk. She replaced them with a pair of scissors, the pattern she and Kelly had designed for the Egan family quilt, and a pattern for the main family crest appliqué.

"This was going to be a surprise for you." Emma sat on the sofa. "Kelly and I designed a quilt based on the Egan family crest. Would you like to help?"

Maeve's eyes filled with tears. "Yes, I'd like that very much."

Starting with the red fabric, the two women pinned and cut out several large curled leaf pieces, two sections of the shield, and three helmet plumes. Emma's fingers tingled from the feel of the fabric between her fingers, and soon her creative juices were flowing and her stress levels were lowering. She and Maeve worked silently until Kelly reappeared.

"The poor man misses me like crazy." Kelly switched off the phone and tossed it back and forth between her hands. "When I told him about Mom, he immediately started searching for a plane ticket online. It took some fancy talking to convince him we were handling things OK without him. It wasn't exactly the truth, but not quite a lie, right? He worries enough as it is."

"It's a good thing you handled it that way, or we'd have our hands full keeping track of both Patrick and Dottie Faye." Maeve finished cutting out another leaf and added it to the growing pile.

Kelly exchanged her slippers for sneakers. "I'm going in search of food and to see where Dottie Faye is. Want to join me?"

"I'll go with you." Maeve dropped another leaf on the stack. "Emma, you coming?"

"No thanks. I'm enjoying the feel of fabric in my hands again. I think I'll just work on the quilt and take pleasure in some peace and quiet for a while. I might even do some yoga." Emma maneuvered the scissors around the scalloped edges of a leaf. "But if you come across any fresh fruit, would you bring some back for me?"

"Will do." Kelly stuffed a room key in her pocket. "Enjoy your solitude."

The door closed behind Kelly. Emma closed her eyes,

leaned against the sofa back, and sighed. The sounds of silence were glorious. As much as she loved Dottie Faye, Kelly, and Maeve, she needed alone time too. Sometimes Kelly's huge Irish family overwhelmed her. As an only child, she'd learned to appreciate quiet time with a book, craft, or yoga mat.

Rolling her head from side to side to stretch her neck muscles, Emma sat forward with her elbows resting on her knees and glanced from the sketched quilt design to the pattern pieces. With the red leaves finished, she moved on to the red areas in the upper left square and lower right triangle of the shield. According to the heraldry website she'd checked, the red signified strength, warrior spirit, military, and martyrdom. Maeve and Kelly had strength to spare, as they'd both proven during this trip.

Emma was finishing cutting out the red pieces, including a few small pieces of plumage for the helmet, when the silence was pierced by her cellphone ring. She didn't recognize the number, which appeared to be local. "Hello?"

"May I speak with Emma Cotton?" The vaguely familiar voice had a charming Irish lilt to it.

"Yes. This is Emma."

"This is Paul O'Riley. From the pub. You and your friend asked me to call if Mr. Gallagher should come in." He cleared his throat. "He just ordered a pint and plate of fish and chips. If you hurry, you can catch him before he leaves."

Emma's heart thumped, and she took a deep breath. "We're on our way. Thank you for calling, Paul."

"Anytime. *Slán.*"

Emma immediately dialed Kelly's number. She didn't give Kelly time to say hello before she started talking. "Paul O'Riley just called from the pub where we ate on the way back from Dublin. Liam Gallagher just sat down to a pint and meal. I'm walking out the door now. I'll meet you and Maeve at the lobby. Can you round up Dottie Faye?"

"I'll try to pry her away from the handsome executive she's attached to in the drawing room. See you in a bit." Kelly paused. "I guess this means I'll take the muffin I just grabbed with me, but I don't think your fruit will fare too well in my purse."

"Ditch it. I'll be down in less than a minute." Emma was already dashing down the hallway to the stairs.

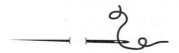

The pub was as dimly lit as last time, but Paul and Colleen had enough customers to warrant an extra server. A squatty young woman, little more than a teenager, was taking orders at a corner booth. Several tables were occupied, but only one customer sat at the bar.

Dottie Faye spotted him immediately and pulled on the sleeve of Emma's pullover. "Look at that gorgeous hunk of man sitting at the bar. He looks like Pierce Brosnan in *The Thomas Crown Affair.*" She cut her eyes at Emma. "He's just about the right age for you too."

"Dottie Faye, may I remind you why we're here?" Kelly asked. "That man may be responsible for Rose's death. Are you really trying to set Emma up with a possible murderer?"

"Oh." Dottie Faye was at a rare loss for words. "Silly me. I was overwhelmed with temporary insanity while looking at quite possibly the most handsome man in Ireland."

"Let's go sit down before someone else walks in and takes the seats next to him." Emma took a step but then looked back at Dottie Faye. "Please behave yourself."

Gallagher had just taken a bite of fish when Emma pulled out the stool next to him, but he nodded as she sat down. Dottie Faye was just about to pull out the stool on the other side of him when Maeve grabbed her arm and guided her in the other direction. "Dottie Faye, we can't possibly discuss our travel plans if you sit way down here."

Kelly slid onto the stool beside Emma. "This place reminds me of the little neighborhood Irish bar back in Mystic Harbor, the one my dad liked so much."

"I'll take that as a compliment." Paul dealt four napkins on the bar with a wink. "What can I get for you?"

Emma ordered a sparkling water, Kelly a ginger ale, and Dottie Faye an iced tea. Maeve asked for hot tea.

"We have iced tea, but I can't guarantee how it tastes. We don't get many requests for it." Paul shuffled past Kelly and Maeve and stopped in front of Dottie Faye's place. "Sure you don't want something else?"

"I'll take my chances with the tea. Bring me lots of sugar, handsome. OK?" Dottie Faye batted her eyelashes. "And lemon."

Paul's eyes coasted from Dottie Faye to Kelly then Emma. "Do you know what you'd like to order?"

"Haven't thought about it yet." Emma cut her eyes to Gallagher and back to the bartender. "What do you suggest?"

Paul wiped his hands on the towel hanging from his belt. "We have great bangers and mash, if you've not experienced it since you arrived in Ireland."

"What are bangers and mash?" Dottie Faye crooked her pointer finger and motioned Paul to come closer. "I'm always up for something new."

"Mashed potatoes and sausages," Maeve explained. "It's one of my favorite Irish dishes. I'll take that."

Can't beat it." Paul wiped a water ring off the bar. "Want to try it?"

"I do." Kelly and Dottie Faye spoke in unison. Emma wrinkled her nose.

Paul smiled at Emma. "I have a nice Caesar salad with your name on it. Eh?" He disappeared after she nodded.

Gallagher took a long pull from his frosty glass and wiped his mouth with a napkin. "Not into Irish cuisine?"

Several seconds passed before Emma realized he was talking to her. "I'm a rabbit food sort of girl."

"Did I hear you say you're from Mystic Harbor, as in Massachusetts?" He took another gulp of lager.

"You know it? Most people have heard of Boston, but few recognize the name Mystic Harbor."

"I've not spoken to anyone from Mystic Harbor in years." He wiped his mouth with the napkin and stuck out his hand. "I'm Liam Gallagher. I spent time in Mystic Harbor in undergraduate school at Hawthorne College as part of a year-abroad program."

Emma introduced him to Kelly, Dottie Faye, and Maeve. "We're in Ireland visiting Kelly's family." Emma watched for a reaction from Liam but didn't see one. Their names didn't seem to register with him. Obviously he hadn't received the messages they'd left for him at the shop, factory, and his office.

"I really liked Mystic Harbor. It reminded me of an Americanized version of the village where I was raised. Is The Chocolate Cauldron still there? A girl I dated a few times was addicted to their chocolate éclairs."

"She must have been related to Kelly." Emma gave her friend a nudge. "She loves them too."

Liam smiled, and Emma realized Dottie Faye was right. He did resemble Pierce Brosnan, in a more rugged sort of way. He seemed rather charming, but then again, so was Ted Bundy, and he was a serial killer. Could this alarmingly likable man have killed Rose?

Paul emerged from the swinging kitchen door and set three plates of bangers and mash and one bowl of salad on the bar. "Everything OK here?"

"Everything except I can't hear a word sitting all the way down here." Dottie Faye leaned so far forward her earrings were in danger of dangling in her mash. "You need to talk a little louder."

"Mr. Gallagher is just reminiscing about his year of study at Hawthorne College," Kelly said. "It seems his girlfriend at the time was also a fan of The Chocolate Cauldron."

Dottie Faye tilted sideways. "Maybe you knew Emma and Kelly's friend Ro—"

"Yes, maybe you met my old boyfriend Roland. Oh, what was his last name?" Kelly cut off Dottie Faye's sentence before she blew their cover.

"Stitch?" Emma smiled. "Yes, it was Stitch. My memory always was better than yours."

"No, I didn't know a Roland Stitch." Liam reached for the check Paul had placed near his plate. "Unfortunately, I must leave for a business meeting, but I've enjoyed tripping down memory lane. The year I spent at Hawthorn College was a highlight of my college days." He pulled several euros from his wallet and placed them on the check before flipping his wallet on its side and removing a business card. He handed the card to Emma. "Please contact me if there's anything you need during your stay. I plan to be in the area for the next week or so."

Emma glanced at the card and extended her right hand. "Thank you, Mr. Gallagher. It was nice to meet you. We'll definitely keep your offer in mind."

Kelly and Dottie Faye slid off their stools to say goodbye to Gallagher. Kelly shook his hand. Dottie Faye linked her arm through his and started walking him to the door. "Has anyone told you that you look just like Pierce Brosnan? And I dare say that is a compliment."

Maeve, Emma, and Kelly watched Dottie Faye put her feminine charm to work. Kelly shook her head and giggled. "I want to be your aunt when I grow up."

Maeve shook her head. "Oh no, the world isn't ready for two like her."

When Liam Gallagher finally broke loose from Dottie Faye's grasp, she returned to the bar just as the bartender began clearing away the empty dishes. After placing the plates and bowls into a plastic bin, he reached for Liam's glass. "Oh, Paul." Dottie Faye lightly brushed his arm. "May I call you Paul?"

He nodded.

"This is by far my favorite establishment in Ireland, and I'd dearly love a souvenir to remember it by." She reached into her bright purple shoulder bag and pulled out a bag. "Do you mind if I take this little old glass? I'll be happy to pay you for it."

Paul's face brightened. "Take it as my gift. I only ask that you fill it only with Irish beverages."

"Every chance I get, handsome. Thank you." Dottie Faye scooped up the glass with a tissue and placed it in the bag. "You made my day."

She pulled a wad of euros out of the side pocket of her purse. "This is to pay our bill. Keep the change." She looked at Emma, Kelly, and Maeve. "Let's go girls."

Paul remained behind the bar as the four women walked to the door. "We'll always have a seat for you here. Come back and see us."

As soon as they reached the car, Emma hugged her aunt. "You are absolutely amazing, although you also almost ruined it."

Maeve pointed at the bagged glass in Dottie Faye's grasp. "But you absolutely made up for it by snagging that glass!"

Dottie Faye put her hand on the front passenger door handle. "You know, that Gallagher is kind of cute in a brooding Irishman sort of way. Perhaps he could be waiting in the wings if things don't work out for you and Dr. Eric Hart, Mystic Harbor's most eligible bachelor."

"Dottie Faye, aren't you forgetting something?" Emma started the van.

"What's that, sugar pie?"

"Liam Gallagher just might be Rose's killer."

Dottie Faye lifted the glass in the air. "I guess we'll find out soon enough."

eighteen

Kelly pushed her dessert plate away, leaving a few crumbs from Nessa's Irish apple cake in the remaining wisps of whipped cream. "With all due respect to Mom, who makes a killer apple cake, I do believe that was the best I've ever tasted."

"Thank you. I'm glad you had the energy to visit after all the excitement of the trip to Kilkenny." Nessa collected the plates from Orrin, Dottie Faye, and Emma, who'd left half her cake on it. She turned to Maeve. "It's doubly nice to have you here."

"If Emma's not going to eat the rest of her cake, I'll take it." Kelly eyed the plate until Nessa put it in front of her. "I hate to see something that scrumptious go to waste."

Emma wouldn't have eaten such a large piece of cake anyway, but her mind was too preoccupied to even taste food. On their way to Nessa's house, they'd stopped by the UPS office and sent Liam Gallagher's glass speeding to the Genetix International lab in Boston. By Friday morning they would know if his DNA matched that found on Rose. "The cake was delicious, but I'm not much of a sweets eater."

"Emma Jane eats like a bird. I have no idea how she does all of the exercising, yoga, and running when she doesn't eat." Dottie Faye folded her napkin and put it on the table. "It's more fun to feed Kelly."

"It's a wonder any of us can eat with Maeve facing trial for murder," Nessa said. "I'm glad you're finally out of that awful place."

"Any news on that front?" Orrin poured another cup of tea and added a splash of milk and spoonful of sugar.

"Mr. Rooney is working on my defense. We've met a couple of times already. I feel better now that the American Consulate is watching the case." Maeve pushed a bite of cake around the plate. "Emma, Kelly, and Dottie Faye did some checking into other possible suspects, and Daniel has been checking into a few things."

Kelly took the last bite of Emma's cake and set her fork on the plate. "A shopkeeper gave the police an alibi for the teenagers, and the entire O'Broin family was in Kilkenny at a christening on the day of the shooting. That leaves the developer, Bartley Foley."

"I don't know about the developer, although he did act pretty strange when we saw him on the beach, but my bet is on those young thugs." Dottie Faye shook her finger. "I just don't trust them. Anyone who'd put a ring in his nose is likely to do anything."

"I know what you mean. Our Bridget thinks she wants a nose ring. She's only thirteen. Where do kids get these ideas?" Nessa asked. "You know, Bridget and John are at the church, preparing for the talent show. Can you imagine what would be said if she showed up with a nose piercing?"

"A nose ring isn't a motive for murder, Nessa," Orrin chided his wife. "My bet is on the O'Broin family. Those types of vendettas run deep and never heal. They easily could have hired someone to kill the old man."

Kelly bit her lip. "All I know is that we need to find out who killed him soon or Mom will stand trial for murder."

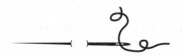

The mist floated over the Cliffs of Moher, but tiny slivers of moonbeams managed to slip through like tiny candle flames leading to heaven. The breeze was quiet, yet strong enough to lift Emma's blond hair off her nearly bare shoulders as she walked along the footpath at the edge of the cliffs. She paused, waiting for the moon to peek farther out of the mist and cast more light on the path. Had she imagined the voice? "Em-ma. Where are you, Emma? Are you still looking for me?"

Emma looked over the cliff. She heard the sea below but couldn't see it. The mist was too thick, becoming a fog. "Em-ma." A moonbeam sliced through the haze. "Come to me, Emma."

Emma took one more step. Her foot was no longer on the path but engulfed in the mist. Where was the moonbeam?

It shone through again, and Rose hovered just off the edge of the cliff. "Come to me Emma."

"Rose!" Emma's eyes flew open, and she threw off the plush comforter as she tried to get her bearings. She could barely breathe, and her heart would surely explode from beating so fast. Emma sat up and switched on the small lamp by her bed. *Get a grip, Emma. Rose is gone. When will these dreams stop?*

But Emma knew when they'd stop. When Rose's killer was caught and locked away forever.

She slipped out of bed and peeked through the curtains to look at the sea. The darkness of night was tinged with lighter shades of blue, although the ocean wasn't visible yet. Emma's heart rate dropped back to normal, but she felt antsy and unsettled.

There was only one cure for antsy. Running.

She changed into running tights, a tank top, and a jacket before lacing up her shoes and tiptoeing through the sitting area, where Dottie Faye was asleep on the sofa. Her aunt had refused to sleep in a bedroom just in case the banshee returned. It might be best not to tell her about the spectral Rose beckoning Emma into the sea. She slipped her phone into her jacket pocket and scrawled a hasty note on the desk pad. "Gone running. Emma."

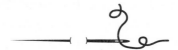

The concierge, housekeeping staff, and restaurant chefs were already bustling around the first floor when Emma skipped down the stairs. She took the long hallway to the back of the castle and slipped out the solarium to the terrace and passed the pool on her way to the beach path.

Emma hadn't been for a run since arriving in Ireland, and she missed it. Starting with a brisk walk, she soon started jogging and eventually set a respectable running pace. Settling into the run, Emma let her thoughts wander to the people she'd met in Ireland. She was amazed at the bond between Kelly and Maeve and their Irish relatives they'd either never met or hadn't seen in decades. The entire Egan family was pulling together to help Maeve. And the O'Broins, especially Rowena, seemed like a loving family, proud of its history. Could someone in the O'Broin family really have killed Hugh Slane as Orrin suggested?

Deep in thought, Emma was startled when she glanced toward the dunes and recognized the dead man's cottage. She slowed to a stop and gazed at the cottage, willing it to give up some clue to its owner's killer. "If only your walls could talk," she muttered into the wind. "What would they say?" Emma studied the tiny house and wondered just how the killer got in the cottage in the first place. What would she give for a police report?

She was jolted from her ruminations by a huge Irish wolfhound barreling straight for her. Taken aback by its sheer size, Emma breathed easier when she saw its tail wagging. She wasn't in danger of being attacked. Then she remembered Maeve's tale of meeting Hugh Slane on the beach and the giant dog who'd greeted her. This must be his dog.

"Hey, you! I told you, no press." Bartley Foley emerged from the dunes, screaming and running at Emma full throttle.

She shook off her fear and turned to run but stumbled into a wall of dog fur. By the time she regained her footing, Foley was close enough to grab her arm. As he twisted her around to face him, she reached into her pocket and pulled out the mini canister of hair spray that she packed when she found out she couldn't travel with pepper spray. She pointed it at his face, hoping he couldn't see what she was really holding.

He held his hands up and backed up a step. "OK, put the Mace down. Tell me why you're stalking me."

"I'm not stalking you." Emma lowered the canister but kept it ready in her hand. "I was out enjoying a morning run until you accosted me."

"You weren't running when I saw you. Sure looked like you were casing my house."

"*Your* house?"

"Yes, my house. So tell me why you're here." His eyes told her he wasn't about to let her go without an answer.

"My friend, Maeve Quigley, has been arrested for Hugh Slane's murder, although she's innocent. I'm trying to find out who killed him so I can clear her name." Emma returned Foley's glare. "You're the developer who's been forcing property owners to sell so you can destroy this gorgeous coast with gaudy, high-rise vacation condos. I understand Mr. Slane was one of your last holdouts. That gives you motive."

Confusion swept across Foley's face. "You mean you're not a reporter? Then why were you here with Brendan Egan, the guy from the *Western News Leader*? Who are you?"

Emma shook her head. "Brendan is Maeve Quigley's nephew. He was helping Kelly, Maeve's daughter and my business partner, find Slane's real killer." Emma stopped to consider if she should really give Foley her name. "I'm Emma Cotton. Kelly and I own a quilt design and restoration business near Boston."

Foley fished a photo from his shirt pocket and held it out to Emma. "This is me with my Uncle Hugh, my sister's brother." He watched Emma examine the photo. "I never would have displaced him from the cottage."

"People have killed family members for less." Emma handed him the photo.

"Maybe so, but the economy here has been so bad that development of this property hasn't been an option. I would have allowed Uncle Hugh to live out his days in the cottage." Foley's face softened. "I loved the old man. I'm trying to find out who killed him too. I really don't think your friend did it either. With my uncle's past, I don't know where to start. I've hired a private detective."

Emma studied Foley's face. He seemed sincere; maybe they could work together in solving Hugh Slane's murder. "I can tell you, Maeve was thrilled when she met your uncle. She enjoyed their conversations and was enthralled with his stories of her father. She is not a murderer."

Foley patted the dog's head. "By the way, this is Fionn, Uncle Hugh's dog."

"Maeve told us about Fionn." Emma scratched the giant

dog behind his ears. "We don't even have a police report. Do you?"

"I do. If you give me an email address, I'll send you a copy."

Emma wanted more information before giving him any of her personal information. "Explain how you're related to Hugh Slane."

"My mother was Hugh Slane's younger sister, Anna Slane Foley." Foley was silent for several seconds. "Uncle Hugh returned to Merrow as the hermit Mick when he heard Ma's health was failing. She died eleven years ago. He never told me how he found out she was sick."

"Do you have any proof that what you say is true?"

"You won't find proof of Hugh Slane's existence since about 1984, when he decided to leave the IRA and go into hiding, but you can find plenty of information on my business dealings online."

Emma smiled for the first time since Foley had approached her. "I've already done that. You have quite a history."

"Indeed. Some of it isn't flattering. But I'm a businessman, not a murderer." Foley reached into his back pocket and produced a wallet. He opened it and removed a business card. "You can reach me anytime at this number and email address. I only ask that you not give it to anyone else. I keep my business to myself. But I believe we can help each other."

Emma took the card and glanced at it before putting it in her jacket pocket. "I'll talk to Maeve and Kelly, and we'll get back to you. I agree that we can probably help each other. Right now, I need to go. My aunt and friends will worry if I'm not back for breakfast."

She turned and trotted in the direction of the castle. When the beach curved and she was sure Foley couldn't see, Emma stopped running, pulled out her cellphone, and dialed

Brendan. Emma recounted her conversation with Foley and asked Brendan to check out the developer's story. He agreed to do some snooping and suggested a stop at Egan's Pub to talk with the old-timers about the Slane family.

"And Emma, don't go visiting with Foley alone again. Don't forget the goons he sent after us," Brendan said. "I'll call you as soon as I find out anything. Be careful."

Be careful. It didn't seem to matter how careful they were, trouble always seemed to find them.

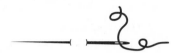

Egan's Pub was buzzing with stories of Hugh Slane—his falling-out with Frank Egan and the alleged O'Broin family vendetta—when Emma, Kelly, Maeve, and Dottie Faye arrived just after the dinner hour. By that time, many drinks had been poured and speculation about the identity of Slane's killer was rampant. Old Connor Egan sat at his usual table, telling tales of the old days, but similar conversations were going on all around the pub.

Connor waved them over and motioned for his son Eamon to find three more chairs. While they stood waiting, Dottie Faye tapped Emma's shoulder. "We're not going to learn anything new from Maeve's uncle." She patted the sunflower behind her ear. "My Dottie cam and I are going to play some pool. Ta-ta!"

Kelly laughed. "I've seen Dottie Faye play pool. Those guys will have no idea what hit them."

"Very true," Emma said. She sat in the chair Eamon pulled up for her and looked around the table at lots of new faces. Could any of them be the killer? She discovered that few around the table, except a couple of old-timers, had actually met Hugh Slane, although his friendship with Frank Egan and Cormac O'Broin was legendary, as was Cormac's death.

Connor slammed his glass down on the table. "Let's drink a toast to my niece Maeve." He waited until the room quieted and glasses were raised. "May joy and peace surround you, contentment latch your door, and happiness be with you now, and bless you evermore."

"Here, here!" Voices and glasses raised in unison to toast the daughter of the legendary Frank Egan. Maeve seemed embarrassed by the attention and relieved when Connor slipped back into storytelling.

He regaled them with tales of prize fish caught by Hugh and Frank, the first time Cormac asked a girl for a date, and how Meggie Egan was heartbroken when her middle son immigrated to the United States. Emma didn't learn much in the way of information to help clear Maeve, but she did take pleasure in watching her friends hear stories about Frank Egan. At one point, they were held spellbound when a short man with long white hair and a beard stood up and sang a ballad about the three revolutionaries and their friendship.

A bevy of Egan cousins, children, and grandchildren of Owen, the youngest Egan brother, had just arrived and joined the group around Connor's table when Dottie Faye flounced up and sat in the chair next to Emma, who was hoping for information. "Anything?"

Dottie Faye shrugged. "Just that Hugh Slane was known for years as Mick, the crazy old hermit on the beach who's now a martyr." She adjusted the sunflower. "I have it on tape."

One of Connor's cronies drained the rest of the ale from his glass and slammed it on the table. He looked at Dottie Faye and his face broke into a grin. "Is this the woman you were telling us about, the one who was visited by the banshee?"

"The one and only." Dottie Faye sat up straight and stared down the table. "Twice."

"Twice?" The old man's eyes widened under his bushy white brows. "Oh, that's not good." He angled his head toward Connor. "Connor, did ya not tell her about the story of Two Visits?"

"I did not." Kelly's great-uncle was smiling behind the napkin he'd just put to his lips. "I wasn't so sure Mrs. Sinclair was ready to hear it."

Seamus Fitzgerald, the village storyteller, kept Dottie Faye's attention with a tale about an American woman who visited the nearby town of Clifden about fifty years before and fell in love with a young fisherman. "The day before they were to wed, the handsome lad went out on his last fishing trip. As night fell and he still hadn't returned, the beautiful young woman was visited by the banshee." The old man shrieked and pulled at his matted mane. "She was convinced her intended had drowned at sea, but her family just as surely believed it was only a nightmare and assured her the wedding would go on as scheduled." He paused and moved his eyes around the room. "On her wedding day, as she started walking into the church in her white gown, the woman was visited again by the banshee. Knowing her true love was gone forever, the beautiful bride's heart gave out … just as his car pulled up to the church." Seamus wheeled around and pointed a gnarly finger at Dottie Faye. "Beware of the two-banshee visit."

"Oh, that's OK." Dottie Faye waved her fingers in the air. "I determined the first banshee I saw was for Hugh Slane. The second one was probably also for somebody else. So, I'm good."

nineteen

"Don't you think we should have gotten Gallagher's DNA test results already?" Kelly swirled the ice around in her glass of soda with the straw. "It's been four days since we sent the sample."

Emma had been thinking the same thing. "If we don't hear anything today, I'll email the lab." She looked over the castle's glistening pool and studied the horizon, where blue sky met aqua sea. The view was gorgeous, but with two killers still on the loose and Maeve facing trial, she couldn't fully enjoy it.

"I'm tired of everything being so uncertain. It would be nice to at least know where we stand with Gallagher, since we can't seem to make any headway in clearing Mom." Kelly pushed up the sleeves of her cardigan. "The authorities didn't seem to be in any hurry to find other suspects. But I'm glad Mr. Rooney is representing her."

"Maeve seems to be taking things in stride now that she's out of jail. I'm glad we talked her into getting a massage. It should help her deal with the stress." The breeze blew a lock of hair in Emma's eyes and she brushed it back with her fingers. "Dottie Faye is having a good time. She sure has been gone a lot."

Kelly chuckled. "Maybe she's ghost hunting. Or should I say banshee chasing?"

"I'm not sure which is worse, but she sure does keep things interesting." Emma glanced at her watch. It was nearly three thirty, and the day was wasting. "I need to do something productive. If I can't solve a murder, then I think I'll go work on Maeve's quilt for a while."

"Good idea. I'll help." Kelly stood up and stretched. "Do you mind if we stop by the drawing room for a little snack?"

Emma shook her head and pushed out her chair. "You know, one of these days, your metabolism is going to tank, and you'll have to start running with me."

"Walking, yes. Running, never," Kelly replied. "I have this fear of blowing out my knees."

Emma and Kelly strolled through the castle, stopping from time to time to admire a piece of artwork. They were paces from the drawing room door when they heard Dottie Faye's laughter. They found her sitting on the sofa between two ruddy men in golf attire.

"Dottie Faye, we were wondering what happened to you," Emma said. "It sounds like you've been having a good time."

"These fine gentlemen were telling me about the perfect golf swing and invited me to play a round with them tomorrow." She slapped each man on his knee. "I don't know which is more ridiculous, the thought of trying to walk on a golf course in heels or how I'd look in a pair of those." Dottie Faye pointed to the men's golf shoes, her bangle bracelets jangling on each arm.

"That's quite a toss-up, I'd say," Kelly snorted.

Emma was saved from commenting when her cellphone rang. "It's Brendan." She pressed the talk button and said hello.

"Hi, Emma. Am I on speakerphone?"

"No."

"Good. Keep it that way." He sounded serious. "I have some information. Can you slip out without your aunt and Kelly so we can talk privately?"

"Well, I was thinking about going for a run this evening.

But sure, I can walk instead." Emma realized all conversation in the room had stopped. "Where?"

Brendan gave her directions to a walking trail on the far side of the village.

"Sounds good. I'll meet you there. Yes, I'm looking forward to it too." She switched off her phone and pushed it into her jeans pocket.

Emma felt her face burn. "Brendan just asked me to take a walk with him."

Dottie Faye clapped her hands to a symphony of clanging bracelets. "Goody, goody, goody!"

The men on the sofa exchanged puzzled looks, making Kelly laugh. "Don't worry, she's not crazy. But she has been trying to marry Emma off for years."

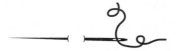

The sun was just starting to dip in the sky when Emma and Brendan walked through the car park to the walking trail. They were silent while crossing a boardwalk over a small wetland that led to the dirt trail on the other side.

Emma jumped when her arm brushed his. "What did you find out?"

"We traced all of Foley's various corporations. There were several; that's what took me so long to get back to you. While he does seem to be a ruthless businessman, it doesn't appear he's done anything illegal. He's been investigated several times, mostly for suspected antitrust law violations, but never arrested."

"Go on. There must be more." Emma picked up the walking pace.

"Not much more, I'm afraid." Brendan pumped his arms slightly to keep up with her. "Foley was telling the truth. He really is Hugh Slane's nephew, although that doesn't necessarily exonerate him. The Garda doesn't seem to have any other suspects at the moment, so it looks like your entourage won't be leaving Ireland anytime soon." He stopped walking and turned to face her. "I'm glad."

Emma's heat sank. Brendan was right; he hadn't given her much to go on. "So, what do you think we should do next?"

"How about dinner?"

"Right now?"

"Why not? You must be getting tired of pub grub by now. A friend of mine runs a trendy place in Clifden specializing in healthy, delicious food. You'll be amazed at what his chef can do with vegetables." Brendan looked in her eyes and grinned. "It's casual, so we can go as we are. We can be there in twenty minutes tops."

The food sounded good to Emma, and maybe talking over dinner would lead to more ideas to clear Maeve. "Ahhh, vegetables. A man after my own heart."

Brendan held his arm out for Emma to take. "Indeed. Shall we go?"

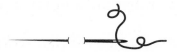

"So, how was your dinner with Brendan?" Dottie Faye put down her magazine when Emma walked in the door.

Emma supposed it had been naïve to hope her aunt would be asleep before she arrived back at the castle. After all, it was just after ten o'clock, and Dottie Faye was a notorious night owl. "It was nice. The food was delicious."

Kelly's bedroom door opened. "You're back. How did it go?" She plopped into the chair next to the sofa.

"I told you everything he knew when I called to let you know we were going to Clifden," Emma said. "We went over all the details at dinner, but we couldn't come up with any new angles or suspects."

Dottie Faye patted the sofa cushion next to her. "Sugar, we weren't referring to information about the old man's murder. We were asking about your dinner date."

"It wasn't a date. It was just two people having dinner and talking." Emma sat on the sofa, unlaced her walking shoes, and slid them off. "His friend's restaurant was small and cozy, but the food was healthy and served like a work of art."

Dottie Faye looked at Kelly and rolled her eyes. "Do you think she's doing this on purpose?"

"Let me try." Kelly leaned forward. "Emma, what did you think of my cousin Brendan?"

"He was very nice and wouldn't let me pay for my dinner." Emma's hand flew to her mouth. "Oh, does that make it a date?"

Kelly and Dottie Faye burst into a gale of laughter. Kelly picked up one of the accent pillows from the chair and hurled it across the room toward Emma. "Yes, you goof!"

When the laughter subsided, a yawning Emma stood up. "I think it's time for me to say good night."

"Good night, hot stuff," Kelly said as Emma's door closed.

Emma was relieved to escape the interrogation. After completing her nighttime routine, she switched on her laptop to check her email before going to sleep. She scanned her inbox deciding which pieces to open and which to save until morning. She read a quick update from Kathleen letting them know everything was great at the shop and that Ichabod the cat was behaving himself. Then she deleted three pieces of spam before spying a message from Genetix. "Kelly, you'd better come in here," she yelled.

Kelly, Maeve, and Dottie Faye came barreling into the room just as Emma clicked to open the email. "I have an email from Genetix." She held her breath and slowly exhaled. "It appears that Liam Gallagher is not our killer. His DNA doesn't match the scrapings from Rose's fingernails."

"Oh, sugar, I'm so sorry." Dottie Faye sat on the bed and put her arm around Emma. "I know you were counting on Liam Gallagher being a match and putting an end to all of this."

"Look at the bright side, Emma," Kelly said. "It's got to end soon. We only have two suspects left, Danielle Moore and Olivia Stewart."

"Yes, but both of them are women. Rose had skin cells from a man and a woman under her nails." Emma closed the email and shut down her computer. She needed sleep. "I'm going to bed now."

"Things will look better in the morning, Emma. You'll see." Dottie Faye blew her a kiss and followed Kelly out of the room.

Emma turned out the lamp and burrowed under her covers. As exhausted as she was, sleep evaded her. How could Liam Gallagher be innocent? He'd avoided them in Dublin and had them run off the road on the way back to the bed-and-breakfast, or at least that was what she had assumed. She rolled over and punched her pillow. They were out of male suspects. Could one of the two women left as suspects have been helped by a man who wasn't a classmate?

"Oh, Rose. I wish you could tell me the truth," Emma whispered. "Have I been unreasonable and stubborn in investigating your death? Was this trip to Ireland just a mistake—a mistake that landed Maeve in jail?"

twenty

Sleep was elusive. After checking the clock hourly between midnight and 5 a.m., Emma tossed back the covers and faced the day. A peek out the window confirmed that it was pitch-black outside, and everyone else was slumbering. Needing to deal with excessive worry, she pulled on her yoga pants and a loose-fitting shirt and donned running shoes. If the fitness center was open, she'd recharge her batteries with an hour of yoga. Leaving a note on the desk and slipping the room key in her pocket, Emma tiptoed past a snoring Dottie Faye.

She crossed the back of the castle, passed the solarium, and was pleased to find the fitness center empty. Standing just inside the door, Emma inventoried the equipment offerings. There were three rows of cardio equipment included treadmills, elliptical machines, and stationary bicycles. Weight machines filled the center of the room, with free weights and benches lining the side. Emma walked the perimeter of the gym and found a multipurpose room with yoga mats and assorted other equipment. When she found a dimmer switch on the lights and a sound system offering different types of music, she knew this was the place to regain her focus with some yoga.

She turned on a Sounds of Nature soundtrack, spread a mat on the floor, and stretched out on her back to begin meditation and visualization in the Corpse pose, pushing the ironic name out of her mind with controlled breathing. Fully relaxed, she moved through the deliberate Sun Salutation poses, stretching her entire body before focusing on standing positions for balance, and finally deep stretches on the floor.

By the time the melodic sounds of nature faded away, Emma had recharged her batteries and was prepared to take the next steps, whatever those might be, in solving the two murder mysteries. It was time to take determined action. She retraced her path back to the room to wake Maeve, Kelly, and Dottie Faye.

She was surprised to find the room empty. Dottie Faye's blanket was crumpled on the sofa. Emma folded it and went to peer into the open door of Kelly's room. Her bed was vacant and unmade. Returning to the sitting room, she checked the desk. At the bottom of the note she'd left was Kelly's rounded cursive: "See you at breakfast."

Emma took a quick shower. After partially blow-drying her hair, she dabbed on a bit of makeup, pulled on a pair of khaki slacks and a red short-sleeved sweater, and headed to the dining room. She walked from one side of the room to the other, but saw no signs of Kelly or Dottie Faye. Odd. The note said, "See you at breakfast." What had happened to them? Feeling her heart begin to race, Emma took a deep breath and let it out. No need to overreact. She strolled into the lobby and found Kevan at his post by the door. "Good morning, Kevan. Have you seen my aunt, Maeve, and Kelly?"

His eyes twinkled. "I think you'll find them in the drawing room. There's a fresh batch of cookies and a new group of businessmen in there."

"I understand." Emma chuckled. She was relieved she found them so easily. "They shouldn't be too hard to find."

"Indeed. Have a grand day."

"You too, Kevan."

Emma heard Dottie Faye's laughter before she reached the drawing room door.

"There's Emma." Dottie Faye waved her over to the sofa where she was sitting between two men in casual business attire. "Yoo-hoo! Come over here and meet Scott and Ryan from Atlanta. They're in Ireland for a business conference."

Emma smiled, barely glancing at the men. "Nice to meet you." She reached out a hand to Dottie Faye to help her up. "Dottie Faye, I hate to rip you away from your friends here, but we have things to do."

"Spoilsport." Dottie Faye waved Emma's hand away and stood up. "But OK."

Maeve joined Dottie Faye and Emma, and the trio stood watching as Kelly strategically placed one more cookie on her plate. Emma motioned them toward one of the game tables. "Let's sit there and figure out our next move before Kelly goes into sugar shock."

They clustered around the table, Emma with her bottled water, Kelly clutching a cookie, and Dottie Faye still ogling the men out of the corner of her eye. "I owe you two and Maeve an apology for dragging you on this expensive trip before thinking things through properly. I can't believe Gallagher's DNA test was negative. I was so sure he was the killer."

"Don't worry about the expense, sugar. You know I have that covered; put money out of your mind."

Emma looked at Maeve and Kelly, marveling at their strength. Guilt swept over her. "It's my fault Maeve is in trouble. I'm so sorry. We're going to get her out of this mess, I promise."

Maeve put her hand over Emma's. "Don't worry. I'm innocent. Everything will be OK."

"It won't start being OK until we determine our next move." Emma took a sip of water. "Any ideas?"

Kelly shook her head, but Dottie Faye's hand went up. "I

do." She lowered her arm. "That handsome Liam Gallagher said to give him a call if we needed anything. He gave you his card, so he must be sincere." She leaned back in her chair, clearly proud of herself. "Maybe he can help Maeve."

"That's a great idea, and we can also ask him about Rose and her last night of class," Emma said, standing up. "We'll have to return to the room first. I didn't bring my purse or cellphone down with me."

Kelly pulled her phone out of her pants pocket. "I programmed his number into my phone."

She dialed Gallagher's number and held the phone out to Emma. "Want to do the honors?"

Emma shook her head. "No, you go ahead."

Holding the phone to her ear with one hand, Kelly tapped her fingers on the table with the other. "Mr. Gallagher?" The tapping stopped. "I'm Kelly Grace, from Mystic Harbor. My friends and I met you at O'Riley's Pub several days ago." Kelly paused. "You were so kind to share your business card and encourage us to call if we needed anything. The truth is, we're sort of in a pickle and could use your help. Are you still in Merrow?"

Kelly was silent for a minute before speaking again. "Three o'clock at O'Rileys?" She looked at Emma and Dottie Faye, smiling when they nodded their approval. "Sounds perfect. We'll see you then."

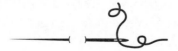

Liam Gallagher was sitting in the same seat at the bar when Emma led Maeve, Kelly, and Dottie Faye into a nearly empty O'Riley's. He turned around on the barstool when he heard their voices and slid off it when he saw them.

"Thank you for meeting us." Kelly said.

"Anytime." Liam pointed to a corner table. "Perhaps we should sit over there, out of the way."

"Do you want your usual?" Paul O'Riley materialized on the other side of the bar. "A pint for Liam, and a water, soda, and iced tea for the ladies?"

Liam nodded. "Put it on my tab, Paul."

He waited by the table as the women sat down and pulled up an extra chair between Emma and Kelly. "It's been a long time since I've heard the phrase 'in a pickle.'" A slight smile tugged at his lips. "You sounded serious on the phone. What can I do for you?"

"We have to tell you something first. We weren't quite honest with you about our reason for being in Ireland." Emma pulled Liam's quilt square from her purse and hid it on her lap. "We came here specifically to find you."

"Me?" his brows furrowed. "Why?"

"Emma and I were best friends with Rose Peterson from childhood until she died the night of your last class at Hawthorne College." Kelly looked across the table and paused. She resumed talking when Emma nodded, urging her to continue. "Emma and I never believed Rose's fall was an accident. Until recently, we didn't have enough information to try to piece together what happened."

Dottie Faye stirred a packet of sugar into her iced tea. "That's when I come into the story. You see, I needed to borrow a quilt to add some color to one of the rooms in my home. I rummaged through Emma's storage closet to find one." She shuddered. "What I found was a hideous quilt of mismatched squares and clashing colors. But my discovery got the ball rolling on investigating Rose's murder—the way the cops *should* have done."

Confusion swept across Gallagher's face. "What does this have to do with me? Other than the fact that I was in the design class."

Emma opened Liam's quilt square and flattened it on the table.

He stared at it and whistled. "Now there's something I never thought I'd see again. Why do you have it?"

"It was part of the quilt I found in Emma's closet." Dottie Faye said, blowing on her red nails and rubbing them on the front of her purple blouse.

Liam laughed and traced the diamond and circle shapes incorporated into the red, navy, white, and green designs. "I was quite enamored with American baseball and became quite a Red Sox fan. I've come a long way in the world of textile design since then."

They all chortled at the wild design and colors until Emma steered the conversation back on track. "For fifteen years I've tried to figure out what happened to Rose, but the Mystic Harbor Police Department ruled her death accidental and refused to reopen the case. Each year on the anniversary of her death, I've paid a visit to the man who was in charge of the investigation. He just brushes me off like a mosquito," Emma said. "But I've never given up."

Emma and Kelly took turns telling him the story of their investigation into his former professor's death. When they finished talking, Gallagher leaned back in his chair. "I get it. I was the next guy on the list. That's why you're in Ireland. Now I'm the suspect."

"Not anymore." Dottie Faye leaned so close to Liam that Emma thought she'd fall off her chair. "I swiped your beer glass last time we were here. Your DNA doesn't match the skin found under Rose's fingernails. You're cleared."

"Impressive."

Emma couldn't tell if he really was impressed or irritated, so she was silent until he spoke again.

"What do you want from me?" he asked.

She rubbed the quilt square between her thumb and forefinger. "What can you tell us about the last night of class? And do you remember anyone wearing a necklace with a raven charm?"

Liam closed his eyes and thought for a minute. "I remember two girls, Danielle Moore and Olivia Stewart, who sat next to me in class." He smiled. "They were inseparable best friends and wore matching raven necklaces. I remember the necklaces vividly because I had a huge crush on Olivia at the time."

He took a long pull from his glass. "I'm afraid I don't remember much about the last class. I was angry for not having had the courage to ask her out, and I knew I'd soon be returning to Ireland. When class was over, I stayed just long enough for a quick goodbye, and then I left the building so my face wouldn't betray my emotions."

Dottie Faye sighed. "Such is the course of youthful love."

"Indeed." Liam picked up his quilt square. "I can't believe this scrap of fabric led you to me. I just wish I could be of more help."

"Maybe you still can, Mr. Gallagher," Kelly replied.

"Call me Liam, please."

"We've had some strange things happen since we landed in Ireland," Kelly continued. "Perhaps you can help us sort them out."

"Such as?"

"For starters, we left messages for you at your shop in the village, the factory outside of Dublin, and your offices in Temple Bar. Your employees were hostile, and obviously you didn't get our messages." Kelly took a breath. "Then we were run off the road on our way back from Dublin."

"The messages were from you?" Liam was clearly surprised. "My staff thought you were there to harass me about a disgruntled employee. This is rather embarrassing, but I'm afraid they were trying to protect me. You see, I had to fire two of my long-time managers for drinking on the job. They'd been threatening to discredit me and leak misinformation to financially ruin the company." He took a breath. "I apologize for my staff's behavior, and it will be addressed immediately. I can't explain the car incident. I'll look into it just in case, but I can't imagine anyone in my company would be involved."

"There's more," Kelly said.

Liam lifted his hand to signal Paul. "Another round, please. This might take a while."

"While we were in Dublin, my mother met an old man while walking on the beach. A few days after we returned to Merrow, he was found dead in his cottage, and my mother was arrested for his murder." Kelly's voice wavered a little. "Of course, she didn't do it. She didn't even know the man."

Kelly stopped talking as Paul placed four glasses on the table and returned back to the bar.

"Go on." Liam reached for his pint.

"We began investigating two murders, Rose's and the old man's. We couldn't let Maeve languish in jail." Emma glanced around the room to make sure nobody was listening. "Things began to get stranger."

Emma, Kelly, Maeve, and Dottie Faye each pitched in to tell about the events surrounding Emma's assault at the Cliffs of Moher and Kelly's plunge into the sea.

Liam shook his head. "I'm sorry. I can account for your treatment by my staff, but I have no idea who's responsible for the others."

He sat quietly as the women explained Bartley Foley's connection to Hugh Slane.

"Could he have killed his own uncle?" Emma asked. "Or is Slane's murder connected somehow to his past as an IRA operative?"

Liam smiled. "I think you've been watching too many movies."

"There's also the O'Broin family," Dottie Faye piped up. "Don't forget them."

"Yes, and then we have the O'Broins." Kelly looked at Liam. "You grew up in the village, so I'm told. Are you familiar with Cormac O'Broin?"

"I've heard the legend, that's all. The family moved inland long before I was around." He raised his eyebrows. "Surely you don't think the family would have Slane killed after all this time."

"I hope not. I really feel for Mrs. O'Broin. I don't know how I'd cope if I lost my husband, especially so violently. She seems to have forgiven, but we have to look at everything in order to prove my mother is innocent. The local authorities don't seem to care about anything but pinning this murder on Mom."

"I wish I could be of more help. You might want to contact a private detective." Liam seemed sincere. He unclipped his cellphone from his belt, pulled up his directory, and wrote a name and phone number on a napkin. "I use Terence Campbell from time to time for background checks. He's honest. If you call, tell him I sent you."

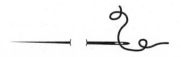

Emma climbed into bed and tried to feel optimistic. Liam Gallagher might not have provided much insight into Rose's death, but at least they were down to just two suspects, and both of them were in the United States. Tomorrow she'd call Bartley Foley and tell him she'd like to partner with him on finding his uncle's killer, since Brendan had cleared him. If he'd changed his mind about working together, then they'd call Liam's PI. She felt herself drifting off to sleep and prayed to be free of nightmares.

Her sleep was pierced by a blood-chilling shriek, and Emma fought through a sleepy haze. *Is this a dream? Where's Rose?* She rolled over, rubbed her eyes, and sat up. She was awake. Someone was screaming.

Emma leaped from the bed and ran into the sitting room, nearly colliding with Kelly and Maeve, who had just entered the room from the second bedroom. Dottie Faye sat cowering on the sofa with the blanket pulled up to her chin, mumbling incoherently. Emma ran to the sofa while Kelly dashed to the door and looked up and down the hallway.

"Dottie Faye, you're safe now. Take a deep breath. Can you tell me what happened?" Emma wrapped her arms around her aunt and waited for her to calm down enough to speak.

Kelly returned. "No one in sight. How strange." She knelt on the floor beside Dottie Faye, whose face was regaining its color. "What happened?"

Regaining her composure, Dottie Faye sat up and blinked. "It was horrible. It was this grotesque creature in the shape of a black horse with glowing red eyes. It murmured 'Hugh Slane, Hugh Slane' over and over until I threw a copy of *Soap Dish Gossip* and hit it broadside. Then it moaned and screeched. And disappeared." She shuddered. "What was it?"

"Are you sure someone didn't just pull one of those

mounted heads down from the hallway and use it to spook you? After all, they are pretty creepy." Emma was weary of being wakened in the middle of the night by phantom creature burglars.

"Hmmm." Kelly tapped her lips with her fingers. "If I didn't know better, I'd say you were just visited by the pooka."

Dottie Faye's eyes bulged. "The polka?"

"No, *pooka*. In Irish folklore, the pooka can be a benign or malevolent creature. It's a shape-shifter and supposedly can appear as a black horse, goat, or a rabbit."

"Why visit me?"

Kelly winked at Emma. "I don't know. You're just lucky, I guess."

Emma yawned. "Would you like to sleep with me tonight? There's plenty of room."

"Emma Jane, women in our family don't shy away from scary things. I'll be just fine on the sofa. You go on to bed now." Dottie Faye shooed her off the sofa. "Go on."

Emma and Kelly returned to their rooms.

When they woke the next morning, Dottie Faye was missing.

twenty-one

Inspector Bailey looked at Emma as if she were a two-headed cyclops. "You're telling me your Aunt Dottie Faye Sinclair has seen two banshees and a pooka?"

"Please don't put words in my mouth, Inspector Bailey. I'm only repeating the descriptions Dottie Faye gave us of these creatures she's been seeing." Emma was well aware the story sounded ridiculous.

"None of us actually saw any of them except Dottie Faye. But yes, those were the two thoughts that came to my mind too—banshee and pooka." Kelly's eyes darkened and glared at the man sitting on the sofa.

Maeve had pulled up a chair to sit by her daughter. "Inspector," she interjected before Kelly could continue, "we're not saying we believe in them, mind you, we're just telling you what Dottie Faye described."

Garda Lowney snickered from just inside the doorway where he was maintaining their privacy. The snickering stopped when the inspector cast a dirty look his way.

The inspector returned his attention to the women. "And the last time you saw her was around midnight or so?"

Emma and Kelly, who were sitting in the chairs facing him, nodded in unison.

Inspector Bailey stood up. "That's all for now. I'll be in—"

The doors to the drawing room flew open. "Oh goody, you're already here, Inspector!" Dottie Faye waltzed in wearing black from head to toe with a duffle bag over one shoulder. "You saved us a phone call."

She eased her duffle bag to the floor and put her hands on her hips. "I know who killed Hugh Slane, and I can prove it. Not to mention who threw Kelly overboard on the ferry." She licked the pointer finger of her right hand and made an imaginary hash mark in the air while making a sizzling sound. "You all should see the looks on your faces."

"Gobsmacked would be the word, Dottie Faye. Utterly gobsmacked," Kelly said. "Boy, are we glad to see you."

Emma jumped up and hugged her aunt. "I'm glad to see you in one piece. Now, tell us everything."

Dottie Faye's eyes twinkled. "You really want to know?"

"Mrs. Sinclair, please do go on. And sit down," Inspector Bailey urged.

"Well, if you insist." Dottie Faye grinned. "I just couldn't sleep after last night's visitor. After all, I'd been accosted several times since setting foot on the Emerald Isle. I was beginning to take it personally."

While Emma and Kelly took the inspector's spot on the sofa, Dottie Faye pulled her bag over to one of the chairs, sat down, and yanked out a small camera. "I set out to catch that banshee after it visited and embarrassed me just outside the drawing room the other day. Do you girls remember the first shopping trip I took to the village alone?" Dottie Faye looked at Emma and Kelly. She resumed her story after they nodded. "First I scoped out the old man's cottage and planted a camera there. I knew everyone was wrong. That banshee was not looking for me."

Inspector Bailey cleared his throat. "Show us what you have."

Dottie Faye squished between Emma and Kelly on the sofa. She moved a stack of magazines and a bowl of potpourri and set the camera on the coffee table. Inspector Bailey walked behind the sofa, looking over their shoulders, as Dottie Faye pushed the Play button.

Once the camera focused, Emma recognized the four young men in black as some of the hoodlums they'd seen in the village. She leaned forward and watched them ransack the place, looking for something.

The dark-haired ringleader grabbed the arm of a short blond running his hand over the back of the sofa. "Stephen, how could ya be such an *eejit* to lose your St. Christopher here and not know it?"

Stephen yanked his arm away. "Don't you be giving out to me, Gavin. You're the one who shot the geezer."

Kelly gasped and turned around to look at the inspector. "I told you she didn't do it."

Dottie Faye nudged her. "Keep watching. There's more."

On the screen, Gavin shoved Stephen. "Dry up. I didn't mean to do it. I just picked up the old gun to scare the man. I didn't know it was loaded."

"I found it! Remember how he grabbed at you as he went down?" The voice came from off camera.

"Good on you, Mark." Stephen crossed the room and took the chain from Mark's outstretched hand. "Molly and I had a scrap when she found out I lost it. She was so mad, she might have gone to the Garda and changed her story on us. We shoulda been back to get it sooner."

"You know the Garda and all the others were poking around here after the old man was found dead," Gavin said. "That Yank they arrested and her friends." He snickered. "The old dame was a good one to pin it on."

"I hear something out there. Let's go." The off-camera voice spoke again. All Emma could hear was a rustling sound.

Dottie Faye switched off the camera. "That was me they

heard. I was hiding in the bushes outside." She pulled a piece of equipment out of her bag that looked like the bell of a small tuba. "I was listening on my Super Sleuther Conversation Magnifier. When they walked up to the house, they were boasting about dropping the younger one in the drink." She looked at Kelly. "They were talking about you. I think they meant to kill you."

"How lovely." Kelly's lip quivered. "Thank you, Dottie Faye." Kelly took a deep breath. "Dottie Faye, did you hear the hoodlums say anything about assaulting Emma at the Cliffs of Moher?"

"Nothing. Not on the tape nor listening outside." Dottie Faye's eyes followed Inspector Bailey as he walked around the sofa. "I guess that will be a question for the inspector to ask."

He reached for the camera. "I'll need to hold this for evidence.

"Sure. You can take it. There's plenty more where that came from."

"All of you will need to come down and give a statement. The sooner you do this, the sooner we'll be able to drop the murder charges against Mrs. Quigley."

Kelly pulled her phone from a pants pocket. "Gladly. We'll be on our way as soon as I call Mom's attorney and have him meet us there."

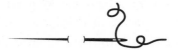

Emma and Kelly sat in a waiting area and watched Dottie Faye follow Garda Lowney into a room just as Inspector Bailey led Maeve and Mr. Rooney from the other direction into a room across the hall.

"Do you think your mom will ever get over Dottie Faye being the one who cleared her?"

Kelly chuckled. "Oh, I imagine Mom will grudgingly thank her when the shock wears off. Dottie Faye will rub it in for a while, and by the time we get back to Mystic Harbor, they'll be back to trying to outdo each other."

"You're probably right." Emma smiled and shook her head. "Whatever will we do with those two?"

"I guess the only thing we can do. Love them."

Before Emma could reply, a Garda approached. "Kelly Grace and Emma Cotton?"

"Yes." Kelly stood. "I'm Kelly Grace. This is Emma Cotton."

"Inspector Bailey asked me to take you to Mrs. Quigley. We're going to pick the suspects up now. Mrs. Quigley asked that you wait with her." He motioned them toward the hall.

As soon as Kelly entered the small square room, she darted to Maeve and hugged her. "It's almost over, Mom. Mr. Rooney will see that the charges are dropped."

Maeve kissed Kelly's cheek and released her. "Not soon enough."

This definitely hasn't been the trip we expected." Emma gave Maeve a quick hug. "But you've survived it."

Irving Rooney, who'd been discreetly leaning against the wall and studying his notes during the conversation, crossed the room. "Everything will be fine shortly."

The door opened and Dottie Faye sashayed through it. "There's nothing like being questioned about two different investigations, Hugh Slane's murder and the pooka and banshee incidents." She looked at Maeve. "From some of the questions they asked me, I think they believe the two might be related somehow. When I get my camera back, we'll have to look at the video again. Maybe it will show a connection."

Nearly an hour had passed before Inspector Bailey finally returned. "We're ready to do the lineup."

"Inspector, may we stay here with my mother?"

"Please, Inspector." Maeve looked him in the eyes. "I'd like them here."

Inspector Bailey looked at Dottie Faye. "Very well, as long as you stand by the door and don't say a word."

He dimmed the lights in the room, and while lights illuminated the room on the other side of a window, no one had noticed. "Mrs. Quigley, several men will file in front of you. They won't be able to see you. I know we have the taped admission, but we need to link them to Hugh Slane's residence before the murder. Look at them carefully. If there's anyone you recognize from that day at Hugh's home, tell me his number and I'll have him step forward."

Maeve stared through the glass. "Number two and number five, for sure." She chose the ringleader, Gavin, and the necklace owner, Stephen. "I'm not sure about the others. Maybe."

The men filed out of the lineup room.

"What happens next, Inspector?" Maeve asked.

He turned the lights back on. "They will be fingerprinted and will remain in custody during an investigation. You're free to go. Mr. Rooney has already taken care of the necessary paperwork."

Dottie Faye scrunched up her nose. "Inspector, why would Maeve's fingerprints be on the gun when theirs weren't?"

"Most likely the murderer had on the gloves he's in the habit of wearing," Garda Lowney answered for the inspector.

The inspector led the women and Rooney out of the room. He paused in the hallway just outside the door. "You and Mrs. Sinclair will likely be needed to testify in court, if the case goes to trial."

"I understand." Maeve looked at the window that had allowed her to identify the killers without them seeing her and put her hands on her hips. "I wish they'd give me five minutes with those boys. I sure would like to give them a piece of my mind. Do you suppose they have any idea what they've done and the pain they've caused so many people?"

Kelly grinned. "It sure is nice to see the fire back in your eyes."

"It's good to have it," Maeve said. "Let's go back to the castle. I don't ever want to see the inside of this place again."

"I'm good to go." Dottie Faye held up her camera and motioned to a Garda strolling toward the reception area. "That nice young man gave me back my camera."

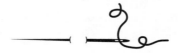

"I never thought I'd see so much of the inside of an Irish police station." Maeve looked back at the Garda station until Emma pulled the minivan around the first corner on the way back to the bed-and-breakfast.

"You shouldn't have to see it again," Kelly said. "Mr. Rooney should be able to handle everything from here."

Dottie Faye leaned forward. "Aren't you forgetting something? Banshee? Pooka? We still have a mystery to solve."

"That's true." Maeve glanced over her shoulder to the backseat at Dottie Faye and Kelly. "Who do you think is behind this foolishness?" Maeve asked.

"There could be many people behind it, but someone who works at the bed-and-breakfast must be involved because they had a key to our room," Kelly said.

"And they don't know we're smart enough to know

mythical creatures don't exist," said Maeve. "Good idea. But if I was being haunted, I'd want to stay awake, waiting on them when they come through the door so I could give them a scare instead. From what you've said, they're bound to do it again."

"I like it." Dottie Faye rubbed her hands together and laughed with a pseudo-sinister flair.

twenty-two

Emma felt silly crawling under the covers fully clothed, but Dottie Faye had insisted everyone be prepared for the next "haunting." For some reason, her aunt had it in her mind that a banshee would show up that night. They'd all consumed copious amounts of Irish tea after dinner in hopes of being awake, should an intruder make an appearance. As tiring as the day had been, the caffeine and excitement were doing their job. Emma's eyes were wide open.

The suite was quiet. There were no ticking clocks or roaring winds to break the silence. The Dottie cam was in place and focused on the suite entrance. All the lights were out, although Emma knew Dottie Faye had a flashlight nestled under the covers with her.

When the outer door creaked open, Emma threw off her covers and tiptoed across the bedroom. *Dottie Faye was right!* When the outer door closed, Emma slowly crept from her bedroom into the sitting room. To her left, Kelly entered the room at the same time.

"Gotcha!" Dottie Faye shouted from the sofa as she blinded the banshee with the flashlight. The two younger women dashed forward to subdue the very human apparition. With Emma and Kelly holding the struggling woman's arms, Dottie Faye snatched the white wig off her head, freeing long auburn tresses to cascade to the shoulders of a gossamer gown. "You won't be predicting the death of anyone else, you fake. Who are you?"

The young woman didn't answer.

Maeve, who'd followed Kelly into the room, switched on the lamp at the end of the sofa. "So this is what I've missed while I've been in jail. Fake banshees?"

Dottie Faye switched off her flashlight and stared at the woman, who was now struggling to free herself from Emma and Kelly's grasp. "Oh, relax, screaming meemie. Who are you?"

She tossed her head back and glared at Dottie Faye. "I'm an actress."

"That doesn't tell us much," Emma said.

Maeve padded to the suite door and leaned against it.

"I'll tell you, if you let me go." The young woman pulled her arms away from Emma and Kelly. "My name is Meghan. I was hired to scare the brassy American."

"What? Did you hear that?" Dottie Faye turned wide eyes to Emma. "She called me brassy!"

Emma went to the small desk on the other side of the sitting room and picked up the phone receiver. "I'm calling the night manager. Security can take care of this." She dialed the front desk number, and a few moments later, she was explaining the night's events.

"The manager will be here shortly." Emma walked back to stand in front of Meghan. "You said someone hired you. Who?"

"I don't have to tell you." Meghan tossed her hair behind her shoulder.

Emma inhaled. "Maybe not, but you might want to tell the manager—unless you want to spend the night in jail."

At an impasse, the women wordlessly stared at each other until a knock sounded on the door. Maeve opened it and stepped aside as the manager and a security guard entered the room.

"I'm Will Dolan, the night manager, and this is Red Vaughan." Dolan looked at Meghan and blinked. "I remember you. I had to run you and the Duncans out of the solarium after midnight last night. The room had already been closed for an hour. I'd wondered what you'd been up to." He looked at Emma. "Tell me what happened here."

She explained about the previous banshee sightings as well as the pooka visit. Dottie Faye took over and described what had happened up until Emma and Kelly grabbed Meghan.

Red Vaughan scribbled notes as the story was told. When the women finished talking, he looked at the manager. "Would you like me to call the Garda?"

"I think that should be up to Dottie Faye." Emma looked at Maeve and Kelly. "Don't you think?"

They nodded in unison.

"She's an actress trying to make a living. I understand that. I've been somewhat of an actress myself." Dottie Faye turned to the manager as if she'd reached the end of the red carpet. "I don't think calling the Garda is necessary—they've probably been here more in the past two weeks than they have in the last two centuries—if Meghan gives up the names of the people who hired her."

Meghan visibly squirmed. "It was the Duncans. They said they tangled with this crazy American lady the first morning after checking into the castle. Said she disturbed their breakfast, and she deserved to be taught a lesson in manners."

"Well, Meghan, Officer Vaughan is going to escort you off the premises. If you step foot on this property again, you will be arrested. Do you understand?" Dolan turned to Dottie Faye and handed her his business card. "I will deal with the Duncans. They may have thought their little prank was humorous, but I assure you this establishment does not. May I have a copy of the video you took for our files? My email address is on the card."

"I don't know how to do anything that advanced, but in the morning Emma can do it for you. Right, Emma Jane?"

"Yes, first thing in the morning." She looked at her watch. "I'd like to get a few hours of sleep tonight."

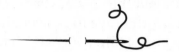

Emma leaned against the back wall of Egan's Pub and smiled when the vibration of music and dancing tickled her spine. Everyone in the village must have turned out for the celebration of a local legend and the end of a bitter feud. Perhaps they were curious to see if the families would peaceably gather in one place for the first time in six decades.

She was surprised to see Cormac O'Broin joining the traditional Irish band on the fiddle. Dottie Faye was enthusiastically learning the dance steps to an Irish reel, adding a few square-dance moves she learned growing up in Vicksburg.

"Surely my Uncle Hugh, Cormac O'Broin, and Frank Egan are looking down on this scene and smiling." Emma was startled to find Bartley Foley's face close to hers. "They'd not miss a *céilidh* as fine as this one, especially one attended by all of their families. Thank you for your part in bringing us all together."

"You're welcome, except I think the praise should go to Hugh's giant of a dog. Evidently, Fionn was the one who connected Maeve with your uncle."

"Ah, yes. Uncle Hugh's gentle beast. He's now happily residing with my daughter, Margaret, in the village." He nodded toward the bar. "She's the beauty chatting it up with the bartender, who I understand is somehow related to Frank Egan."

"Beats me." Emma laughed. "I can't keep everyone in the Egan family straight."

"I think I'll head over to find out. We fathers must keep a watchful eye, even when our children are grown."

"I imagine so. It was nice to meet you, once I got past being afraid of you." Emma blushed when he kissed her cheek before weaving his way through the crowd to the bar.

Emma stood watching the dancing until Brendan returned his cue stick to the rack next to the pool table and approached her.

"Look over there, under my granda's portrait." Emma's eyes followed Brendan's gaze. Daniel, who'd returned home from Castlebar about an hour before the celebration had started, and Maeve sat laughing at a corner table, their conversation filled with animated hand gestures. "Da and Aunt Maeve are finally catching up."

Kelly walked up and took each one of them by the arm. "Come with me. I want to show you something." She guided them to the far side of the pub to Connor Egan's usual table, where he sat with his head bent closely to Rowena O'Broin's.

Brendan brushed his hands across his eyes. "Would you look at that? Cormac O'Broin's bride and Frank Egan's brother deep in conversation. I can almost hear the wounds healing."

The microphone popped and Brendan, like everyone else in the place, looked at the band.

"May I have your attention, everyone?" The band spokesman held up a drink. "As a native of this village, I propose a toast to the ties between the Egan, Slane, and O'Broin families. May the friendship between them never again be torn asunder." He paused for a minute as everyone in the pub drank to that. "Cormac O'Broin, grandson of *the* Cormac O'Broin, will join us again onstage to perform a new version of *Three Connemara Lads*, first written in the 1950s by an unknown musician in the village. Cormac has written a final verse to commemorate tonight's reunion of the families."

Cormac stepped to the microphone and began to sing a cappella to a silent crowd. After a few lines, the band joined in. Brendan bobbed his head as Cormac sang one verse about each of the friends, followed by the traditional last stanza recounting his grandfather's death and the resulting feud between the families. The band played an instrumental riff and softened when Cormac joined them singing:

"Young Cormac did not die in vain,
His country is now at peace.
Frank sought to protect his family,
His love of Ireland never ceased.
Rebel Hugh lived a life on the run,
Auld Mick lived alone on the beach,
Three friends brought together again
By the death of auld Hugh Slane."

Cormac bowed his head as loud applause erupted when he sang his last note.

"Thank you. Now I'd like to recognize the four Americans who brought us together this evening. First we have Maeve Egan Quigley, Frank's daughter, who met Hugh Slane just before he was murdered. Then there's Maeve's daughter, Frank's granddaughter, Kelly Grace, who with her friends Emma Cotton and Dottie Faye Sinclair left no stone unturned to prove Maeve didn't murder Hugh."

Kelly pushed Maeve forward. "Go say something for us."

Maeve shook her head at first, but at more urging from Kelly and Emma, she finally stepped onto the stage and took the microphone from Cormac.

"Thank you for the warm welcome." Maeve looked around the room. "We wouldn't be here tonight, celebrating the end of a very long feud between three families, if the man I knew as Mick hadn't lost his life. But I know that Mick—that is, Hugh—would have happily sacrificed his life to see this happen for the families of men he dearly loved."

Maeve paused to compose herself. "I personally owe my freedom to a woman who has tested my Irish temper for years. I know some of you were irritated at the way Dottie Faye Sinclair harped on banshees and other aspects of Irish culture. But if she hadn't been relentless in her pursuit of the truth, I'd still be in jail, and this celebration wouldn't be happening. So, I thank you, Dottie Faye, for refusing to be left behind. And I thank you all for welcoming us into your families."

When she stepped from the stage, Connor Egan, Rowena O'Broin, and Bartley Foley were waiting for her with Kelly, Emma, and Dottie Faye. "Thank you for this beautiful celebration," Maeve said as her composure crumbled and her eyes filled with tears. "I wish we didn't have to leave tomorrow, but Kelly and Emma have a business to run."

"We—Rowena, Bartley, and I—plan to stay in touch and keep the memories of Frank, Cormac, and Hugh alive," Connor said. "But we'd like to plan an annual gathering of the Egan, O'Broin, and Slane families. Of course, we welcome you to visit anytime, as often as you like."

"I—I mean *we* would really like that," said Maeve. "Of course, you must know by now that Emma and Dottie Faye are honorary members of the Egan family, right?"

"Well, top o' the mornin' to ye!" Dottie Faye said in her best Southern Irish brogue. "I guess I'll be wearin' the green from now on."

Maeve laughed and actually put her arm around her nemesis. "Don't worry. We'll work on that accent before our next trip to the Emerald Isle."

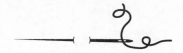

Mystery Sampler Quilt

Create your own mystery sampler quilt with blocks designed by Emma and Kelly and inspired by each book in the series! You'll find a Cotton & Grace block pattern in every Annie's Quilted Mysteries book. At the end of the series, the last pattern will include finishing instructions that will tell you how to stitch the unique blocks together to create a beautiful, one-of-a-kind quilt.

Highland Plains

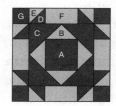

Highland Plains
12" x 12" Finished Block

Specifications
Finished Block Size: 12" x 12"
Skill Level: Intermediate

Cutting

From Light Fabric:
Cut 2 (5¼") squares.
   Subcut in half on both diagonals
   to make 4 B triangles.
Cut 4 (2⅞") squares.
   Subcut in half on 1 diagonal to
   make 8 E triangles.
Cut 4 (2½" x 4½") F rectangles.

From Dark Fabric:
Cut 1 (4½") A square.
Cut 2 (4⅞") squares.
   Subcut in half on 1 diagonal to
   make 4 C triangles.
Cut 4 (2⅞") squares.
   Subcut in half on 1 diagonal to
   make 8 D triangles.
Cut 4 (2½") G squares.

Assembly
1. Stitch a B triangle to opposite sides of the A square; press seams toward B (Figure 1). Repeat on the remaining sides of A.

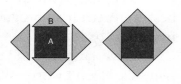

Figure 1

Center Unit

Figure 2

2. In the same manner, stitch a C triangle to each side of the A-B unit to complete the center unit (Figure 2); press seams toward C.

3. Sew a D triangle to an E triangle (Figure 3); press toward D. Repeat to make a total of eight D-E units.

Make 8

Side Unit
Make 4

Figure 3　　　　**Figure 4**

4. Stitch a D-E unit to each end of the F rectangles to make four side units (Figure 4); press toward D-E units.

5. Sew a side unit to opposite sides of the center unit to make the block center row (Figure 5); press seams toward the center unit.

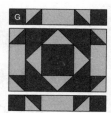

6. Stitch a G square to each end of the remaining side units again referring to Figure 5; press seams toward G. Sew the pieced strips to the top and bottom of the center row to complete the block; press seams away from the center row.

Figure 5

HELPFUL HINTS

• Choose light and dark fabrics for this block. Use scraps from other projects, or purchase fat eighths (9" x 22") or fat quarters (18" x 22") to make one sampler block.

• Cut individual pieces from scraps, or cut strips and then individual pieces from strips if using yardage or large pieces of fabric. For example, to cut several 2½" squares, cut a 2½"-wide strip the width of the fabric. Subcut the strip into 2½" squares.

• Use a ¼"-wide seam allowance for all seams and stitch with right sides together.

• For more detailed help with quilting techniques, go to QuiltersWorld.com and choose Quilting Basics under Quilt Essentials, or consult a complete quilting guide. Your local library may have several on hand that you can review before purchasing one.

Annie's Quilted Mysteries™

COMING SOON!

STAB STITCHED

For once Emma and Kelly's search for Rose's killer doesn't lead them far and wide. Olivia Stewart, one of the last suspects on their list, lives in Lantern Cove, a short drive from Mystic Harbor.

But when a wealthy friend of Dottie Faye is discovered stabbed to death, and Dottie Faye is arrested for murder, Emma and Kelly find themselves on a different manhunt. They now have to dovetail their investigation with a desperate attempt to clear Dottie Faye's name.

Don't miss the next book in this
exciting new series from
Annie's Quilted Mysteries!

Annie's®

AnniesFiction.com

PERSPECTIVES IN EXPERIMENTAL LINGUISTICS

AMSTERDAM STUDIES IN THE THEORY AND HISTORY OF LINGUISTIC SCIENCE

E. F. KONRAD KOERNER, *General Editor*

Series IV – CURRENT ISSUES IN LINGUISTIC THEORY

Advisory Editorial Board

Volume 10

Gary D. Prideaux, Ed.

Perspectives in Experimental Linguistics

PERSPECTIVES IN EXPERIMENTAL LINGUISTICS

PAPERS FROM THE UNIVERSITY OF ALBERTA
CONFERENCE ON EXPERIMENTAL LINGUISTICS

(Edmonton, 13-14 October 1978)

EDITED BY

GARY D. PRIDEAUX

University of Alberta

AMSTERDAM / JOHN BENJAMINS B.V.

1979

CONTENTS

PREFACE

GARY D. PRIDEAUX
University of Alberta

For many years, experimentally oriented language study occupied a peripheral niche in departments of linguistics and psychology. Over the past few years, however, interest and research in experimental linguistics has shifted more toward centre stage, perhaps because of the growing recognition that purely theoretical formulations and speculations about language must necessarily be tested against the empirical facts of language knowledge, use, and acquisition. The increasing awareness of the crucial role of empirical studies has produced enormous gains as the discipline of linguistics struggles toward scientific maturity. In particular, considerable attention has been directed toward foundational issues, with the result that many of the familiar and once unquestioned claims and assumptions associated with the study of language have been called into question, notions such as what a language is, the competence-performance distinction, the infamous derivational theory of complexity, and the assumption of the primacy of syntax.

The growing interest in experimental issues has forced linguists to borrow experimental methodologies from their psychologist and engineer neighbours, as well as to develop new means of their own for the study of language phenomena. Imaginative and innovative techniques have been required in order to tap, albeit indirectly, native speaker judgements about acceptability, paraphrase, ambiguity, semantic similarity, perceptual distinctions, and many other aspects of

VII

language use. Along with the adoption and invention of novel methodologies for the collection of data has come an increasing awareness of the extreme complexity and variety in the kinds of factors which influence language behaviour, ranging from 'purely linguistic' phenomena such as grammatical complexity to aspects of 'world knowledge' as distinct from grammatical knowledge, and from extremely subtle sociolinguistic and dialectal distinctions to varying problem-solving strategies which subjects may employ in various experimental situations. Furthermore, experimentally oriented linguists have been forced to acquire skills quite foreign to those traditionally associated with training in descriptive linguistics. Today the experimental linguist must be far more than an armchair theoretician. He must have an understanding of experimental design, statistics, physics, and calculus, and one of his primary research instruments is now the computer.

Because of the importance of the empirical study of language, the Department of Linguistics was formed within the Faculty of Science at the University of Alberta, with graduate research programs in psycholinguistics and in speech production and perception. On October 13-14, 1978, the Department hosted a conference focusing on 'Perspectives in Experimental Linguistics'. It was realized that since the range of experimental topics in linguistics is so broad, it would be virtually impossible to sample from every area while at the same time maintaining a high quality of papers and providing adequate time for extended discussions. As a result, six scholars were invited to present substantial contributions and six others were asked to present invited commentaries based on their prior reading of the invited papers. Extensive discussion sessions were also scheduled. To the best of our knowledge, this conference was the first of its kind to be held in Canada, and due to its success, a decision was made to publish the papers as soon as possible. Included here are revised versions of the six major presentations, plus an Epilogue, representing the closing session of the conference, chaired by W. J. Baker. That session was intended as a kind of 'summing up' and open discussion of many of the recurrent themes of the conference. A general bibliography is also included.

PREFACE

The conference could not have taken place without the
financial assistance of the Social Sciences and Humanities
Research Council of Canada, the Conference Committee and
the Faculty of Science of the University of Alberta. Our
gratitude is extended to each of these agencies as well as
to the Canadian Linguistic Association for its assistance.
Professor E. F. K. Koerner provided considerable editorial
guidance during the preparation of the manuscript for publication, and his assistance is greatly appreciated. Finally, it must be acknowledged that all the financial support would have been useless had it not been for the liter-
ally tireless work and enthusiastic good humor of
Mrs. Helen B. Hawkes, the Administrative Assistant in the
Department of Linguistics. To her goes a hearty thanks
from the more than seventy conference registrants.

Edmonton, Alberta
May 1979

PHONETICS AND PHYSIOLOGY: SOME CURRENT ISSUES

PHILIP LIEBERMAN
Brown University

1. Introduction. I will discuss some current issues,
e.g., the status of systematic phonetics, speech encoding,
property detectors, and models of speech perception in
terms of our current knowledge of phonetics and the physiology of speech production and perception. I'll first
briefly sketch the relevant background of what we seem to
know, i.e., those theories that have not yet been refuted
though they have been tested many times. I'll then discuss
what we think we know, i.e., some new theories that are
consistent with available data. I'll try to limit the discussion to problems that can be tested and explored using
the technology that is presently available or seems likely
to become available in the near future.

2. The Source-Filter Theory. The source-filter theory of
speech production is perhaps the best example of a theory
that reflects what we probably know. Johannes Muller
(1848) developed the theory in an explicit form in the early 19th century that speech is the result of a source of
acoustic energy being filtered by the airways above the
larynx. The theory of course had been the basis of the
18th century speech synthesizers of Kratzentein (1780) and
von Kempelin (1791) but Muller put the theory into an explicit testable form. He also differentiated between the
quasiperiodic laryngeal source of voiced sounds and noise
excitation. The properties of the human supralaryngeal
vocal tract are well known because of the studies of people
like Chiba and Kajiyama (1941), and Fant (1960). An explicit quantitative theory for the acoustic properties of
the supralaryngeal vocal tract has been developed that can

be reduced to various forms of automata that will predict the filtering action of the supralaryngeal airways, given their area function. The supralaryngeal vocal tract model has even been tested by means of studies which have calculated the output of a vocal tract configuration whose output was not available for comparison with the predicted filter function. The chimpanzee supralaryngeal vocal tract, for example, is a 'one tube' system that essentially consists of an oral cavity. (The pharynx in non-human primates does not form part of the direct airway from the larynx to the lips.) The predicted output of the non-human primate supralaryngeal vocal tract was calculated in Lieberman et al. (1972) by means of a distributed constant computer model for a chimpanzee attempting to make its 'best' approximation to the human vowel [i]. No chimpanzees or other non-human primates had been recorded at that time making vocalizations that were in any sense [i] like. The predicted output and supralaryngeal vocal tract configuration are shown in Figure 1. Vocalizations with these predicted formant frequencies were independently recorded from a gelada monkey in a study by Richman (1976). The sound that Richman considered to be typical of gelada [i]'s had the formant frequencies of the human vowel [I] as the computer model predicted. The model also correctly predicts the behaviour of human speakers who suffer from craniofacial anomolies and who have pathologic supralaryngeal vocal tracts, for example, of patients who have Cruzon's and Aperts syndromes. The source-filter model can predict deficiencies and suggest more effective programs of speech therapy and reconstructive surgery. This marks a new application of the source-filter theory of speech production that is at the same time a test of the theory and a practical, humane application.

Although most aspects of the source-filter theory constitute what we might term a stage I level of knowledge, as certain as anything human is, some aspects are at stage II, i.e., more uncertain. The effects of nasal coupling still have to be explored in detail for both normal speakers as Fujimura has been systematically doing by means of computer controlled X-rays and acoustic analysis, and for pathologic conditions which represent more complex problems.

3. <u>Phonology</u> <u>and</u> <u>the</u> <u>Constraints</u> <u>of</u> <u>Speech</u> <u>Production</u>. The dynamic control of the supralaryngeal vocal tract is also a stage II problem. This uncertainty is, of course, vexing to some people but we must look on its more joyous aspect since it presents problems that are interesting and affords an opportunity to demonstrate the power of phonetics. The relationship between prevoiced stops and

/i/ ●──●			/ɑ/ ■--■			/u/ ▲·······▲		
Formant	Freq.	Freq./1.7	Formant	Freq.	Freq./1.7	Formant	Freq.	Freq./1.7
1	610	360	1	1220	720	1	830	490
2	3400	2000	2	2550	1500	2	1800	1060
3	4420	2600	3	5070	2980	3	4080	2390

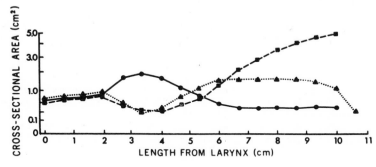

Figure 1

nasalization, for example, is a useful example. Linguists often draw charts on blackboards and pieces of paper. One common picture shows the different, independent components of a linguistic theory. At the top of the picture we can see a box labelled semantics. This holy mystery is of course a significant, if intractable level, of linguistic science and the present lack of experimental semantic methodology makes it possible to formulate very important, complex theories that only certain people can understand. The next level of linguistic theory is typically a box labelled syntax. The next lower level is a box labelled phonology. At this level we can make use of detailed phonetic data that people more or less agree on, except for phenomena like stress and intonation. The last and lowest box is the phonetic level.

4. <u>Prevoiced Stops and Nasalization</u>. Two recent developments demonstrate that this little box linguistic theory is not especially productive. The various `phonologic' phenomena that cause prevoiced stops to undergo various changes when they occur in intervocallic position are not generally viewed in relation to the physiology of speech production, nor is there any hint that the suposedly independent phonetic dimension of nasalization has anything to do with prevoicing in anything other than a strictly distributional sense. Prevoiced stops, however, require an airflow through the larynx during the primary stop

occlusion. One strategy to effect this airflow is to employ a nasal airflow. In an ongoing comparative study of Portugese and Spanish, Maia (in preparation) proposes to explain some of the differences between Spanish and Portuguese stop contrasts in terms of nasalization. A series of supposedly abstract phonologic rules can be motivated in terms of the possibility of maintaining a transglottal airflow for voicing by means of airflow through the nose. A stop in the neighborhood of a nasal `segment´ is also more likely to retain its voiced character.

This brings us to the more general question of segmentation and speech encoding. Some linguists are beginning to adopt the position that there is no segmentation whatsoever at the phonetic level. The basis for this position rests on phenomena like that of prevoicing and nasal assimilation plus the perceptual encoding and decoding that has been discussed for many years by the Haskins Laboratory research group in connection with the `motor theory of speech perception.´

5. Encoding. Figure 2 shows a typical illustration of speech encoding. The word **bat** was synthesized by means of a two formant speech synthesizer. There is no clear segmentation; the formant frequency pattern that defines the initial [b] melds into that of the [ae] and that goes into that of the final [g]. Cineradiographic evidence of speech production also shows the absence of segmentation at the articulatory level. Studies like those of Gay (1974) and Nearey (1976), moreover, also show that there is no clear evidence for segmentation at the level of muscular commands as monitored by EMG techniques. We thus can pose the question, is there a biological basis for phonetic segmentation? Is segmentation perhaps a carryover from our orthographic system?

6. Neural Property Detectors. Some recent and some `older´ psychoacoustic data are consistent with the theory that there exists a set of neural property detectors that respond to specific acoustic patterns in the speech signal of an invarient segmental basis. Figure 3 shows a four formant plus burst synthesis of the consonant-vowel syllable [da]. This particular syllable was one of a set synthesized in a study of Stevens and Blumstein (1978). A number of such stimuli were synthesized. When listeners are asked to identify the first 26 msec of this particular sound they identify the sound as [da] 90% of the time. The listeners behave very differently than do listeners who are asked to identify stimuli synthesized on the older two and three formant synthesizers typical of those used in the now

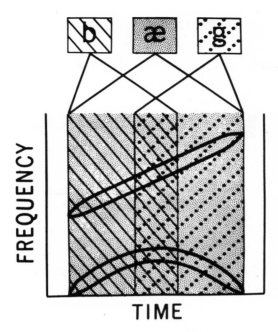

Figure 2

classic Haskins experiments. When listening to the Haskins' stimuli listeners had to hear the entire syllable
before they could reliably identify the stop. These differences probably rest in the fact that the newer synthetic
speech stimuli are more fully specified than the older 'i-
mpoverished' stimuli used in the Haskins experiments. The
result of experiments over twenty years ago by Halle et al.
(1957) that gated out short segments of natural speech are
in accord with the responses of listeners to these new synthesized four formant plus burst stimuli. Listeners who
heard about 20 msec of the onset of a CVC syllable identified the initial consonants, on the average, about 80% of
the time. I'd like to propose that there exists an en-
semble of 'templates' or neural property detectors that respond to fully specified consonant-vowel and
vowel-consonant speech sound clusters. Stimuli that are
not fully specified can also trigger these templates but
with lesser accuracy and with slower response times. These
templates form the basis for various classes of speech
sounds.

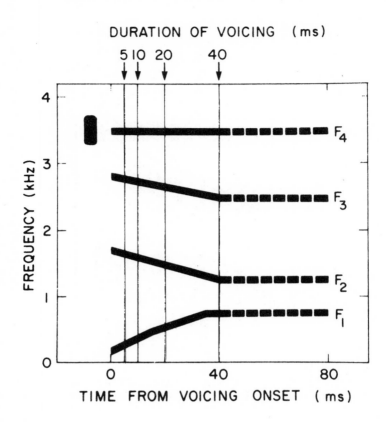

Figure 3

I would also propose that certain classes of speech sounds occupy a more central place in human languages because they make use of 'better' biological mechanisms. The stop sounds, for example, can be viewed as speech sounds that match the quantal constraints discussed by Stevens (1972) and thus make use of templates that probably are innately determined in <u>Homo sapiens</u>. These templates appear to be present in human infants at three weeks of age since these subjects display the same categorical classes as adult speakers. Other speech sounds, which are less prevelant across different languages, probably do not involve innately determined templates. I'll return to discuss the possible evolution of these templates in relation to speech production and the 'base' level of speech communication present in other mammals in a later section.

In regard to acoustic features, in the sense proposed by Roman Jakobson, I would propose that they represent secondary, derived properties of the speech sounds and templates. In other words, the basic psychologically `real' level perceptual unit is the speech sound cluster and its associated ensemble of templates.

7. The `Motor Theory of Speech Perception'. The templates form part of a phonetic system that is `matched' to a greater or lesser degree in all animals to the constraints of the speech production system. The basis for the `motor theory of speech perception' thus rests in the match between the templates that form the basis of speech perception in Homo sapiens and the speech producing physiology of Homo sapiens (Lieberman 1975), in particular, the quantal formant frequency patterns of the stop consonants. The attractiveness of the motor theory of speech perception, which has a long history dating to at least the last decade of the 19th century, rests in this match. However, there are good reasons for believing that there is no active device that compares the incoming speech signal with a `reconstructed' or `internally generated' speech signal as the motor theory claims. In other words, there is no neural `decoder' that actively matches the incoming speech signal againt a modelled signal. I'll return to this point.

8. A Model of Speech Perception. Figure 4 is a diagram of the levels of analysis that I would propose for a model of the perception of speech. A preferatory remark is in order regarding the relation between a model and its implementation. A physicist may model certain aspects of the activity of a heat engine by means of the Carnot cycle. This model relates input and output temperatures and the engine's efficiency. If all that one knows about a particular heat engine is the model exemplified by the Carnot cycle, it is not possible to tell whether the engine works by means of pistons, rotors, turbines, vanes, etc. The model and its implementation are distinct, and the physicist is not making any claims regarding the model's implementation when he presents the model. Linguists and psychologists often confuse the claims of a model with the implementation of the model. The `analysis by synthesis' model for formant attraction described by Bell et al. (1961) and by Halle and Stevens (1959) is a case in point. The computer program of this model made use of one register of a computer to calculate the formant frequencies of an incoming speech signal by subtracting from the input signal the transfer function of a particular first formant frequency, a particular

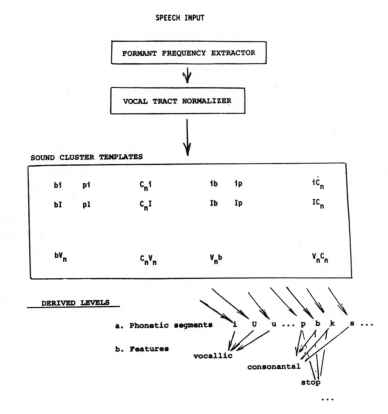

Figure 4

second and a particular third formant frequency and systematically changing these formant frequencies, noting the residue. The combination of first, second, and third formant frequency which, when subtracted from the input speech signal, left the smallest residue was selected as the 'correct' solution. The model was based on Fant's (1956) demonstration that the transfer function for each formant frequency could be combined in a linear manner for a non-nasal vowel. The filter function of any first formant frequency could thus be added to that of any second formant frequency, etc. It therefore was possible to systematically try out the effect of adding all possible first formant frequency filter functions to all second and third formant frequency patterns allowing all possible permutations. The `best` combination of F1, F2, and F3 was thus the one that most closely matched the incoming speech signal.

The analysis-by-synthesis model was interpreted as a sign that formant frequencies were determined by human listeners by an `active` process in which the effects of single formant frequencies were added together in one `arithmetic` register. The process in some ways was analogous to the operation of the rules of the English stress cycle formulated by Chomsky and Halle (1968). However, the proces could just as well have been implemented by using a number of artihmetic registers operating in parallels. This would have made the process faster. The model also could have been implemented by having a number of `templates` equal to the total number of combinations of all possible formant frequency triads and matching the incoming speech signal against the members of the array of templates in one parallel operation. This last solution, that of an array of templates, would yield the highest operating speed. Looking at the `outside` of three black boxes that made use of these different alternatives would yield the same input and output relationships except for operating speed. It would be impossible to tell what was going on inside the various black boxes unless one knew the operating speeds of the possible components. In the discussion that follows I'll present a number of black boxes that together constitute a model of a recogniser of certain speech sounds. I'll discuss data that argue for the reality of some of these boxes and some data that hint at the formal implementation of these boxes in the human brain, but I don't make any guesses about the neural implementation of the boxes.

The first box in Figure 4 is labelled Formant Extractor. An obvious question is why have a formant extractor at all? At least two radically different theories have been proposed that would not make use of a formant extractor. The theory proposed by Jakobson, Fant, and Halle (1958) in _Preliminaries_ _for_ _Speech_ _Analysis_ can, for example, be interpreted as a model that makes use of various measures of the power spectrum of various sounds without ever considering the actual formant frequencies of particular speech sounds. The distinctive feature Graveness versus Acuteness, for example, can be defined in terms of the frequency balance of the overall acoustic spectrum without considering formant frequencies. Sounds that have relatively more acoustic energy at high frequencies are Acute, whereas sounds that have more energy at low frequencies are Grave. The Compact-Diffuse dimension likewise can be defined in terms of the overall spectrum. Sounds in which acoustic energy is concentrated in a particular portion of

the spectrum are Compact, sounds that involve an energy
'spread' across the spectrum or in different parts of the
spectrum are Diffuse. Computer (and pre-computer) automatic speech recognition systems have been implemented that
made 'distinctive feature' decisions to identify speech
segments by means of such spectral decisions (Chang 1958;
Hughes 1960; Forgie & Forgie 1960, 1962). These systems
did not make use of any formant extraction device. They
instead operated directly on the spectrum deriving the distinctive feature decision by means of filter banks and ana-
log circuits that computed spectral peaks. All of these
systems, however, operated with less effectiveness when the
fundamental frequency of phonation of the speech samples
that they analyzed was high. This was to be expected; if
the fundamental frequency of phonation of a speech sample
is, for example, 200 Hz instead of 100 Hz, then there will
be half the spectral detail present since acoustic energy
will be present at intervals of 200 Hz rather than 100 Hz.

If human speech perception thus involved some procedure that was analogous to the procedures used in automatic
speech recognition schemes that make use of the 'raw'
acoustic spectrum, we would expect to find that speech perception was a function of the fundamental frequency of
phonation. Speakers who has high f0's would be less intel-
ligible, all other things being equal, than speakers who
had low f0's. This assumption was widely held for many
years. Women thus were supposed to be less effective as
radio announcers or commentators than low pitched men. It
was simple to test this theory. Data (Moslin & Cowper
1975) show that women with average f0 of 250 Hz are as in-
telligible as men whose average f0 is 120 Hz. The equal
intelligibility of voices that have low and high fundamental frequencies of phonation is thus consistent with a process that involves decisions made on formant frequencies
rather than the raw acoustic spectrum.

9. <u>Formant</u> <u>Extractors,</u> <u>Nasalization</u> <u>and</u> <u>Errors</u>. It is interesting to note that the procedure that is presently most
often used for the estimation of formant frequencies by
means of computer implemented analysis, Linear Predictive
Analysis (Atal & Hanauer 1971) is subject to the same sort
of errors as human speech perception. Nasalization, which
opens a side branch in the acoustic supralaryngeal filter,
introduces poles and zeros into the transfer function and
makes a linear approximation impossible. The error rate
for LPA goes up with nasalization. Human listeners also
make almost ten times as many errors when they are asked to
identify nasalized vowels (Bond 1976). The higher error
rate for nasalization also occurs for native speakers of

languages like Portuguese, which have nasalized vowels
(Maia, in preparation). The lower frequency of occurrence
of nasal vowels in the languages of the world thus may stem
from the inherent properties of the human formant extraction device which makes more errors when the formant frequencies of nasal sounds are derived.

In a meaningful sense LPA derives from the same source
as the `analysis by synthesis´ model of Halle and Stevens
(1959). Fant (1956) showed that the solution to the vocal
tract transfer function could be derived by a linear super-
position of the transfer functions of individual formant
frequencies for non-nasal sounds vowels. The `analysis by
synthesis´ model, however, implies a rather different model
for speech perception than the proposal that I´ve made. It
(Bell et al. 1961) will compute formant frequencies but
also eliminates the separate stage of formant extraction.
The computer implemented analysis by synthesis scheme of
Bell et al. (1961), for example, in deriving the formant
frequencies, could have assigned them into different vowel
categories. Models for speech perception such as those
propoed by Liberman et al. (1967) and other exponents of
the `motor theory of speech perception´ attempt to classify
incoming vowel sounds in terms of invariant vocal tract
shapes or motor commands that, in turn, specify the vowels
in traditional phonetic theories. The problem with these
schemes is really a more general problem, i.e., the failure
of traditional phonetic theory at the descriptive level.

Data derived from frames of a cineradiographic study
of speech production, e.g. Ladefoged et al. (1972) and
Nearey (1976), where the contour of the tongue and other
anatomical features were sketched during the production of
the vowels of English for a number of different normal native speakers of English, show that different speakers make
use of different tongue contours that are not in accord
with the claims of the traditional´ phonetic theory that
has been developed from Melville Bell´s mid-19th century
studies. Tongue height and the anterior-posterior location
of a hypothetical `point of articulation´ are supposed to
specify vowels according to this theory. The height of the
tongue, for example, in the production of the vowel [I] is
supposed to be greater than it is for [æ] or [e]. This is
not necessarily the case (Lieberman 1977). Although some
speakers, in fact, systematically produce vowel distinctions by means of differences along the hypothetical dimensions of Front versus Back and High versus Low as Bell
(1867) and Jones (1919) claimed, many speakers do not. The
data of Russell (1928) demonstrate the general deficiencies
of the traditional 19th century phonetic theory based on

classificatory invariant articulatory distinctions for vowels. Russell's data were derived from still X-rays of a
large sample of speakers across the 'front' and 'back' of
vowels where the dimensions Front versus Back refer to the
hypothetical 'point' of articulation with reference to the
palate. Russell's data were ignored by most phoneticians
who apparently believed that the discrepancies that Russell
found between X-ray data and the claims of the traditional
theory were due to alignment problems in Russell's X-rays
or generally sloppy procedures. These claims regarding the
deficiencies of Russell's data appear, to me, to be
self-serving in view of the lack of experimental controls
in the studies that found no problems with the articulatory
Bell theory. Recent carefully controlled cineradiographic
studies like those of Perfell (1969), Houde (1967), Ladefoged et al. (1971), and Nearey (1976), however, are consistent with Russell's data and refute the 'traditional'
phonetic theory (Lieberman 1976, 1977).

10. Vocal Tract Normalization. Nearey's work (1976) is,
in particular, significant since it establishes that vowels
can only be classified after a process of vocal tract normalization. The process of vocal tract normalization involves a scaling of the formant frequencies that, in effect, takes into account the fact that the formant frequencies of a vowel or any other speech sound are a function of
the overall length of the speaker's supralaryngeal vocal
tract.

11. Speech Development in Children. Data on the acquisition of speech by children address two issues: first, the
innate basis of the formant frequency normalization 'd-
evice' and, second, the phonemic versis phonetic dichotomy
that has been part of all linguistic theories since de
Saussure. The data that I'll discuss form part of a comprehensive acoustic analysis of the development of speech
in normal children from birth through the preschool years
(Lieberman, in press). We have systematically recorded and
analyzed the utterances of a small group of normal children. Our objective has been to gather quantitative acoustic data that are sufficiently detailed to develop and test
hypotheses that bear on the biological bases of language.

We started the study by recording, at weekly or two
week intervals, the utterances of five children whose ages
ranged at the start of the project from 16 weeks to five
years. All of the children were raised in upper middle
class, monolingual English speaking environments in Providence, Rhode Island. As the project went on we 'lost' some
of our subjects when it became difficult to schedule

recording sessions or when the family moved and we added
three more children. Two of these children were started at
10 and 12 months respectively, to focus on the transition
from babbling to word acquisition. The third child was
first recorded one week after birth. We have also recorded, at intervals, one child raised in a bilingual
Polish-English and five children in Korean speaking environments to acquire data that address specific hypotheses.

The recording sessions typically involve the child and
his or her mother interacting in situations that are normal
in the context of the child's maturation. In the early
months of life the child may be recorded while eating or
bathing; in later stages of development the mother and
child may be `reading' picture books aloud or playing games
with various toys. Older children have been recorded as
they engage in monologues or converse with their parents,
other people, or the recording crew. We used Nagara type
4.2 portable tape recorders at a tape speed of 7.5 ips using 1.5 mil Scotch Low Noise tape. The tape recorders have
been used with battery supplies to cause the least pertur-
bation of the children's home environment.

A study of the development of vowel production necessarily depends on having acurate formant frequency measurements. We adopted a systems approach to meet this problem
and tailored our recording techniques to optimize the measurement of formant frequencies from speakers who have extremely high fundamental frequencies. We have emphasized
recording breathy voice excitation, which yields noiselike
excitation of the supralaryngeal vocal tract's filter function by using directional AKG D900 microphones positioned
close to our children during the early stages of their
lives. As the children mature and grow accustomed to the
presence of microphones, recording, etc., we have in certain cases used electret condenser microphones attached to
the child, near his or her mouth.

12. Analysis. We analyzed the tape recordings made under
these conditions, which emphasized breathy excitation, with
spectrograms made on Kay Elemetrics Type 6061B Sound Spe-
ctrographs using 90 Hz and 600 Hz bandwidth analysis filters. Figure 5, for example, shows two spectrograms of the
word [dagi] produced by speaker JB at age 91 weeks. The
lower spectrogram was made with an analyzing bandwidth of
90 Hz; the upper with a filter bandwidth of 600 Hz. A Kay
type 6067C scale expander was used in both cases and calibrating signals spaced at one kHz intervals were put on
both spectrograms.

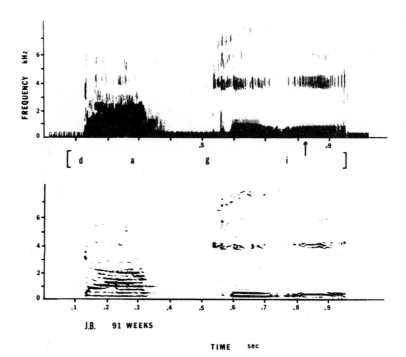

Figure 5

The use of 90 Hz and 600 Hz bandwidth spectrograms,
the scale expander and calibrating signals which we check
against a signal generator is standard procedure for all
our analyses. The increased bandwidth of the 600 Hz analyzing filter makes it possible to estimate formant frequencies for fundamental frequencies up to at least 250 Hz
whereas it is quite difficult to estimate formant frequencies with the usual 300 Hz 'wideband' analyzing filter of
the sound spectrograph when the fundamental frequency exceeds 150 Hz (Lieberman 1977). The arrow symbol that appears after 0.8 sec on the upper spectrogram indicates the
point at which the formant frequencies of the vowel [i]
were measured for this utterance. We made formant frequency measurements for vowels at points like that indicated by
the arrow where 'steady state' conditions occurred. Formant frequencies were not discernable in all utterances
even with these techniques. The fundamental frequency of
phonation of the utterance displayed in Figure 5 ranged between 300 and 250 Hz so the formant frequencies could be

derived by means of the averaging technique inherent in the use of the 600 Hz bandwidth analyzing filter. The formant frequencies of the vowel [i] which are at approximately 0.5, 4.2 and 6.0 kHz are measurable, but note the `extra' dark `bars' that occur during the [a] which are the results of nasalization. The [a] in Figure 5 is nasalized and the formants and antiformants of the nasal airway make it difficult to derive the formant frequencies of the [a]. In cases of doubt, which were many, we simply did not use the utterance; for example, if it was too nasalized or if the fundamental frequency was too high and there was not sufficient breathy excitation present to resolve the formants. The data that we shall discuss in this report is drawn from a corpus of approximately 18,000 spectrograms, of which approximately 50% were discarded for the above mentioned reasons.

13. Classification of vowels. The process of perceptually identifying vowels in the non-cry utterances of very young children is not easy. The children in their babbling stage may not be referring to any known referent objects, actions, or requests so it is difficult to determine what they are attempting to say, if indeed they are attempting to produce any specific vowel. Despite these difficulties there is general agreement on at least the range of sounds that very young children produce during the initial stages of babbling.

Perceptually based phonetic transcriptions of the sounds that children make in the first three months of life are in substantial accord (Irwin 1948; George 1978). The transcriptions of phonetically trained listeners responding to the sounds that children make as they grow up in an English speaking environment are in accord; the `front' vowels of English excepting [i] occur. It is in the latter stages of babbling that some phoneticians claim to hear children producing the phonetic repertoires of languages other than the one of their immediate linguistic environment (Jakobson 1940). Since we were expending a great deal of effort to derive reliable acoustic data we assessed our phonetic classifications of the vowels that the children produced.

We used two different procedures to check the consistency and validity of the perceptually based phonetic transcriptions we made of the childrens' vowels. The first method we used was applied to the utterances of speaker LS who was recorded from the age of 16 weeks onwards. All of the tape recordings for this speaker were transcribed by a single phonetically trained investigator (RB). We assessed the consistency of these transcriptions, i.e., would other phonetically trained listeners agree with these transcriptions by preparing a tape recording that contained 89 'identified' vowels. The sample was drawn from tape recordings that had been made when the child was 16 and 62 weeks old. The child was still in the babbling stage at 62 weeks.

Each stimulus was repeated 16 times in a random sequence on this tape recording and the recording was then independently transcribed by six different phonetically trained listeners who transcribed every stimulus on the tape. The listeners were able to stop the tape recording, change their transcriptions, go back over sections, etc. In other words the six listeners were asked to transcribe the tape as though they were making the primary transcription, the object being to make as accurate a transcription as possible from the tape recording. The overall agreement between the six listeners and the person who originally transcribed the tape recordings was 73%; 76% of the vowel stimuli recorded at 16 weeks and 70% of those recorded at 62 weeks were in agreement with the original transcription. Of the total number of vowels identified at least 4 of the 6 listeners agreed with the original observer. Within this subset of vowels the overall consistency was 81%.

We also used a second method to transcribe the tape recordings to achieve consistent classifications for sounds that were perceived as vowels of English. The transcriptions of the tape recordings of speakers JB, FR, RC, and GR were made by a panel of three phonetically trained listeners who each independently listened to the tape recordings. Vowel stimuli were only plotted on the graphs that will be presented for these speakers when the three listeners were in agreement. The overall agreement of these three listeners was 74%, which turned out to be essentially the consistency derived in our test of the consistency of a single phonetically trained listener.

In addition to the vowels that were consistently identified as vowels of English, we recorded many other vowel-like sounds. We also analyzed some of these sounds in connection with that aspect of Jakobson's (1940) theory claiming the production of vowels that do not occur in English during the babbling stage of children raised in an English speaking environment. We will return to these data later.

14. <u>Acoustic</u> <u>Data</u> <u>and</u> <u>Observations</u>. We will first present data for one child, LS, who was babbling throughout the

period (16-64 weeks of life) that we shall cover. Child
LS, who is a normal male, was recorded at the intervals
noted in Table 1, which also notes the total number of occurrences of each vowel identified and plotted through week
64. As the entries in Table 1 show, vowels like [u], [o],
[ɔ], and [i] occurred infrequently throughout the data
sample and not at all before week 16. The absence of [i],
[u] and [a] from the early vocalizations of children is
consistent with the data of George (1978) who notes their
complete absence before age 13 weeks and infrequent occurrence in the weeks thereafter in a sample of 29 normal
children. The most common vowels are [æ] and [ɛ]. In Figure 6 the ranges and means of F1, F2, and F3 are plotted
for [æ]. Note the high absolute value of these formant
frequencies; F3 is about 5 kHz which compares with values
of about 2.5 kHz for adult males (Peterson & Barney 1952).
In Figure 7 F1, F2, and F3 are plotted for the vowel [i].
Note that F3 is about 6.5 kHz for [i]; it is about 3 kHz
for adult males. There is little change in the average
values of the formant frequencies for speaker LS's vowels
from weeks 16 to 64. This to be expected since there was
probably little change in his supralaryngeal vocal tract's
length as his height changed only 3 inches through this
period, from 25 to 28 inches. The length of the supralaryngeal vocal tract is closely correlated with overall
growth in this period of life (George 1978). It thus is
very probable that the overall length of his supralaryngeal
vocal tract did not change very much throughout this period. X-rays of our subjects which would have established
the growth pattern of their supralaryngeal vocal tracts
would have been useful but cannot be made within present
ethical guidelines for research.

Speaker LS's vowels cannot be regarded as simple imi-
tations of the formant frequencies of adult speech. They
have the correct spectral patterning. F2 and F3 converge
in the mid-frequency region for [a], while F2 and F3 converge at the high end of the spectrum for [i] (Figure 7).
However, the absolute values of the formant frequencies are
completely outside the range that occurs for adult speech
and are consistent with the short length of the child's supralaryngeal vocal tract. Note also the variation in the
formant frequencies that was measured for particular vowels. This is especially so for vowels like [i] and [u]
which appear infrequently and later than other vowels.

The development of speaker LS's acoustic vowel space
can be seen in the graphs that follow, in which the first
formant frequency of each identified vowel is plotted with
respect to the ordinate. In Figure 8 these vowels are

Weeks:

	16	17	18	19	21	22	23	24	25	26	29	31	33	35	36	37	38	41	43	45	47	48	51	54	57	60	62	64
i		1				1				2		2			2		1	3	6	1		3		3	8	4	2	5	5
I	3	4		3	1	5	2	3		1	3	2	6		3	2	7	13		2	6	3	17	6	2	5	6	9
e		1				1	1	1	1	2	3		3			1	1	4	1	1	1		2	9	3	5	1	4
ε	18	20	6	7	2	11	12	22	6	16	8	2	12	17	5	4	7	20	2	8	17	6	14	7	6	16	10	13
æ	13	2	5	4	1	16	6	8		4		2	6	2	2	1	6	7	2	12	10	19	3	14	3	9	5	1
a		3		1	1					1			2	6	2		1	3	1	1	6	5	5	1	3	2	3	1
ʌ	9	9	1	1	1	3		4			1	3	3	2			1	9	1	4	10	13	11	6	4	5	6	
ɔ											1						1								2			
o																1			1		1	1	2	1	3			
U	8	4	6	3	1	3	3	9		3		1	2	2	2	3	4	6	2	4	4	6	7	5	7		7	3
u								1		1															1	2		

Table 1

The number of occurrences of each individual vowel per week

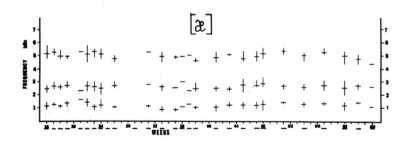

Figure 6

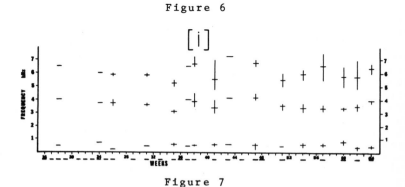

Figure 7

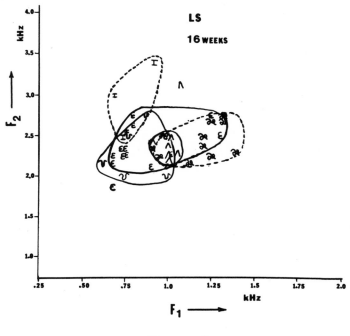

Figure 8

plotted at 16 weeks where there is considerable overlap for
all the vowels identified [I, ε,æ, ʌ , and U]. In Figure 9
the identified vowels recorded in week 24 are plotted.
Note that the formant frequencies of [u] have dropped on
the plot, that [æ] has moved rightwards, i.e., Fl has been
raised. It would appear that in this time period the vowels produced by LS are moving into the acoustic positions
which resemble a rudimentary vowel triangle. In Figures 10
and 11 the vowels identified during weeks 41 and 62 are
plotted. Note that the general trend towards expanding the
acoustic vowel space continues, though the trend may not be
apparent if we simply compare the vowels recorded during
two single weeks. For some reason, which we do not know,
the formant frequencies of the vowels plotted during week
41 overlap more than those plotted in weeks 24 and 61.
Some of the sounds that we identified as [I]'s in week 41
have formant frequency patterns that would make them [i]'s
but their durations are too short (about 80-100 msec). The
child is not yet coordinating the formant frequency pattern
and temporal pattern of English vowels. In week 62 (Figure

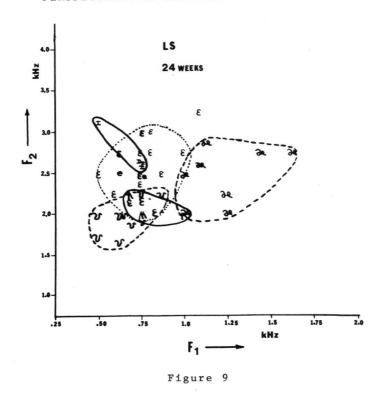

Figure 9

11) this overlap disappears.

One question that comes to mind is whether the formant
frequency patterns of the vowel sounds that we were not
able to identify as vowels of English fall outside of the
range of the acoustic vowel space of the vowels that we
were able to identify. We therefore plotted all of the vowels that we were able to identify during week 64 together
with F1 and F2 of all the other vowel stimuli that we were
able to measure on spectrograms, though we could not reliably identify them as vowels of English. A total of 48
unidentified vowels are plotted. The total acoustic vowel
space of the unidentified vowels is quite similar to that
of the identified vowels. When we pooled the identified
vowels for weeks 62 and 64, there was virtually no difference except for the cluster of unidentified vowels that
occupy the position that should be filled by [u]. These
sounds were nasalized; the spectrograms show the presence
of additional nasal formants, which may account for their

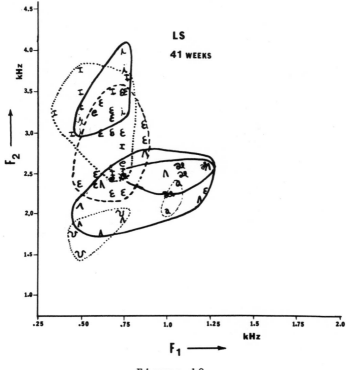

Figure 10

not being identified as English [u]´s. In general, the unidentified vowels were nasalized.

     The trend towards elaboration of the acoustic vowel
space that is evident in speaker LS was also evident for
other children.   In Figures 12 and 13 the vowels plotted
for speaker JB for weeks 66 and 147 are derived from her
productions of meaningful words.   Our transcriptions continued to be phonetic rather than phonemic when children
produced meaningful words.   Thus we transcribed a sound as
an [I] when it occurred in a word where the child should
have been producing an [æ].   Note the change in the
'shape' of her acoustic vowel space as well as the fall in
the absolute values of the formant frequencies which is
most apparent in F2 for [i].

     The same trends are apparent in Figures 14 and 15 for
speaker FR, a boy, who was producing meaningful sentences
throughout the period that we recorded him.   Note the fall

in Fl for [i] between the vowels recorded in weeks 125 and 169 in Fl that are plotted in Figures 14 and 15. Note also that the formant frequencies of the vowels are moving towards a better fit with the acoustic vowel space typical of adult speakers of American English. When the data on Figures 14 and 15 are compared with those of Peterson and Barney (1952) for adults and older children it is apparent that speaker FR has moved his [I], [ɛ], and [æ] vowels into better alignment along the `acute´ [i]-[a] axis (Jakobson et al. 1952) and [ʌ] and [o] along the `grave´ axis. The trend towards `perfecting´ the acoustic vowel space thus continues from babbling well into the phonologic and syntactic stages of language acquisition.

These formant frequency data address two issues. The most obvious acoustic distinction between the formant frequencies of the vowels of these young children and the vowels of older chldren and adults is the higher values of the formant frequencies. The younger and smaller the child, the higher the formant frequencies are for specific vowels. F3 for speaker LS is about 6.5 kHz for [i] at ages 50-60 weeks, 5.5 kHz for speaker JB from 81-96 weeks, and 4.5 kHz for speaker FR from 125-161 weeks. As the children grow their formant frequencies fall. There is no evidence that children attempt to mimic the absolute formant frequencies of the adult speech that they hear. This is so even for vowels, where, in theory, the child could shift the formant frequencies towards the lower frequencies of adult speech. Computer modelling frequencies for vowels like [æ], [I], [ɛ], [U], etc., than those that follow from the relatively short length of the child's supralaryngeal vocal tract for vowels like [i], [u], and [a]. A child could by means of `compensatory´ manoeuvers, e.g., lip rounding, produce an [I] vowel that has lower formant frequencies than we would expect if we considered the length of the child's supralaryngeal vocal tract. The acoustic data that we have presented, however, shows that the formant frequencies of these vowels ([I], [æ], [ɛ], etc.) are in `proper´ relation to those of vowels like [i] and [a] where the supralaryngeal vocal tract effectively constrains the possible absolute values of the formant frequencies that would yield the proper spectral relations that define the vowel acoustically (Stevens & House 1955). This is quite apparent in the plots for children producing vowels in meaningful words, e.g. Figures 12-15. studies (Stevens & House 1955) demonstrate that a speaker can produce lower formant

The higher values of the formant frequencies for vowels like [i], [u], and [a] follow from the fact that the

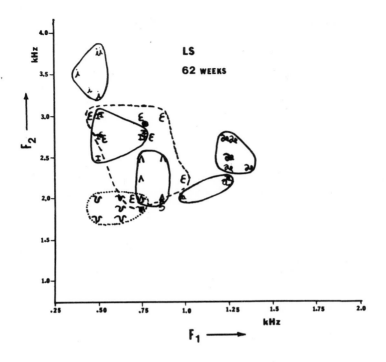

Figure 11

child can in no way imitate the absolute values of the formant frequencies of the vowels that he hears from his or
her parents, or from older children. Although some degree
of variation is possible in the production of vowels like
[I], [ɛ], [æ] , etc., where a speaker with a shorter vocal
tract can, in theory, produce a formant frequency pattern
having absolute frequency values that we might expect to
find in the acoustic vowel space of a speaker having a
longer supralaryngeal vocal tract, we don't find that either. The children produce vowels whose formant frequencies
are consistent with their shorter supralaryngeal vocal
tracts. This fact can be explained if we hypothesize the
presence of a perceptual mechanism that is present in all
normal human beings that `normalizes' incoming speech
sounds in terms of the presumed length of the speaker's supralaryngeal vocal tract and that likewise allows the child
to `know' that it has produced an equivalent signal as it
listens to its own speech. The development of an approximation of the acoustic vowel space of English during the

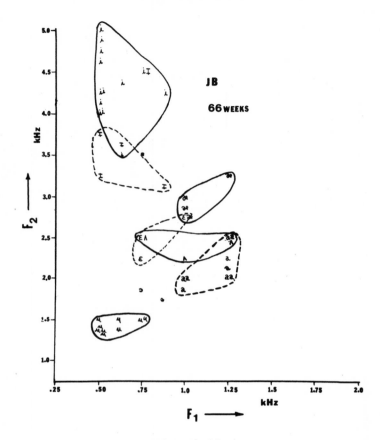

Figure 12

babbling stage of speech by the children argues for the
early presence of this perceptual normalization mechanism,
indeed, for the presence of an innate species-specific
neural mechanism.

Cineradiographic data on the speech production of
adult speakers shows that there is no set of invariant supralaryngeal vocal tract shapes that all speakers of a particular language use to generate the vowels of that language. Different speakers, for example, use different supralaryngeal vocal tract manoeuvers to generate the vowels [I]
and [ε]. Therefore, there cannot be a set of innately determined instructions for specific supralaryngeal vocal

tract maneuvers that the child brings into play as it begins to produce the vowels of English. Indeed, the child
has no way of determining what specific supralaryngeal vocal tract shape might underlie the production of the formant
frequency pattern that specifies its mother's, father's or
older sibling's production of the vowel [i]. (Nor can anyone do this, which argues forcefully against a strict 'motor theory' of speech perception.) The child thus has to
imitate the <u>acoustic</u> signal that specifies the vowel [I] to
produce that sound. The child, however, cannot produce the
formant frequencies of the adult speech that it hears; its
supralaryngeal vocal tract is too short, but it apparently
never attempts to mimic the lower formant frequencies of
the incoming adult speech. Children instead produce 'equivalent' formant frequency patterns that are scaled to their
shorter supralaryngeal vocal tract length. Moreover, as
children grow the formant frequencies of their vowels continually fall. The only plausible hypothesis that can account for these data is the presence of an innately determined vocal tract normalization mechanism.

Note that we have not made any claims regarding either
the neural implementation or the functional modelling of
the normalization mechanism. The normalization could be
effected by means of an algorithm like that proposed by
Nearey (1976) in which the formant frequencies of the incoming speech sound are divided by a vocal tract normalizing factor. The listener could derive the normalizing factor from the formant frequencies of vowels like [i] which
yield effective indices of the speakers' supralaryngeal
vocal tracts (Nearey 1976) or the burst frequencies and initial formant frequencies of 'quantal' consonants (Stevens
1972; Stevens & Blumstein 1978). The normalization mechanism, however, might not be implemented by means of the
active computational process that we have outlined. Human
beings may instead be equipped with arrays of all possible
formant frequency patterns corresponding to all possible
supralaryngeal vocal tract length. The listener, on receiving the incoming speech signal and making an estimate
of the presumed length of the supralaryngeal vocal tract,
would classify the incoming vowels in terms of the appropriate patterns inventory that would specify the total
acoustic vowel space of the speaker producing the incoming
speech signal.

The process would have to be 'plastic' in the sense
that different dialects and languages make use of different
acoustic partitionings of the acoustic vowel space deli-
mited by the quantal vowels [i], and [a] (Lieberman 1976,
1977). The plasticity would be manifested in the child's

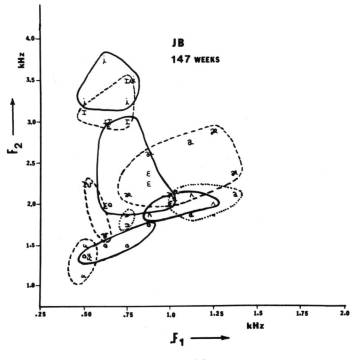

Figure 13

setting up different acoustic partitionings of the available vowel space by means of either different neural acoustic `templates´ or property detectors, or neural implemen-
tations of appropriate algorithms. The gradual elaboration
of the acoustic vowel space and even more gradual `perfe-
ction´ of the acoustic vowel space that we can see in the
formant frequency data of the children whose vowel production we followed is consistent with the hypotheses that the
normalization device is innate and manifests itself at the
start of babbling and that the process of forming appropriate vowel categories for a specific language is gradual and
plastic.

        This brings us to the second issue that the formant
frequency data address. There seems to be a gradual and
consistent `improvement´ in the children´s productions of
the vowels of English from the earliest stages of babbling
well into the state (three years of age) where the children
are using meaningful sentences and are conversing with the

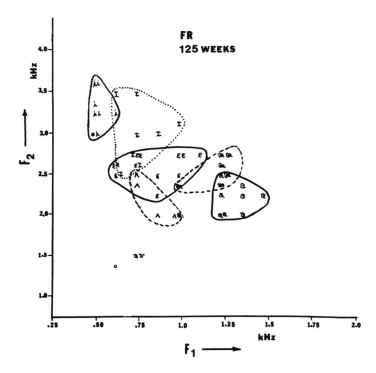

Figure 14

experimenters. Though we cannot tell whether the children
are attempting to produce the vowel sounds that they hear
when they babble, there does not appear to be any `abrupt´
break or discontinuity in their behaviour as they go from
the babbling to the phonologic stage of language acquisition. The perfection of the vowel repertoire that is manifest in the better approximation of the child´s F1 versus
F2 acoustic vowel space continues well into the state when
the child is acquiring other aspects of language, morphology, syntax and semantic interpretation, at age three years.
There thus cannot be a dedicated´ language learning device
(in the computer terminology sense of the word `dedicated´)
that applies itself to one task at a time as various linguists have suggested. The child simultaneously is per-
fecting phonetic, morphological and syntactic abilities.

     There is yet another question that these data address
but do not resolve. Jakobson (1940) claimed that the child
in its babbling stage produces the sounds of all human

languages as well as the sounds of its linguistic environment. Although we have not found acoustic evidence that would support the hypothesis that the child is producing non-English vowels even when we take account of all the vowels that we can measure during a recording session (Figure 10), we still cannot rule out this hypothesis. The general trend of the data seems to be more consistent with the alternative hypothesis that the child during the babbling stage is attempting to imitate the sounds of his or her linguistic environment, producing many sounds that are, in fact, not satisfactory English vowels (when the linguistic environment is English) because of errors. A phonetician who had a wide linguistic background might interpret the child's errors as the sounds of another language because they, in fact, fit more closely into the acoustic template of the sound that occurs in another language, e.g. Swedish, where the acoustic vowel space is partitioned differently (Lieberman 1976, 1977). When a child enters the phonologic stage we can bring contextual dues to bear on the problem of assigning a child's error signal into the proper linguistic category of English if the child is attempting to speak English. The child's phonetic ability is also gradually improving and fewer errors occur. The hypothetical abrupt change in behavior (Jakobson 1940) that is supposed to occur between the babbling and phonologic stages of language acquisition thus may be a consequence of a different frame of interpretation that the phonetician brings to bear on the question of classifying the child's speech sounds. (a) Contextual cues are available to aid in the perception of speech; contextual cues play an important role in the classification of the sounds of adult speech is normal conversation (Lieberman 1963, 1967). (b) The child's phonetic ability also is continually improving.

15. <u>Babble</u> and the <u>Phonetic/Phonemic Distinction</u>. Our most recent data on the development of speech focuses on the transition from babbling to the production of words and sequences of words. There is no evidence of a discontinuity between these two 'stages' in the child's production of the formant frequency patterns that specify vowels and consonants. Children gradually seem to gain control over their speech producing system and produce more consistent acoustic signals. If there is a distinction between the phonetic and phonemic levels, it is not apparent in this data. The children do appear to take account of syntactic boundaries when they produce sequences of words. The duration of a word becomes shorter when it occurs in a non-final position in a breath-group (Kubaska, in preparation).

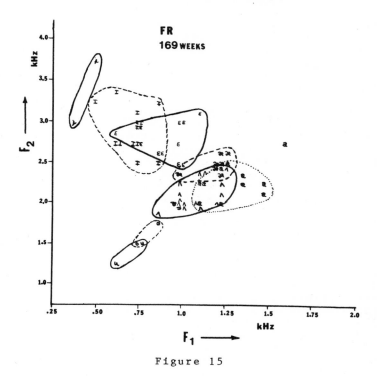

Figure 15

16. **The Systematic Phonetic Level.** Theories like that
proposed by Chomsky and Halle (1968) claim that the output
of the grammar is a segmental transcription at the systematic phonetic level. This level entails a transcription
of an utterance in which all phonetic contrasts that can
occur in any language are noted, whether or not they occur
in the language being transcribed. Any trained reader thus
could convert the transcription into a correct speech signal without knowing anything else about the language or
dialect of the transcribed utterance. The theory thus im-
plicitly claims that there exists a set of segmental
phonetic elements that all languages draw upon to derive
their phonetic and phonemic inventories. Languages that
have different phonetic inventories differ insofar as they
make use of different subsets of the total set of phonetic
elements. This scheme, at first reading, seems very reasonable; it would appear to provide a description of how a
language sounded rather than simply noting the phonemic
contrasts. There are, however, serious problems.

It is not clear that the differences between the speech sounds that occur in different languages can be specified in terms of a set of phonetic segments that do not overlap at the acoustic level. The 'recipes' that specify phonetic elements in the rather traditional phonetic theory of Chomsky and Halle are the usual articulatory specifications of 19th century phonetic theory. These descriptions are supposed to serve as instructions for the phonetician acting as a human speech synthesizer. However, the transcriptions simply do not work. Many of the phonetic symbols and feature ensembles (they amount ot the same thing) refer to different acoustic signals in different languages, e.g., the symbol [b] refers to very different sounds in English and Spanish, the vowel [u] to different sounds in English and Swedish, etc. (Lieberman 1976, 1977). As I noted earlier, the articulatory recipes are misleading and sometimes irrelevent.

There are, however, more serious problems. Careful perceptually based, e.g. Moulton's (1960), studies of Swiss German dialects and acoustic analyses, e.g., Labov's (1972) New York City dialect studies, show that different dialects slice up the F1 versus F2 acoustic vowel space that specifies vowels in different ways. The parts of the vowel space that 'belong' to different vowel classes vary. Part of one vowel's acoustic space in one dialect may belong to part of another vowel's space in a second dialect, while the remainder belongs to a third vowel that also maps onto other areas of the acoustic vowel space. The distinctions between the two dialects can only be captured by different partitionings of the acoustic vowel space.

17. <u>Distinctive</u> <u>Features</u>. We might attempt to salvage the systematic phonetic hypothesis by means of a hypothetical set of features which would suffice to describe the sounds used in all languages through suitable combinations. This is in effect the solution of Jakobson in <u>Preliminaries</u> <u>to</u> <u>Speech</u> <u>Analyses</u> (1952). The 'atomic' features combine to make up the sound 'molecules', if I can be permitted to make a physical analogy. This solution, however, hinges on the psychological reality of the features.

Some feature contrasts do appear to relate to neural property detectors. The feature of voice onset, for example, which appears to be one factor that differentiates sounds like the English stops [b] and [p] seems to be structured by auditory mechanisms that are present at birth in human infants (Eimas et al. 1971) and which also probably are present in other species like chinchilla (Kuhl & Miller 1975). Recent studies, however, suggest that voice onset

is not the sole factor that differentiates these stop contrasts. The amplitudes of bursts in stops that have identical voice onset differentiates English stops. A [p] will
have a greater burst amplitude than a [b]. Mothers speaking to their children in the period when the children are
first beginning to acquire words that differ with respect
to the [b] verses [p] speech sound contrast will enhance
either, or both, the bursts and voice onset times of the
[p]. The data suggest that the children's acquisition of
the [p] is facilitated by well formed exemplars (Moslin
1978). While we could logically factor out the burst and
voice onset distinctions and treat them as independent features, the mothers produce them as integrated acoustic patterns.

18. Place Distinctions and Adaption. The acoustic patterns that convey place distinctions for stops also appear
to be perceived in terms of the integrated acoustic pattern. The adaption paradigm that has been used in the past
few years (Cooper 1974) generally will result in the greatest shift of the perceptual boundaries of a stop contrast
like [b] versus [d] versus [g] when the adapting stimulus
most closely matches the acoustic parameters of the speech
signals that the subjects identify after they hear the
adapting stimulus. If, for example, we presented fully
specified synthesized speech signals to listeners along the
voiced [b]-[d]-[g] stop feature dimension we would shift
the boundary closer to [b] if the listeners heard an adapting [b] sound than if they heard an adapting [m] sound.
The adapting effect is about twice as great when we adapt
the [b] than the [m]. This result could be interpreted as
indicating that adaption is best if the adapting sound is
closer to the acoustic parameters of the signals presented,
and that features are secondary derived properties of
speech sounds. The results of this adaption experiment,
however, are also consistent with the hypothesis that we
have in place in our brains sets of fully specified acoustic patterns that specify speech sounds in terms of all of
the acoustic parameters that are relevant.

19. Fully Specified Neural `Templates'. If we present
listeners with a set of partially specified synthetic
speech sounds along the [b]-[d]-[g] dimension, the greatest
shift in the perceptual boundary occurs not when the adapting stimulus is also a partially specified [g] but when it
is a fully specified [g]. The listeners' behavior is consistent with the theory that the adapting stimulus that
works the best is that which most completely triggers the
acoustic `templates' that are in the listener's brains.
These acoustic templates obviously would have evolved to

respond to real, completely specified sound patterns rather than the partially specified acoustic patterns that can only be produced on a speech synthesizer. In experiments that involved adaption with both partially specified and fully specified synthesized stimuli (where the partially specified stimuli had formant transitions but lacked bursts), the fully specified adapting stimulus produced the greatest shift (Stevens & Blumstein 1978).

The results of other types of psychoacoustic experiments are also consistent with the hypothesis that we have sets of fully specified acoustic patterns in our brains, i.e., neural property detectors, that respond to complete speech sounds. The identification of the rounded versus unrounded vowels [y] and [u:] of Swedish is, for example, at the chance level for speakers of English (Stèvens et al. 1969) though English speakers make use of the rounded feature in the production of the vowels [u], [o], [U], etc. Speakers of English can discriminate between these vowel stimuli, but they can't use them as productive speech sounds. These results, I propose, would also occur in any systematic study of vowel identification versus discrimination for vowels that are not speech sounds in one language but occur in another. Non-native listeners of a second language would not be able to identify the fully specified acoustic signals that differentiated vowel contrasts even though the `distinctive feature' contrasts that a linguist could derive to describe the salient acoustic contrast occurred in their native language. Our speech perception mechanism thus, in my view, is not particularly economical in terms of the memory locations that it uses. The speech sounds of a language have neural representations in terms of the fully specified acoustic patterns that make up these sounds. Some of these acoustic patterns are probably innately determined or need very little shaping up. These are the highly valued sounds of human languages that occur most often e.g., the quantal vowels and consonants (Stevens, 1972; Lieberman 1970, 1976, 1977). Other neural property detectors are the result of exposure to particular linguistic environments, they are the result of a `plastic' process that allows us to respond in an `automatic' way (Lieberman 1975, 1977) to sounds that are of particular interest or utility to us.

Different languages and dialects thus have different inventories of speech sounds. Some speech sounds differentiate words more often and are `phonemic,' others are conditioned by other sounds and are `phonetic' but the phonetic sounds are also essential in that they yield many of the acoustic cues from which the so-called phonemic sounds can

be inferred in the actual production and perception of
speech where the acoustic cues that would transmit the
`phonemic´ distinction may not be present (Lieberman 1965).
Distinctive features are secondary, derived analytic properties that can serve to classify the total set of acoustic patterns or a particular language or dialect. They are
`universal´ only in the sense that similar sound patterns
occur in different human languages because of the biological factors that structure all human languages and cultural
similarities. The only universal level thus is the biological level.

20. <u>Systematic</u> <u>Phonetics</u>. The arguments concerning systematic phonetics that I´ve tried to develop are perhaps easier to follow if we were to consider a hypothetical analysis of the range of cookies that are available in pastry
shops in New York City. Let us suppose that all the pastry
shops claim that they bake their own cookies on their premises. One cookie gourmet, a native New Yorker, suspects
that this is not the case and develops the theory of systematic cookie variation. He claims that all the cookies in
New York City come from the Universal Cookie Works which
has available a variety of different cookie types. If his
theory is correct then all of the cookies available from
any pastry shop can be drawn from this universal set of
cookie types. A second cookie gourmet, however, rejects
this theory; he claims that there is no central cookie bakery. There is, however, a central cookie supply ware-
house, The Universal Biological Supply House, that supplies
all the pastry shops with flour, sugar, butter, chocolate
chips, etc. Each pastry shop then bakes its own cookies;
the range of cookies thus cannot necessarily be described
in terms of a subset of specified cookie types. Although
there is a general notion of what a chocolate chip cookie
is at the `phonemic´ level, wherein it can be differen-
tiated in all shops from a banana cookie, at the phonetic
level you´d have to specify the particular pastry shop to
get an accurate description of the cookie to a gourmet
cookie phonetician. Though the supplies of The Universal
Biological Supply House (a distributor of organic foods)
are in a sense the universal level, they can be combined in
many ways. The discerning cookie gourmet will realize that
different pastry shops have developed different approaches
to the art of cookie making. Thus the most meaningful description of cookies from the Fifth Avenue pastry shop
would be to note that all of the cookies tend to be sweet
and crunchy, whereas the Lexington Avenue pastry shop´s
cookies are always soft. If a guide to cookies were to be
published, it would be useful to specify the products of
each pastry shop in terms of these `pastry shop specific

redundancy rules'.

20. <u>Conclusion</u>. To conclude, most scientific theories are initially based on much intuition and little data. I don't propose to labor on the relative balance of intuition versus data that underlies the discussion of the neural property detectors that I've presented, but it seems that a level at which we respond to fully specified acoustic patterns that differentiate speech sounds must be the primary level of speech perception. If one considers human evolution in terms of the principles that generally govern the general process of evolution by means of mutation and natural selection, this would follow. In other words, if our linguistic abilities evolved, subject to the same principles that operate with respect to the evolution of all other aspects of the behaviour of all other animals, then we would have evolved neural property detectors that responded to fully specified speech sounds. It is, for example, impossible to produce an isolated onset spectrum or an isolated F2 pattern unless one uses a speech synthesizer. If hominids evolved neural devices that facilitated their perception of conspecific speech sounds, as is the case for the neural devices that appear to operate across the range of species from frogs to Japanese Macaque monkeys, then we also have fully specified property detectors and there is no level of systematic phonetics. There is, however, a productive structuring of phonetic possibilities, phonologic processes and syntactic possibilities in terms of the constraints of the speech physiology. As we learn more concerning the biological bases of speech production and perception, we'll learn more about the general structure of other 'levels' of language.

ICONIC PERSPECTIVES ON LINGUISTIC EXPLANATION

W. C. WATT
University of California, Irvine

1. Introduction. Linguistics and iconics--the study of
visual language-like systems such as the alphabet--have
pursued rather different lines of development. Modern or
generative linguistics, true to the 'essentially rationalist' views with which it was imbued by its founder, has
traditionally set as its goal the discovery of the putative
abstract cognitive device that underlies linguistic behavior at a level well removed from direct observation; while
iconics, born of practical and computational concerns and
thus of a more empiricist cast, from its inception has been
oriented towards constructing a theory capable of explaining more-or-less observable behaviour, whether in the laboratory or in the relics of archaic writing. To a point,
each history is no doubt self-justifying: a natural language is not, of course, directly observable, since it is of
unbounded size; while the number of alphabetic letters, or
even of Chinese characters, is finite. Or, to take a quite
different dimension, the abstraction away from speaking and
hearing to a more abstract level, in linguistics, may seem
intuitively warranted to many, on one ground or another,
while the analogous abstraction away from writing and reading may strike many as dubious

On the other hand it would be astounding if, unlike
any other science, either linguistics or iconics could proceed directly to its goal with no false turns or missteps,
not to say pratfalls. Iconics in its early years strikes
me as having been overly devoted to empiricism, with
scarcely any rationalist leavening at all; and linguistics,
as I have argued rather too much elsewhere (1970, 1973,

1974a,b), has unduly penalized itself for its adherence to its high degree of abstraction. Put into more conventional if also somewhat misleading terms, linguistics has paid ra her too much attention to `competence´ at the expense of `performance´, while iconics has taken the opposite tack. The penalties, in either case, are not difficult to catalogue, I think.

But that will not be my purpose here. Rather, what I want to do is to show how iconics is improved by widening the scope of its inquiry to accomodate a wide range of data from extremely disparate sources, while at the same time keeping its nose fairly close to the ground, so to speak; to argue that, conceivably, this `rationalist-empiricist´ approach may serve linguistics as an example; and, above all, to show how a close scrutiny of the range of data argued to be properly within the province of any adequate theory of iconics, suggests that so-called `performative´ matters associated with the different roles are best explained, in effects and causes, by separate and distinct grammars, with little or nothing to be gained by the construction of a more abstract account in which those two roles, as with those of speaker and hearer in linguistics, are merged.

To make the mission of this paper perfectly clear, however, what I will <u>not</u> do is suggest that linguistics and iconics are so alike, whether in object of inquiry or in preferred methodology, that what is true of iconics must be so of linguistics: any such claim must await much further evidence. Which is only to say that, w ile the general parallels between the two disciplines, as bearing on such issues as `competence´ and `performance´ for example, seem moderately clear, the more specific parallels that one might be tempted to draw, as between `speaker/hearer´ and `writer/reader´, can only be cited, at this point in ongoing research efforts, as provocative.

2. Though some other visual systems have been studied (the best examples are Faris´ description of Nuba body-paintings (1972) and Stokoe´s analysis of Ameslan, the gestural language of the American deaf (e.g. 1972), the systems that have received most attenton have been alphabets, and it is to this rich area that we will devote our attention below.

An alphabet has two functions: to be written, and to be read. Oddly, these two functions are in unremitting conflict. This conflict is owing to the fact that any attempt to increase the efficiency with which an alphabet is written, <u>de</u>creases the ease with which it can be read: to

simplify the letters, hence ultimately to make them more
alike, is to make them harder to distinguish. This point,
self-evident once stated, has gone almost unremarked in the
generous literature on the subject; without it, much is obscure that could be clear. But first a couple of other
points of clarification. To provide a satisfactory account
of an alphabet an iconic analysis must, obviously, provide
an explanation for why it has the symbols it has instead of
some other symbols, except of course where mere accident
can be shown to have operated. Or at least this must be so
if the alphabet in question is not a congeries of arbitrary
and unrelated forms, and it can scarcely be that, since
even on the slightest reflection one has to admit that, of
a set of candidates for proposed future inclusion in an
alphabet that one is familiar with, some are better than
other, which must mean that one has formed an intuitive
idea of homogeneities among the existent letters, hence an
intuitive idea of the `relative well-formedness´ of pro-
posed additions. For instance, any addition to the
upper-case or majuscule alphabet of (say) five or six letters from the lower-case or minuscule alphabet, seems
anomalous, on an intuitive level, which must mean that both
the majuscules and minuscules have properties as sets which
inhibit addition of members from one to the other. But a
set in which homogeneities are perceived cannot be a congeries. No student of modern linguistics, it seems to me,
can fail to agree that such intuitions--such tacit
knowledge--must be among the more interesting facets of the
alphabet that any serious iconic theory is obliged to explain. Relating this to our previous point, such a theory
must explain whether the homogeneities that obtain among
(say) the majuscules are primarily among their kinesthetic
or their visual properties: whether, that is, they are primarily consequences of how they are written or of how they
are read. Or, not to prejudge the matter, of both equally,
perhaps.

    The point just made is hardly a deep one, it seems to
me; and yet it manifestly demands a great deal of any iconic theory. Both comments apply to the next point as well.
Since its origins in the Near East at around the end of the
second millennium B.C., the alphabet has undergone a not-
able evolution to reach its present form; and surely, except where demonstrably arbitrary, this evolution must be
accounted for by any adequate iconic theory. With what
sort of `evolution´--I use the term in its most guarded
sense--are we dealing here? To illustrate, let me propose
that we adopt, subject to all sorts of subsequent cavils,
the proposition that `Phylogeny recapitulates ontogeny´,
meaning that the history of a system like the alphabet in

part exhibits the same sort of alterations as are introduced by children when learning that system. Or rather,
mislearning that system, for the alterations in question
are the products of children's 'mistakes'. (It is possible
to argue that the errors in question are not the children's
innovations but the adults' insistence that those innovations be discarded; but I leave that for another time.)
Suppose we also adopt, just for the sake of argument, the
proposition that the mistake most typically made by a child
learning an alphabet is 'homogenization': that is erroneously making one letter more like its fellows than it ought
to be. As one example, a mistake made by many children
learning the alphabet is the reversal of 'S' to make it
more like 'Z'. On the 'recapitulation' proposition, 'homogenization' must also be a prime feature of alphabetic history. Picking up our earlier point, this process of homogenization might be one of kinesthetic or of visual attributes; an homogenization that results in greater similarities in the way the letters are made, or an homogenization
that results in greater similarities in the way the letters
appear.

I take it that at least part of the foregoing discussion has taken place at the 'explanatory' level of grammatical adequacy adumbrated by Noam Chomsky in a number of pu-
blications (most clearly perhaps in Aspects of the Theory
of Syntax), in that any theory that accounts for the very
membership of the set of items under analysis, must make
contact with the deep cognitive level of explication defined as distinguishing that level. Yet on the other hand,
how is this 'explanatory' analysis to be derived? How can
one get a handle on the 'homogenizations' which, on our hypothesis at least, make a cardinal contribution to the basic nature of that which is to be explained? Can there be
any doubt that the activities of children must be observed
before any accurate notion of their homogenizations can be
obtained? Or any doubt that the same observation holds for
the putative homogenizations of adults? Or, in sum, can
there be any doubt that an adequate 'explanatory' iconic
theory must rely on the results of observation and experimentation?

On the other hand it would be easy to overdo the notion that what is to be 'explained' in iconics is iconic
performance as contrasted with iconic competence. The
'competence/performance' distinction, as put forward for
linguistics in e.g. Chomsky (1965), is of course relevant
to iconics also, though in the latter discipline the two
notions are distinguished less by their putatively different relations to such notions as 'knowledge' and

`execution´ than by their relation to distinctive criteria
of economy. The `competence´ economy criterion can be ta-
ken as minimizing the size of grammars, or rule-sets, necessary to specify the iconic system in question--<u>ceteris
paribus</u>, of course--while the `performance´ economy criter-
ion can be taken as minimizing the individual derivations,
or rule-actuations, by which elements of the system are actually produced. Thus by the `competence´ criterion a set
of rules for specifying (say) the English majuscules would
be more highly-valued than another if both specified the
same system (the majuscules as `correctly´ determined) and
if the first contained fewer symbol-tokens than the other
(again <u>ceteris</u> <u>paribus</u>); while by the `performance´ criter-
ion a set of rules for specifying the English majuscules
would be more highly-valued than another if the first produced the individual letters with fewer steps, with fewer
rules, or in general with less effort. In sum, then, it is
easy to ascertain whether a set of symbols like the majuscules has come into being exclusively in obedience to
`competence´ or `performance´ criteria, or in obedience to
both: the `competence´ criterion is obeyed just to the ex-
tent that the derivations of letters are homogenized to the
point where the specification of the entire set of letters
is minimized; whereas the `performance´ criterion is obeyed
whenever an individual letter has a simpler (shorter) derivation at the cost of requiring special rules hence at the
cost of lengthening the grammar and incurring a `compe-
tence´ diseconomy.

Nothing could be clearer than that a system of letters
like the English majuscules does, in fact, in part obey a
`competence´ criterion of economy. Taking a kinesthetic
example, consider the program for composing a majuscule `A´
as a series of traverses upon the figure of Figure 1. Majuscule `A´ is commonly made with five strokes of the
writing-instrument: (1) the stroke BA, on the page; (2) the
stroke AB, off the page; (3) the stroke BD, on the page;
(4) the stroke DF, off the page; and (5) the stroke FG, on
the page. Now, certainly a four-stroke `A´ is easier, and
such an `A´ is possible just by omitting stroke (1) and by
putting stroke (2) on the page. Why then is four-stroke
`A´ avoided? It seems that, basically, the reason is that
five-stroke `A´, by beginning with a downwards stroke, con-
forms to the great body of letters that begin the same way;
then, that five-stroke `A´ is preferred because it obeys a
<u>general</u> rule: "Begin any letter with a downward stroke if
its leftmost line is vertical or near-vertical". To return
to the issue addressed a little earlier, it seems that in
this instance writers prefer a `competence´ notion of
economy, one which minimizes the number of rules for

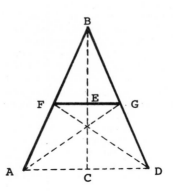

Figure 1
Strokes for `A´

composing the set of letters as a whole (= the `lang-
uage´), to a `performance´ notion of economy in which, by
increasing the grammar by one special rule ("Begin `A´ with
an upwards stroke"), the individual derivation or composition of `A´ is made easier.

     The case of the alphabet shows us that the competence
criterion must be a very powerful one indeed: it is so powerful that it is invoked in the learning of a mere
twenty-six items; our putative invocation of this principle
in the course of learning a natural language need by no
means be attributed to the sheer impossibility of learning
a language sentence by sentence or even paradigm by paradigm. If it is so powerful, so inevitable a learning-tool,
we should scarcely be surprised to find it widely used in
forming the grammar of a language: and, in fact, those who
have advocated investigation of the possibility that a performance criterion is sometimes invoked in the learning of
a language, have hypothesized only that such a criterion is
invoked under certain specified circumstances. In particular (Watt 1970), under the circumstance that a child learning a language will not displace a simple derivation of a
given paradigm--for example, the Truncated Passive--in favor of a more complex one obeying the competence criterion,
even though the more complex one leads to a more economical
grammar. That is, on this hypothesis, the performance
criterion leads in language only to the retention of a derivation, in the case of interest of a derivation producing

a competence diseconomy, because such a derivation must be preemptive. (In the case of the Truncated Passive, for example, the evidence is that it is in fact learned first (Bates 1969), and so, on this hypothesis, its early and presumably primitive derivation ought to be retained on performance grounds.) This hypothesis has little bearing on the learning of the alphabet, however, on two grounds. First, because (with one proviso) the alphabet is taught by teachers who know the entire set, to children who learn several letters at once; `A´ is not acquired first and in isolation, and so the simpler four-stroke derivation has no chance to preempt. And secondly, in iconics a `performance´· criterion can be brought into play at a late date, as see below.

Returning to our opening question, then, it does seem possible that iconics, like linguistics, must invoke the competence principle of economy, whether to predict forms not yet observed or to make predictions of other kinds--with, again as in linguistics, the qualification in favor of facilitated performance for forms learned first and in isolation. (This is the `proviso´ mentioned just above: if a child learns `A´ first, and is free to follow his own compositional program of making a four-stroke `A´, it may be hard for Teacher to persuade him to adopt the more laborious, though more general, five-stroke `A´.) To take a very persuasive instance, iconics ought to be able to invoke the competence principle to predict that the child learning the alphabet will `over-generalize´: that he will himself invoke the principle in such a way as to run afoul of the exceptions to generality that society insists be honored. In linguistics, instances of such behavior are all too familiar, for example in the well-known cases where children start off using <u>broke</u> for the Past of <u>break</u>, then learn that verbs take their Past by adding <u>-ed</u> to the stem, whereupon they say <u>breaked</u>, after which they learn that <u>break</u> is an exception. We note, just in passing, that the term `over-generalization´ is a bit misleading, for all the child is doing is `generalizing´ in the way he always does; it is society that insists that he break his pattern, essential to the learning process and almost always successful, by `<u>under</u>-generalizing´. And in iconics there are instances just as compelling. The pattern of learning the alphabet proceeds, for most children, in three clear stages:

I. The letters are, on a random basis, written from left to right (to produce e.g. `B´) or from right to left (to produce `q´);
II. All of the letters are written from left to right,

so that `B´ is always produced rather than `ᗺ´; but
also so that `ᒋ´ is produced instead of `J´;
III. `J´ is learned as an exception.

These stages--precisely parallel, it seems to me, to those
by which <u>break</u> is finally learned--are predicted, or explained, only by recourse to a competence principle of
economy, one by which the learner tries valiantly to form
the most general generalization he can, and only later
learns the lamentable exceptions. I say "lamentable" because, after all, if the learner were allowed to have his
way, and turn `J´ around, he would ´improve´ the alphabet
in exactly the sense that the next generation of learners
would have an easier time of it.

Suppose that phylogeny does recapitulate ontogeny.
Suppose that we identify the learner´s tendency to generalize with the tendency to `homogenize´ mentioned earlier.
Then we should expect that, every time a `lamentable excep-
tion´ is ignored, an homogenization would result; the
learner´s tendency to homogenize would then be an historical process which ought to condition historical change in
the alphabet. This observation, by returning to an earlier
point, lays the groundwork for a further one.

3. The evolution of the alphabet proceeds along two distinct paths, and these can be identified with the two
strands just sketched: those of competence versus performance, of facilitation of individual items versus homogenization of the whole.

The learner of an alphabet does not have much control
over the system he is learning, and it is too much to expect him to abandon his strategy of
generalization--essential to him to disentangle the
right-facing letters from their forbidden left-facing
counterparts--in order to facilitate the production of particular letters. But once he has mastered the system, he
does control it, and as soon as he is freed from societal
restrictions, which by and large are limited to the
elementary-school class-room, he may well resolve to ease
his lot. He may impose a late `performance´ criterion and
shorten individual derivation, e.g. by making a four-stroke
`A´, if he thinks about it and if above all he has a great
many `A´s´ to compose. Indeed, if he is producing letters
for his own eyes alone, he may proceed in the facilitation
process so far as to change the form of `A´ itself, perhaps
in the direction of `Ⱥ´.

This is what the Greeks did. Once they controlled the
alphabet and used it a great deal the need for facilitation
bore in upon them very strongly, it would seem, and their
records show precisely the kinds of `performance´ facilita-
tions we should expect, including the one just given.
Indeed, at a later point they carried this process even
further, curvelinearizing the letters so that `A´, to con-
tinue the same example, became `α´. In fact most of the
Greek minuscule letters have the same kind of relation to
the corresponding majuscules: they involve a minimization
of the effort required to draw the majuscules, which minimization takes the form of first reducing to a minimum, or
close to it, the path required to traverse the majuscule,
and then curvilinearizing the result. This is a particular
process; it is supported by ample evidence from Greek inscriptions; and it can be identified with the promptings of
performance.

The other basic tendency observable in the history of
the alphabet can be identified with the promptings of competence: this is the homogenization broached earlier. This
tendency brings letters closer together, irrespective of
the efficiency with which individual letters are made, and
therefore sometimes in such a way as to reduce that efficiency in the most graphic way possible. As one instance,
the alphabet that the Greeks inherited from the Phoenicians
contained a lambda much like the modern `L´. It was the
only letter like it in the alphabet: the only letter which
was composed by drawing a vertical stroke downwards followed by an augmentation at the bottom of the letter-space.
In all other such cases the augmentation began at the top.
In many Greek epichoric dialects a change took place: `L´
became `ᐸ´, and ultimately through another process `Λ´,
thus classic Greek `Λ´ and modern `L´--descended from Eubo-
ean Greek through Etruscan and Latin--are variants of the
same letter. We may identify this as a competence change,
one due to homogenization, precisely because it makes lambda more like the other letters, even though at a cost of
adding a third (invisible) stroke to lambda´s composition;
we can do this with confidence because the contrary change,
that which would for example change `ᐸ´ to `L´ against the
general pattern, seems never to have occurred.

I said at the very beginning that an alphabet is realized in two modalities, composition or production and
reading or reception, and that these two are in unremitting
conflict in that any attempt to homogenize the letters
makes them harder to distinguish. This general comment and
the discussion just devoted to homogenization combine to
suggest that the `competence´ historical force leads to an

increase in recognitional or reading difficulty, and so
should be inhibited by a countervailing force. And so it
is: no Greek epichoric alphabet contains both '∧' for lambda and '∨' for gamma, for instance: the gamma preempted the
'∨' spot and, seemingly, inhibited movement of lambda in
its direction. What then, if anything, is the force that
countervails the performance tendency: what inhibits simplification of individual letters? The answer is twofold.
First, simplification can produce homogenization 'by accident', so to speak, in which case the countervailing force
is just the one named above; and secondly, even if simplification does not produce homogenization the process can
nevertheless be inhibited by a general conservative tendency: don't change any letter so much that the next scribe
can't read it. By implication, this tendency will permit
only small changes between one scribal generation and the
next: though in the long run the cumulative changes may be
quite considerable, of course. It takes, in fact, the
trained eye to discern the Greek majuscules behind their
minuscules, let alone the modern English majuscules behind
the modern English minuscules or, to refer to an even
greater divide, the majuscules behind the cursives.

To sum up, an alphabet appears to obey two 'evolutionary' tendencies each of which is impeded by an inhibitory counterforce from attaining its logical end. The
'competence' force tends to homogenize the letters, and its
end result would be complete homogenization, the merger of
all letters into one Ur-letter; but the need to retain discriminability amongst the letters nips this tendency in the
bud. The 'performance' force tends to simplify the individual letters, and its end result would be something like
shorthand; but the 'competence' counterforce preserving
discriminability, plus a general conservative force, tend
to slow this process and to obstruct its progress, except
amongst scribes (like modern secretaries) with special
training, so that it too never gets very far. Along both
dimensions of evolutionary change, then, an equilibrium is
established.

By its very nature an alphabet exhibits in sharper relief whatever traits it shares with language: for instance
there are certainly 'artificial' or individual evolutionary
changes in language, too, but they do not typically have
the effect they do in iconic change, if only because changing one word in 20,000 has a smaller proportional effect
than changing one letter in 26. From this sharper relief
one might conclude that iconic change is quite different
from linguistic change; that iconic systems like alphabets
are quite different from languages. In my view, however,

the similarities clearly outweigh the differences, which is
what gives iconics the potential of being of interest to
linguistics.

4. But the preceding few paragraphs have been in the nature of a longish digression on the nature of competence
and performance in iconics, at a first approximation, which
we now sum up by saying that it appears that in iconics,
even more tellingly than in linguistics, `competence
economy´ and `performance economy´ are in competition, even
though the two effects involved--respectively, homogenization and individual facilitation--are basically orthogonal
to each other. What determines the form of the present
alphabet--what determines its having the letters it has instead of some other letters--is, of course, the whole process of iconic `evolution´, which, I have said, has both
`competence´ and `performance´ components tending to increase their respective `economies´. The `competence´ component could have been analyzed by guesswork, on the usual
criterion of minimality, though it could never have been
confirmed without a close look at the historical data which
so eloquently substantiate the process of homogenization;
but since the nature of the alphabet is not determined
solely by its `competence´ component this sort of analysis
could never be adequate. Of course observations like the
historical inquiries that have characterized the preceding
discussion are undertaken in linguistics, too: but, since
linguistic change seems to be dominated by `competence´
changes, the `performance´ element rarely receives much at-
tention. The latter can be seen operating most clearly in
the ontogenetic progress of language-learning, on the hypothesis advanced earlier: and this progress, it seems to me
at least, has yet to be taken fully into account within
linguistics itself. (Consider the `idealizations´ under
which language is assumed to be learned in one fell swoop.)
The argument thus far, of course, does have a peculiar fla-
vor, in that it uses historical facts to show that iconics
cannot be done in the absence of `performance´ considera-
tion for linguistics in the study of ontogeny; however, the
general point remains valid dispite this disparity, which
is due in any case only to the fact that the performance
considerations in iconics are more manifest in the historical than in the ontogenetic data simply because the former
have been studied longer and are better understood.

In all, the same criterion of economy that has been
proposed for linguistics--that which, <u>ceteris paribus</u>,
minimizes the number of symboltokens--applies also in iconics; as in linguistics, it seems oblivious to one of the
basic factors determining the form of the object of

inquiry; as in linguistics, achievement of the requisite `explanatory' level of adequacy appears to demand some inspection of `performative' matters.

5. Which brings us, finally, to iconic experimentation and its influence on iconic theory. Over the past twenty years or so there have been several kinds of iconic experimentation performed at various North American universities and elsewhere; they range from the complex reading experiments conducted by Paul Kolers at Toronto (Kolers 1968; Kolers & Perkins 1975) to the exotic stabilized-image research by Pritchard and his associates (Pritchard et al. 1960); they include the derivation of multi-dimensional scaling diagrams, as by Kunnepas, (1966), and the derivation of other sorts of comparative representations as in the work of Peter Dunn-Rankin (1968) at the University of Hawaii. Given my limited compass here however I should like to concentrate on research directed at obtaining `confusion matrices' and on the inferences for iconic theory that may be drawn from such research.

The reader will recall that the alphabet is realized in two quite distinct modalities, the kinesthetic and the visual, from which it should follow that the letters of the alphabet may be expected to have rather different characterizations according to which modality is at issue. And from this it should in turn follow that, since after all it is these characterizations that capture the putative basic traits of the letters, and since letters sharing a high proportion of these traits should be the ones most often confused, then a kinesthetic confusion matrix should look quite different from a visual one.

No kinesthetic confusion matrix exists at the present time, to my knowledge; but from the existing visual matrices, and from presently-available analyses in both modalities, this seems an altogether reasonable inference. The point is brought home when the separate kinesthetic and visual analyses are transformed into multidimensional scaling diagrams like those of Figures 2 and 3, respectively. The briefest glance will confirm that the distances on these diagrams, reflecting degree of dissimilarity, are quite different in the two modalities, graphically illustrating my earlier point that, since in principle homogenization operates autonomously on each of these two independent planes, historical change cannot be adequately accounted for on the more abstract single plane that could be obtained by merging the visual and the kinesthetic modalities.

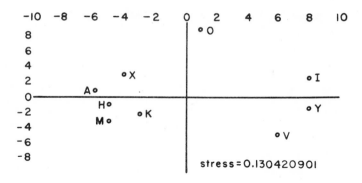

Figure 2

Kinesthetic attributes of several letters

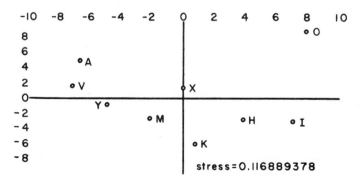

Figure 3

Visual attributes of several letters

With this caveat in mind, let us now look at a purely visual confusion matrix for the English majuscules: in fact, at the most comprehensive such matrix compiled thus far (Townsend 1971). (Actually the matrix under view is one of two exhibited by Townsend in the article cited, but for our purposes this once can stand for both.) The Townsend Matrix was derived, like most others familiar to me, by displaying the letters to Subjects under reduced

visibility--in fact, under such poor viewing conditions
that each Subject's probability of correctly identifying a
letter was only .5--and then keeping track, for each letter, of the probability of misidentifying it as another
letter. A subsection of this Matrix is given in Table 1.

Like any confusion matrix of the letters, Townsend's
contains some correspondences, or misidentification, that
neatly confirm intuition. For example it comes as no surprise that `E' tends to be misidentified as `F' more than,
say, as `M' or `W' or `O'; nor is it astonishing that `M'
and `W' tend to be misidentified as each other. But on the
other hand there are some surprises here as well. For instance, why is `F' thrice as likely to be misidentified as
`L' than as `E' (.07 vs. .02)? That `J' should sometimes
be misidentified as `L' is not surprising: but why is it
just as likely (.03) to be mistaken for `O'? And why is
`W' as likely to be mistaken for `O' as for `M' (.05 in
both cases)?

Or, in short, what implications for iconic theory can
be drawn from the Townsend Matrix, arguably the most comprehensive and most painstaking that has yet been compiled?
The answer, I think, is obvious: though the Matrix will
have to be accommodated in any over-all explanation of how
people perceive letters, there is no easy way of extracting
`features' from the Matrix for the characterization of the
letters in the hope that the degree to which letters share
those features is a predictor of the degree to which they
are likely to be confused. On no immediate analysis of the
constituents of `E', `F', and `L' will `F' be more like `L'
than like `E'. In this respect at least, iconic theory
will have a rather complex relationship to the results of
perception experiments; and the same comment is likely to
hold true for the results of experiments in kinesthetic
confusion, when these become available. (Nor does it seem
probable that the results exhibited in the Townsend Matrix
are owing to an admixture of kinesthetic effects.)

There are, of course, many other perception experiments that could be performed with the letters of the
alphabet; and in time, no doubt, most of them will be. But
inter-letter similarities, and therefore the correct
intra-letter characterizations, may be as difficult to infer from these experiments as from the ones just mentioned.
It may well be, then, that what is indicated is that such
characterizations should be expected to correlate more immediately with more mundane tasks such as sorting and with
the products of ontogenetic observation. Certainly the
last-named kind of data seem to associate far more easily

(Response)

	A	E	F	J	L	M	O	W
A	.58	.00	.01	.03	.02	.00	.01	.00
E	.01	.36	.07	.04	.11	.00	.03	.00
F	.00	.02	.33	.05	.07	.01	.07	.00
J	.01	.00	.01	.48	.03	.00	.03	.00
L	.01	.01	.01	.03	.60	.00	.03	.00
M	.00	.00	.00	.01	.00	.62	.05	.05
O	.01	.00	.01	.02	.00	.01	.51	.01
W	.01	.00	.00	.01	.01	.05	.05	.45

(Stimulus)

(percentage of identification)

Table 1

A partial confusion matrix (after Townsend, 1971)

with intuitive properties of the letters than do those
drawn from confusion studies, suggesting that perhaps confusion studies, or in general perceptual experiments in
which the letter-stimuli are deliberately degraded in order
to foment mistaken identifications, tap recognition strategies, at least in part, that involve characteristics that
lie rather far from 'intuition,' whatever that may mean.
By way of wrapping up this discussion, let us take this
point just a bit further.

The notion that intuitive properties of the letters
merit closer scrutiny is equivalent to the suspicion that
there is very probably some association between the properties of intuition and the properties assigned the letters
by the mind that knows them. Now, by 'intuitive properties' I mean only to designate the traits that anyone would
assign the letters after some study and a little reflection: what I am claiming is that it is probable that there
is a reasonably high likelihood of anyone's assigning them
the same properties, unconsciously of course, as part of
the process of learning the letters and of first putting
them to use. For example, I submit that one intuitively

judges `S´ to be closer to `Z´ than to most other letters;
from this the prediction follows that children will probably make the same judgement. How will they reveal this to
us? At the simplest level, by using `Z´ for `S´ and/or `S´
for `Z´; at a somewhat more interesting level, by so making
`Z´ so that it is more like `S´, or vice versa. That is,
by reversing `Z´ so that it is just an angular `S´. And
this is precisely what many children in fact do, as numerous studies now show. In particular, those studies show
that children reverse either `S´ or `Z´, to such a point as
to neglect a crucial difference, that of orientation. (See
Watt & Jacobs 1975 for futher examples of this phenomenon.)

Since, as I have argued earlier, phylogeny seems in
part to recapitulate ontogeny, and since therefore the
characteristics assigned by our intuitions and by children
seem to motivate historical change and hence the forms of
the letters themselves, it seems not at all amiss to pay
close heed to these characteristics when building an iconic
theory to account for those forms. Yet it would be amiss
indeed to ignore the results of confusion studies, however
`counter-intuitive´ these might be.

Incidently, the Townsend Matrix does **not** predict that
`S´ is very like `Z´; `S´ is identified as itself 43% of
the time, as `Z´ 2% of the time, as `X´ 3% of the time, and
as `H´ or `K´, an anomalous 6% of the time. Perhaps this
indicates that the `intuitively-perceived´ similarity be-
tween `S´ and `Z´ is motivated by kinesthetic attributes,
which of course any matrix of visual attributes--such as
Townsend´s--would be bound to miss. Still, when one writes
the act of composition is followed by an act of
recognition--one sees what one has just done--and if `S´
were as visually different from `Z´ as the confusion stu-
dies appear to suggest, the child making the composition
error might be expected spontaneously to recognize his mistake. But his ability seems to come only after considerable exposure to the alphabet. The same remark applies to
the ancient Greeks, too: why should so many ancient Greek
inscriptions display so many letter-reversals, even on
stone, where the carving of the letters follows well after
their having been sketched onto the block? The tendency to
reverse letters is widespread (see Gross & Bornstein 1978
for summary); but the failure to realize that one has committed a reversal, even after prolonged exposure, is the
fact of interest from the visual side.

6. Conclusion. In this paper I have tried to provide an
introduction to the discipline of iconics and to some of
the ways in which the problems and findings of iconics

bear, however distantly, on some problems and findings of
linguistics.   In   particular   I   have   focussed   on   the
well-known   problem   of   distinguishing   `competence´   from
´performance´ phenomena and on the related problem of determining what bearing, if any, the results of experimentation in the `performance´ realm have on the construction of
the `competence´ theory of the object of inquiry.   I have
urged the view that it is imperative that some kinds of
`performance´ be taken directly into account when building
the grammar; this is tantamount, of course, to arguing that
the `competence´/´performance´ distinction is a bit blurry.
This point has been argued before in relation to linguistics; but the introduction of similar problems from iconics
lends that argument a different, and I hope illuminating,
perspective.

THE SYNTAX AND SEMANTICS OF COMPREHENSION

MARC E. MARSCHARK
University of Western Ontario

1. <u>Introduction</u>.[1] The majority of current psychological approaches to language performance can be dichtomized on the same general basis as most linguistic approaches to language competence. On one side are syntax-oriented researchers, who argue that the interpretation or description of an utterance is both facilitated and determined by its intraverbal structure. This group includes a number of information processing/computer-oriented investigators who depend upon the constituent structure of a segment to drive their linguistic parsers (e.g., Anderson 1976; Anderson & Bower 1973; Norman & Rumelhart 1975; cf. Schank 1973). On the other side are semantics-oriented investigators, who appear to ignore structural characteristics of language in favour of 'higher-order' constructs such as holistic representations, case relations, and knowledge schemas (e.g., Bransford, Barclay & Franks 1972; Neisser 1977). Unfortunately, the nature of this dichotomy has given rise to a corresponding polarization in psycholinguistic research. This appears to have been the result of, in one case, an out-dated view of language comprehension as a passive, pre-programmed system and, in the other, a reaction to structuralist and behaviorist domination of psychology in the not too distant past.

In contrast to the above positions, it will be suggested here that language comprehension is a dynamic process in which the receiver makes use of any and all information available at the time of encoding. That is, comprehension is a stratified process in which semantic, syntactic, and pragmatic (used here in the sense of knowledge of

the world) levels interact with each other. The actual
contribution of each to the comprehension process is seen
to vary as a function of task demands and material attributes among a variety of psychological and linguistic variables (cf. Fillmore 1977; Halliday 1970, 1977; Lakoff
1977). Given this viewpoint, it seems that the most profitable course for linguistic and psycholinguistic research
would be to determine under what conditions syntactic, semantic, or pragmatic information are differentially involved in the comprehension process; in other words, to in-
quire about how these language characteristics interact
with each other and with other aspects of the language situation.

The research that I will describe later represents two
in a recent series of studies that provide some answers to
these questions. In particular, three aspects of language
processing will be considered: 1) subject's perceptual coding strategies as determined by the semantic and syntactic
characteristics of the to-be-processed material, 2) the
concreteness or imagability of the material, and 3) the extent to which relatively formal models of syntax, determined by logical rules, can adequately characterize language performance, which is based on psychological rules.
The latter consideration will be referred to as the relationship between 'possible syntax' and 'utilized syntax.'

2. The Roles of Syntax and Semantics in Comprehension
The constituent structure of a sentence, as reflected in
its surface structure, serves to divide it naturally in a
way that appears to be of some importance to the receiver,
who actively imposes such structure on spoken or printed
prose (Jarvella 1971). Comprehending a sentence is, in
this sense, a non-uniform process that relies on structure
to 'chunk' information. A number of studies (e.g., Abrams
& Bever 1969; Jarvella 1970, 1971) have demonstrated that
the constituent breaks of a sentence allow an interval in
which the receiver can integrate preceding information and
predict likely forms of subsequent information (see also
Bower & Springston 1970; Wilkes 1975; Wisher 1976). The
phrase structure of sentences has further been shown to influence learning speed (Anglin & Miller 1968), immediate
recall (Wilkes 1975), and long-term retention (Kennedy &
Wilkes 1971). These effects all appear to be a consequence
of the role of phrase structure in short-term memory as a
means of organizing the typically rapid rate of linguistic
input. Precisely because of this function, however, phrase
structure is probably of only transitory importance to a
receiver. Although people can, and sometimes do, remember
the original form of a linguistic input, this is not the

usual case. Rather, the input structure of a linguistic
segment (i.e., syntax and verbatim wording) is discarded
rather quickly after it has served its organizing function,
and only the meaning or gist, is retained (Bregman & Strasberg, 1968; Fillenbaum 1966; Sachs 1967).

A variety of studies have demonstrated the importance
of semantic and pragmatic information in sentences and connected discourse. The majority of these, however, have
been concerned not as much with the function of such information in the comprehension process as the nature of their
mental representation. Among the more visible studies are
those involving the retention of theme (e.g., Dooling &
Lachman, 1971; Just & Brownell 1974; Pompi & Lachman 1967;
Yuille & Paivio 1969) and those concerned with semantic integration (e.g., Barclay 1973; Bransford, et al. 1972; Marschark & Paivio 1977; Rosenberg 1968). The general point
made by all of these studies is that the meaning of connected discourse is typically abstracted from the input and
then stored in the form of integrated `surrogate struc-
tures´ such as schemata, themes, or images. A linguistic
segment is thus rarely preserved in a form resembling the
sequential input. While the majority of the above studies
may have been primarily concerned with memory performance,
further research has shown that integration is not merely a
recall phenomenon. Rather it is part of a constructive,
elaborative comprehension process that depends on the analysis of context and pragmatic knowledge as well as syntactic and semantic information (Barclay, Bransford, Franks,
McCarrell & Nitsch 1974; Dooling & Mullet 1973; Sulin &
Dooling 1974; Dooling & Christiaansen 1977).

3. The Role of Material Imagability in Comprehension.
Consider, briefly, the role of pragmatic information in understanding an utterance. Suppose you were asked to remember the sentence, "The scientist observed the bacteria."
Chances are that it would evoke some sort of visual image
involving a white-coated scientist looking through a micro-
scope. But, of course, there was no mention of a micro-
scope in the sentence. This is an example of knowledge of
the world, and specifically knowledge about the size of
bacteria (and the pragmatic problem of their observation),
playing an essential part in the encoding process. Now
consider the sentence, "The report lacked a conclusion."
While it is true that there are a number of inferences or
elaborations that could be made given this information,
there is clearly a difference in the way that one would
deal with this abstract sentence, as compared to the previous, concrete one. In fact, a variety of studies have
shown that concreteness, or imagability, is one of the most

pivotal characteristics of linguistic material, by virtue
of its effects on essentially all phases of encoding, storage, and retrieval (see Paivio 1971, for a review). While
the interpretation of language depends on both verbal (linguistic) and non-verbal (imaginal, pragmatic, etc.) information, to some extent, processing of any particular sentence appears to depend more heavily on one than the other
corresponding to whether the material is concrete or abstract. As the content becomes more concrete, the role of
non-verbal surrogate structures, such as images, increases
as a function of both facility and availability. As would
be expected, the role of structural information decreases
accordingly (Yuille & Paivio 1969).

Consider a study by Begg and Paivio (1969). They hypothesized that the meaning of a concrete sentence can usually be summarised in one organized unit as a complex visual image. Accordingly, they predicted that meaning changes
(i.e., subject-object reversals) in concrete sentences
should be recognized more often than (meaning-preserving)
lexical changes. Since abstract sentences were assumed to
be encoded as sequential verbal strings, closely linked to
the original input, the predictions for those materials was
reversed: lexical changes were expected to be recognized
more often than semantic changes. Their results supported
both of these predictions and the generalization that,
"...concrete sentences are coded primarily in a
imaginal-spatial manner, and aspects of the structure of
sentences which require non-sequential information, such as
meaning, will be retained better than sequential aspects
such as individual words. Abstract sentences, however, are
coded in terms of a verbal sequential process, and the units and their sequential arrangement in the sentences become more important for memory" (Begg & Paivio 1969:826)[2]
Now, if concrete sentences are processed through the formation of integrated images, the elements of which are ipso
facto likely to be the referents of the key words of the
sentence, it seems likely that the comprehension of a concrete sentence is more dependent upon semantic than syntactic information (cf. Paivio & Begg 1971). Similarly, if
processing of abstract sentences is tied to intraverbal
structure, it seems likely that syntactic information might
be relatively more important for their comprehension than
semantic information. The following experiments were designed to investigate the effects of imagability on the relative importance of syntactic, as compared to semantic,
information in comprehension.

4. The Present Research. That the task demands of an experimental situation may interact with various characteristics of the to-be-processed material is not a new idea. The general approach to this problem has concerned the possibility that different requirements imposed on a subject during the comprehension, storage, or retrieval phases of a language processing task may result in qualitative and quantitative differences in strategies (Aaronson 1976), levels of processing (Craik & Lockhart 1972), or retention of prose material (Kennedy & Wilkes 1971; Wilkes 1975). It has further been suggested that such differences may not be consistent across attributive dimensions such as conceptual structure (Kintsch 1974), thematicity (Dooling & Christiaansen 1977) and imagability (Anderson & Hidde 1971). Experiment 1 addressed the question of whether concrete and abstract materials are actually processed in characteristically different manners, as suggested by previous recall studies. Experiment 2 further considered the effects of imagability and task demands on the nature of the encoding process.

EXPERIMENT 1

Experiment 1 examined the possibility of differences in the perceptual coding strategies of subjects hearing high-imagery and low-imagery prose paragraphs. 'Perceptual coding' is used here simply to refer to the loci of subjects' attention during the processing of an input. Now, it was suggested above that the comprehension of high-imagery prose may be more dependent on the semantic than syntactic aspects of a sentence and the reverse was suggested for low-imagery prose. If these suggestions are viable, subjects receiving high-imagary materials should use perceptual coding strategies that devote greater attention to the major content words than any others. Those receiving low-imagery materials should use strategies keyed more to processing at important structural points such as phrase boundaries.

Two methodologies have been developed recently that allow visual (Aaronson & Scarborough 1976) or auditory (Marschark 1978) presentation of prose in a way that permits the evaluation of perceptual coding strategies. A brief description of the auditory presentation method is described below, as it was used in the present experiments. A more complete description of the apparatus, stimulus materials, and normative studies can be obtained from Marschark (1978).

Prose Paragraphs. Ten high-imagery (Hi-I) and 10

low-imagery (Lo-I) paragraphs were selected from those developed by Marschark (1977). The Hi-I and Lo-I versions of
those paragraphs have identical linguistic and conceptual
(propositional) structures as well as identical wording
wherever possible. They are also matched for number of
sentences and the number of words per sentence. The two
versions ·essentially differ only in the concreteness of
their major content words. The mean imagery rating of the
selected Hi-I paragraphs was 5.20 and that of the Lo-I
paragraphs was 2.90, according to an earlier normative study. Marschark (1977) also conducted a normative rating
task in order to obtain information concerning the important (subjective) syntactic characteristics of the paragraphs. The constituent boundaries obtained were thus
operationally rather than formally defined and will therefore be referred to as the `designated syntactic boun-
daries.´ The selected paragraphs were all 5 or 6 sentences
in length yielding 54 Hi-I and 54 Lo-I sentences in all.
Mean sentence length was 16.52 words (range 9-24) and 15.85
words (range 9-25) for ·Hi-I and Lo-I paragraphs, respectively. Examples of the Hi-I/Lo-I paragraph pairs appear
in Table 1.

     Stimulus tapes and Apparatus. All stimulus paragraphs
were recorded with normal intonation on one track of a
stereo tape. A single tone denoted the end of each sentence and two tones signalled the end of a paragraph. As
will be described below, stimulus presentation was controlled by means of inaudible signals superimposed on the
tape; a single signal was placed on the unrecorded track
immediately following each word and tone. Placement of the
signals was a somewhat complicated procedure and will not
be elaborated here.

     A Sony TC270 stereo tape recorder was modified to be
controlled by the signal channel of the stimulus tapes.
Whenever a signal occurred, it activated a circuit that simultaneously stopped the recorder and started timing according to the internal clock of a PDP-12 computer. At
this point, a second circuit turned on a red light just
above the subjects´ control button. This signaled the subject that the tape recorder could be restarted for the presentation of the next word. This procedure ensured that a
subject would wait until the end of each word (and the
starting of the timer) before presenting the following
word. The timing was stopped by the subject pushing a button to restart the tape recorder, thus yielding a
word-by-word latency (i.e., processing time) profile. Latencies were recorded in milliseconds and stored by the
computer. All materials were presented through headphones.

Table 1

Examples of Stimulus Paragraphs

High-imagery

Early in his college career, John Williams was chosen by his hockey coach to receive a trophy from a
professional team. The ceremony proved to be
crowded and was prolonged over a two hour period.
John was excited, however, to receive awards for
scoring and sportsmanship from their star player.
Further, his large size and fast skating helped to
improve opinions of his college's players. Williams went on to become a star centre and gained an
international reputation.

Low-imagery

Early in his college career, John Williams was chosen by his department to receive a scholarship to a
foreign univeristy. The programme proved to be
difficult and was prolonged over a several year
period. John was successful, however, in obtaining
degrees in philosophy and humanities from the in-
stitution. Further, his keen interest and tactful
personality helped to improve opinions of Canadian
students. Williams went on to become a brilliant
philosopher and gained an international reputation.

Strategy questionnaire. A 15-item questionnaire was
constructed for use in a post-experimental evaluation of
subjects' processing strategies. The questionnaire contained a wide variety of possible sentence strategies including rote memorization, comprehension of gist, attention
to grammatical structure, and attention to major content
words. Where applicable, strategies were questioned on the
levels of single words, phrases, sentences, and paragraphs;
each question was rated on a 5-point scale which ranged
from "used very infrequently or never" to "used all or
almost all of the time."

Design and Procedure. Thirteen subjects were assigned
to the Hi-I paragraphs and 13 to the Lo-I paragraphs. Subjects were informed that they would hear a series of sentences, organized into paragraphs, but that they would

receive the words one at a time. They were told that they
would control the rate of presentation by pushing a button
for each new word in a sequence, the only restriction being
that the button was not to be pushed until the red light
had come on. Subjects first received one practice paragraph to familiarize them with the apparatus and procedure.
Each subject then heard a subset of four of the ten test
paragraphs, and each paragraph was presented to five different subjects. The instructions emphasized the importance of understanding the meaning of each sentence, but
subjects were told that after each paragraph they would be
asked for recall. After the last paragraph was recalled,
all subjects filled out the strategy questionnaire The entire experiment lasted approximately 30 minutes.

Subjects. The subjects were 26 native English speakers who had volunteered through sign-up sheets posted
around the University of Western Ontario; each was paid $2
for participating. Subjects were randomly assigned to the
two conditions on the basis of their appearance at the laboratory.

Results and Discussion

The inclusion of the recall task in this experiment
was intended to make the task demands roughly comparable to
those in earlier studies that have involved high- and
low-imagery materials. Examination of the protocols revealed extremely low levels of recall, probably due to the
nature of the task. As the data were theoretically unin-
teresting, they will not be considered further.

Processing latencies. Processing latencies over 4000
milliseconds (comprising less than .3% of the analyzed data
points) were truncated to that value to avoid inflated
scores. A mean latency was then calculated (over five subjects) for each word of a sentence. The mean over all
words in a sentence provided a `mean sentence latency' for
each sentence of a paragraph. Analysis of the mean sentence latencies for the Hi-I and Lo-I materials indicated
that the Lo-I materials were processed at a slower rate,
and that there was significant variation between paragraphs. The paragraph x imagability interaction was not
significant, however, indicating consistency between the
two material sets. Because of the difference in processing
rates for the two groups, analyses involving syntactic and
semantic pprocessing latencies were performed using proportional measures.[3]

The index of semantically-based processing was

essentially that described by Aaronson and Scarborough (1976). This involved the selection of major content words from each sentence: the main subject noun and, depending on the sentence's structure, the direct object(s), the predicate nominative(s), or the predicate adjective(s). Verbs were not included in this index because a number of sentences contained auxiliary or separable verbs which would cause problems for any simple scoring procedure. A proportional semantic index was obtained for each sentence by calculating the mean processing latency over all designated key content words and dividing by the mean sentence latency. A proportional index of syntactic processing was obtained in a similar fashion by calculating the mean proc ssing latency for the single words that immediately preceded each designated syntactic boundary in a sentence and dividing by the mean sentence latency.

The proportional indices were evaluated by means of an analysis of variance which yielded only one significant effect: an imagability by processing strategy interaction. As can be seen from Figure 1, this resulted from the Hi-I materials receiving relatively more semantically-oriented processing than syntactically-oriented processing whereas the reverse was true for the Lo-I materials.

Strategy questionnaire. The strategy questionnaires were evaluated by comparing the rated frequency-of-use of each of the 15 strategies between subjects in the Hi-I condition and those in the Lo-I condition. The only significant differences were that, as would be expected, subjects in the Hi-I condition reported greater frequency of forming visual images to phrases, and subjects in the Lo-I condition reported greater role rehearsal of phrases.

Both the processing and questionnaire data from this experiment thus provide support for the hypothesis that the comprehension processes of high- and low-imagery prose entail different perceptual coding strategies. The comprehension of high-imagery materials, which apparantly involved the formation of complex visual images, entailed subjects' devoting primary attention to the key content words of each sentence and thus, in this sense, was semantically-based. Processing of the low-imagery materials, in contrast, was more closely tied to the constituent structure of the sentences and thus was essentially syntactically-based.

There is another aspect of the findings that merits further consideration. A recent study by Aaronson and Scarborough (1976), obtained a pattern of results quite

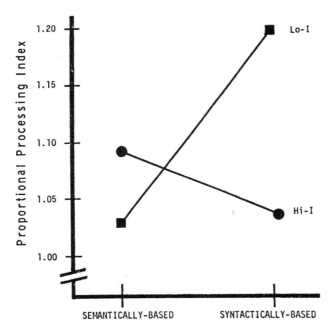

Figure 1

Proportional processing measures for Hi-I and Lo-I
materials: Experiment 1.

similar to those obtained here, but under very different
conditions. They obtained word-by-word reading latencies
for subjects who had received (relatively high-imagery)
sentences under either verbatim memory or comprehension instructions. Their data suggested that the two tasks induced very different perceptual coding strategies, as subjects in the comprehension condition, compared to those in
the recall condition, showed faster processing times,
greater attention to semantic content, and less attention
to the syntactic characteristics of the (relatively
high-imagery) material. Notice that these are precisely
the characteristics that differentiated the Hi-I and Lo-I
groups in the present experiment. This finding suggests

the possibility that the Hi-I and Lo-I materials used here
may have induced different higher-level strategies (namely
comprehension and recall, respectively), despite the fact
that all subjects received the same instructions. The
present results thus may be simply an artifact of differences in subjective task demands and the roles of syntactic and semantic processing in comprehension may be independent of material imagability. Alternatively, however,
there is the possibility that the preference for a particular processing scheme is affected by both imagability and
task demands. The reasoning behind this proposal is that a
semantically-based analysis, akin to a comprehension strategy insofar as it is better suited to the processing of
gist than verbatim information, may be the `natural´ scheme
for processing high-imagery material. This would be a consequence of the ease of representing relevant semantic information in the form of holistic visual images. In contrast, the `natural´ tendency of a receiver confronted with
low-imagery prose may be to impose a structural parse and
attempt a more time-consuming unit-by-unit processing of
the material. This scheme, of course, is typical of a recall strategy. This `strategy differentiation´ interpreta-
tion was tested in Experiment 2.

EXPERIMENT 2

This experiment was similar to Experiment 1 except
that explicit strategy instructions were given before the
task: half of the subjects in each material condition received comprehension instructions (Hi-I COMPREHENSION and
Lo-I COMPREHENSION) whereas the other half received recall
instructions (Hi-I RECALL and Lo-I RECALL). As noted
above, the sentences used by Aaronson and Scarborough
(1976) appear to have been relatively high in imagery value, and it is unclear whether their findings would be expected to generalize to both high-imagery and low-imagery
materials. There are, however, some indications that this
would not be the case. Although recall of high-imagery
sentences typically exceeds that of low-imagery sentences,
Marschark and Paivio (1977) demonstrated that under what
were essentially comprehension instructions (i.e., rating
sentence meaningfulness), subjects were equally able to retain the gist, relative to verbatim wording, of both concrete and abstract sentences (cf. Brewer 1975; Franks &
Bransford 1972). Moreover, this equivalence was found in a
task in which subjects in the concrete condition reported
primary use of visual imagery as a learning strategy whereas subjects in the abstract condition still preferred verbal strategies (Experiment 2). Thus, it appears that comprehension, as well as memory for low-imagery materials,

may involve syntactically-based, verbal strategies. If this is the case, there should be little, if any, difference between the perceptual coding strategies of Lo-I COMPREHENSION and Lo-I RECALL subjects in the present experiment. Aaronson and Scarborough (1976), however, did find a strong effect of comprehension and recall instructions on the perceptual coding strategies employed for relatively high-imagery materials. That relationship presumably should be replicated in the Hi-I COMPREHENSION and Hi-I RECALL conditions of the present experiment. The subjects in the Hi-I COMPREHENSION group should depend on a semantically-based strategy for the reasons noted earlier. Those in the Hi-I RECALL group, however, would have to suppress this natural strategy in favour of a unit-by-unit chunking more conducive to verbatim memory (Aaronson 1976).

Method

Stimulus Materials. Four Hi-I/Lo-I pairs of paragraphs were chosen from the materials used in Experiment 1. Pairs were selected such that the two paragraphs had as high a difference as possible between their imagery ratings. The mean imagery ratings of the four Hi-I paragraphs was 5.32 and of the Lo-I paragraphs, 2.62.

Design and Procedure. This experiment involved a 2 x 2 design in which subjects received either Hi-I or Lo-I paragraphs under either recall or comprehension instructions. There were five different presentation orders of the paragraphs, one for each of the five subjects assigned to each of the four cells. Subjects in the comprehension conditions were told that they were to listen carefully to all of the paragraphs and, to ensure that they were fully understood, questions would later be asked about their content. Subjects in the recall conditions were told to attempt to learn the material word-for-word as they would later be given a verbatim recall test. These instructions were re-emphasized after presentation of the practice paragraph. After completion of the task, all subjects were given a recall test and then filled out the strategy questionnaire described in Experiment 1.

Subjects. The subjects were 20 native English speakers. Sixteen were obtained through the same procedure as in Experiment 1 whereas four were enrolled in a U.W.O. psychology course and received research credit toward a course requirement. All subjects were randomly assigned to the four conditions on the basis of the order of their appearance at the laboratory.

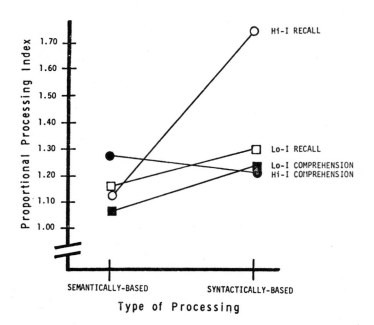

Figure 2

Proportional processing measures for Hi-I and Lo-I
materials under comprehension and recall instructions: Experiment 2.

Results and Discussion

Preliminary analyses of the recall protocols revealed
that sentence memory was quite poor, approaching zero in
many cases. These data were not considered further.

Processing latencies. Processing latencies over 4000
milliseconds (comprising fewer than 1.6% of the analysed
data points) were truncated to that value. Mean processing
latencies were calculated for each word of a sentence and
mean sentence latencies for Hi-I and Lo-I materials were
then compared. Hi-I sentences were processed only margin-
ally faster than Lo-I sentences (424.57 versus 456.06 milliseconds, respectively), but sentences were processed

significantly faster under comprehension than recall instructions (339.67 versus 560.76 milliseconds, respectively). As in Experiment 1, further analyses involving syntactic and semantic processing latencies were performed using proportional measures.

Evaluation of the processing indices indicated that
the coding strategies used with Hi-I materials showed the
characteristic interaction whereby subjects in the comprehension condition, compared to those in the recall condition, paid relatively more attention to semantic aspects of
the sentences and less attention to the syntactic aspects.
Under both comprehension and recall instructions, however,
subjects in the Lo-I conditions attended relatively more
syntactic than semantic aspects of the sentences (see Figure 2). These data indicate that the relationship between
perceptual processing strategies and instructional set reported by Aaronson and Scarborough (1976) holds only for
Hi-I materials. Both the comprehension and recall of Lo-I
materials apparently are based on some sequential,
syntactically-based coding strategy.

The results of Experiment 2 suggested that subjects in
the Lo-I material condition may have made use of a
recall-like strategy, whereas subjects in the Hi-I condition may have used a more comprehension-like strategy. Figure 3 reflects the Hi-I and Lo-I data from Experiment 1
for the subset of materials used in Experiment 2 and the
data from the Lo-I RECALL and Hi-I COMPREHENSION conditions
of Experiment 2. The data from Experiment 2 show higher
over-all levels of processing, probably due to the higher
memory load associated with the task demands. Otherwise,
however, the two graphs are virtually identical, supporting
the strategy-differentiation hypothesis.

The syntactic and semantic processing indices of each
subject were also evaluated over the 'serial positions' of
five sentences per paragraph. Analyses of both indices revealed significant three-way interactions of instructions x
imagability x serial position. The semantic index data are
depicted in Figure 4A. Notice that the two conditions that
induce 'natural' processing strategies according to the
strategy differentiation hypothesis, namely Hi-I
COMPREHENSION and Lo-I RECALL, both show gradual, steady
declines over the course of a paragraph. Aaronson and
Scarborough (1976) have referred to this pattern as a practice effect as it reflects greater efficiency over time.
The two 'unnatural' conditions, in contrast, both show a
fluctuating syntactic strategy which increases slightly
over a paragraph. The semantic index data are depicted in

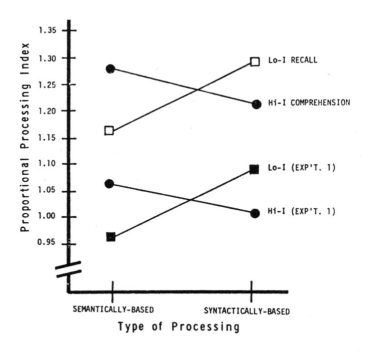

Figure 3

Proportional processing measures for Lo-I RECALL
and Hi-I COMPREHENSION conditions for Experiment 2
compared with data from Experiment 1 for identical
set of paragraphs.

Figure 4B.   While not quite as orderly as the syntactic
data, these reveal two important points. First, the decreases in syntactic processing, reflected in Figure 4A,
were not compensated for by any increase in semantic processing.   Second,   only   the   subjects   in   the   Hi-I
COMPREHENSION condition showed the gradual, steady decline
in processing that appears to reflect a natural processing
scheme.   This is consistent with the data depicted in Figure 2 which indicated that only the Hi-I COMPREHENSION
condition elicited a semantically-based strategy.   Finally,
the declines in both semantic and syntactic processing only
for the Hi-I COMPREHENSION subjects, parallels Aaronson and

Scarborough's (1976) finding, with their relatively concrete materials, that, "For comprehension subjects both
[syntactic and semantic processing] curves decrease with
practice, but for recall subjects there is little if any
decreasing trend in those indices" (p. 64).

Strategy questionnaire. The strategy questionnaire data
were analysed by comparing every two of the four (instructional set x imagability) cells. The analyses indicated
that subjects in both recall conditions, which did not differ between themselves, used phrase rehearsal significantly
more often than subjects in either comprehension condition,
which also did not differ significantly. That is,
Hi-RECALL = Lo-I RECALL > Hi-COMPREHENSION = Lo-I
COMPREHENSION. Subjects in the Hi-I RECALL condition also
used sentence rehearsal significantly more often than subjects in all other cells. The findings regarding phrase
rehearsal provide further support for the strategy differentiation interpretation of Experiment 1: The two levels
of imagability did not differ significantly within either
instructional set, but there was a significant difference
between the two sets. Thus, the only case where a Lo-I
group exceeded a Hi-I group on this syntax-related strategy
(as in Experiment 1) was the Lo-I RECALL > Hi-I
COMPREHENSION comparison.

5. Logical versus Psychological Syntax. One of the oldest
questions in psychology, and perhaps the question, is the
extent to which 'what is in the head' actually reflects
'what is out there.' This is the question of psychological
reality that can be traced as far back as Plato. More recently, Underwood (1966) has drawn the distinction between
functional and nominal stimuli in paired-associate learning, and Tulving (1962) has pointed out that the subjective
organization of a word list does not always coincide with
experimenter-defined organization. We might now ask whether this notion extends to language processing.

In the previous two experiments, the evidence for syntactic processing was based on a normatively-obtained syntax. Actually, this syntax, while apparently rule-governed
and regular, does not represent complete parsing of the
paragraphs. The 'designated' breaks in the 10 high-imagery
paragraphs consisted of 37 divisions at underlying subordinate clause boundaries, 16 at underlying conjoined clause
boundaries, 5 at subject/predicate boundaries, and 1 between a direct and indirect object. The matched
low-imagery paragraphs included 38 divisions at subordinate
clause boundaries, 14 at conjoined clause boundaries, 6 at
subject/predicate boundaries, and 1 between a direct and
indirect object. Now, both experiments have validated the

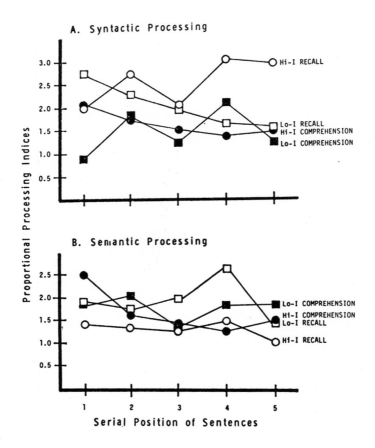

Figure 4

Changes in syntactic and semantic processing over five sentences per paragraph.

psychological reality of these boundaries, at least insofar as they were utilized in the processing task. But one might ask how this utilized syntax compares to a more rigorously defined possible syntax. Essentially, this involves formulating possible syntactic models of the experimental paragraphs and comparing them to the empirically-obtained data.

Toward this end, Peter Denny and I have taken the paragraphs used in Experiment 2 and analysed them syntactically, through the use of several simple rules. First, we have used three categories of syntactic boundaries that intuitively seem to vary in their importance to the sentence. In descending order, these are, Type 1 - boundaries that separate main or subordinate clauses having finite verbs; Type 2 - boundaries that (a) separate subject nominals from their predicates or, (b) separate conjunctions from their clauses; and Type 3 - boundaries that set off (a) non-subject nominals (e.g., direct objects, indirect objects, locative and temporal phrases, etc.) or, (b) units that interrupt larger units. These three classes have been uniformly applied to the materials with four minor qualifications: i) predicate adjectives are considered verbals, ii) participles are considered adjectives, iii) adjectival material is nominal, and iv) infinitives are nominals. We thus have developed one linguistic model of the paragraphs that is identical for the high- and low-imagery sets. For the present purposes, the assessment of the psychological reality of possible syntax relies simply on whether or not subjects use the structure in the comprehension process; that is, whether the constituent boundaries function as natural processing points (Jarvella 1970, 1971).

The first compared the formal syntax of the paragraphs with the normative syntax. The latter had been based on subjects' intuitions about where 'natural' boundaries occurred. In each material set, 23 of the 26 normative boundaries coincided with one of our three types of formal boundary. This agreement, however, was not consistent across the three types. Fourteen of the 16 possible Type 1 boundaries had been distinguished by the normative subjects, but only 7 of 47 Type 2 and 2 of 56 Type 3 boundaries were thus noted. Apparently, those subjects felt only the clause boundaries to be of natural importance. Given the discrepancy between the two syntactic descriptions, the processing data were examined further by calculating mean processing latencies for each of the three boundary types in each sentence. Unfortunately, a statistical comparison of the mean latencies at normative and formal boundaries does not yield information regarding the importance of either with respect to the interaction represented by Figure 2. The analysis did, however, indicate an important point, as only Type 1 boundaries were found to have processing latencies significantly longer than the mean sentence latencies. That is, only at clause boundaries did subjects spend more than ordinary amounts of time. It appears, then, that Type 2 and Type 3 boundaries were of relatively little importance in the processing

task, consistent with the intuitions of the subjects who
supplied the normative syntax data.

6. Summary and Implications. It has long been suggested
that prose materials differing on various attributive dimensions may be comprehended or encoded in characteristically different manners. Typically, however, evidence for
such differences has only been inferred from the quality
and quantity of recall data, sometimes accompanied by subjective descriptions of processing strategies. The present
experiments, however, examined the actual course of perceptual coding strategies as a function of the semantic and
syntactic characteristics of prose materials.

The learning phase of Experiment 1 involved standard
instructions emphasizing both comprehension and recall.
Under these conditions, it appeared that low-imagery materials were processed according to some syntactically-based
strategy whereas high-imagery materials were processed according to a semantically-based strategy. This distinction
received support from both the latency data and the strategy questionnaire. Further, the processing data for the two
conditions in Experiment 1 were quite similar to the data
obtained by Aaronson and Scarborough (1976) for sentences
processed under either comprehension or recall instructional sets. The similarity between their findings and those
of Experiment 1 suggested a strategy-differentiation explanation for the results of the latter. According to this
interpretation, high-imagery materials may 'naturally'
evoke semantically-based, integrative, processing schemes
that appear to be essentially comprehension strategies (cf.
Aaronson 1976). Low-imagery materials, in contrast, appear
to evoke the use of verbal, syntactically-based strategies
that clearly resemble recall strategies. This interpretation was examined further in Experiment 2 where subjects
received either high-imagery or low-imagery materials under
either recall or comprehension instructions. Both the latency profiles and strategy questionnaire data supported
that interpretation insofar as the Hi-I COMPREHENSION and
Lo-I RECALL conditions, respectively, yielded precisely the
same pattern of results as the Hi-I and Lo-I conditions of
Experiment 1. These data also indicated that both the comprehension and recall of low-imagery materials as well as
the verbatim recall of high-imagery materials are dependent
upon syntactically-based encoding strategies whereas the
comprehension of high-imagery materials tends to be semant-
ically based.

Perhaps the most important findings of these experiments were the consistent interactions of instructions and

imagability with processing measures. These results support the intuition that language is a flexible system that makes more or less use of particular sources of information as a function of a variety of variables. Here, for example, the imagability of the to-be-processed material was shown to predict the course of the comprehension process, determining the relative dominance of syntactic or semantic coding strategies. It is assumed, of course, that the type of effects demonstrated here are not restricted to imagability as the independent variable. Some recent studies in our laboratory, for example, have indicated that even subtle variations in the presentation task can greatly alter strategy preferences.

Finally, this research has outlined what appears to be a profitable course by which experimental linguistic and psycholinguists, might develop a characterization of language comprehension. Any search for a unitary process or simplistic model of understanding is obviously doomed from the outset. Whatever the system is like, it must involve a complex of interrelated processes which is probably far from simple. A more profitable approach would be one in which alternative perceptual coding strategies are mapped onto different language situations. This would involve orthogonal manipulation of task demands, context, and material attributes such as semantic and syntactic structure, semantic relatedness of key content words, and conjoint word frequency, just to name a few. In this manner, natural processing schemes can be separated from artificial, task-specific strategies that may be of lesser theoretical importance. Undoubtedly, future language research, in both linguistics and psychology, will have to involve some such framework if our ultimate goal is to be able to evaluate the validity of possible models of language comprehension on the basis of their adequacy in accounting for verbal behavior.

Notes

1. Portions of the research reported herein were supported by grant A0087 from the National Research Council of Canada.

2. Although a number of recent studies have criticized the Begg and Paivio (1969) study on the basis of differential comprehensibility of their concrete and abstract materials (e.g., Johnson, Bransford, Nyberg & Cleary 1972; see, however, Kuiper & Paivio 1977), there remains considerable empirical evidence for the dichotomy they suggested (e.g., Begg 1972; Paivio 1971; Paivio & Begg 1971).

3. Unless otherwise noted, all results discussed were verified by appropriate statistical tests. Those, and only those reported were significant at or beyond the .05 level.

SPEECH SIGNALS, CUES AND FEATURES

TERRANCE M. NEAREY, JOHN T. HOGAN and ANTON J. ROZSYPAL
University of Alberta

1. Introduction. We begin with a brief discussion of four
levels of representation of interest to experimental
phonetics: acoustic segments, speech cues, phonetic features and phonological units. None of these levels is regarded as fully known or firmly fixed and all are subject
to revision or elimination from phonetic theory. Nonethe-
less, we argue that failure to distinguish among such potential levels, as well as other higher linguistic and related non-linguistic factors (e.g., orthograpic interference) can lead to serious misinterpretation of experimental results. Our arguments are developed within a general coding theoretic framework outlined below and they are
illustrated by recent experimental results from our own
laboratories as well as by results from the literature.
Our chief aim is to bring to the surface certain implicit
methodological problems in phonetic research and to suggest
directions for their resolution.

   The first and `lowest´ level of interest is that of
what we will term the `acoustic signal parameters´ which
involves the so called `acoustic segments´ and their
spectral and temporal characteristics. We may also refer
to these as `potential information bearing elements´ of the
speech waveform. This is to be viewed as primarily a descriptive level that serves to segment the acoustic stream
into more or less qualitatively distinct waveform
classes--classes that are readily discernable in common
visual representations of speech, i.e. oscillograms and
spectrograms. These include: silent periods, bursts, voice
bar, fricative segments, aspiration, vocalic rise (formant

transitions), and vocalic steady state, among others.
While the names of some of these segments are influenced by
their general relation to traditional phonetic features,
they are to be regarded primarily as descriptive labels for
portions of the waveform itself and certainly not necessarily isomorphic with linguistic categories of any language.

The second level of relevance is that of the speech
cues, which may be regarded as the basic psychophysical
elements of speech representation. Presumably there is
some orderly relationship betwen this and the level of
acoustic segments--though the relationship need not be one
to one. Thus, for example, if perceived loudness is a relevant speech cue in a given situation, differences in duration of certain acoustic segments may be psychophysically
equivalent to differences in the physical intensity of
those same segments. In such cases it might be reasonable
to consider psycophysically equivalent sets of physically
different signal parameters as conveying the same speech
cues.

The third level of representation is that of phonetic
features. This is the first truly linguistic level to be
discussed. For certain purposes, an analysis may assume a
fairly detailed and structured set of features, e.g. traditional place and manner of articulation features. For other purposes, segment categories roughly the size denoted by
I.P.A. symbols (e.g., phones) will suffice as a kind of
categorical feature. It should be pointed out that we are
here referring specifically to a phonetic and not a phonemic (or other type of phonological) representation.

The fourth level of representation relevant to experimental research is that of the phonological unit or the
phoneme. We will not attempt to define these units here.
However, in the section to follow, we will emphasize the
methodological necessity of distinguishing between the
phonetic and phonological levels.

We are primarily interested in the mapping relationships between the lowest three levels of
representation--from the speech waveform to phonetic features. However, in interpreting the results of experiments
dealing with the speech signal to phonetic level mapping
problem, it is often vital, particularly in considering the
phonetics of running speech, to keep phonological and other
higher level linguistic structures in mind. Before discussing particular issues in phonetic theory, it is therefore
appropriate that we outline our overall view of language as

it relates to the speech signal.

2. <u>A Coding Approach to Language</u>. Our overall view of language bears a close resemblance to the coding theoretic view of Coker and Umeda (1975). The approach outlined below provides a useful framework for discussing some methodological problems in phonetics because it illustrates the necessity of distinguishing among several different types of information from the point of view of their communicative function. The desirability of distinguishing between the phonetic and phonological levels may be clarified by this discussion. In addition, we will consider the relevance of higher level information to phonetic variation and the multivariate nature of phonological oppositions.[1]

There are two types of coding that bear on the four levels of representation mentioned above: (1) error correcting coding and (2) synchronous coding. These were both developed to deal with problems in digital transmission of information and both have received extensive mathematical treatment. All present quantitative applications of the theory have been directed toward engineering problems in electronic communication systems. It is likely that substantial revisions would be required before any quantitative application could be made to linguistic problems. Nevertheless, even a general consideration of qualitative properties of these coding mechanisms serves to highlight certain important issues.

<u>Error correcting codes</u>

The essential property of error correcting codes is redundancy. Certain aspects of the information to be transmitted are encoded in more than one way in the signal. This allows the receiver more than one opportunity to extract the information correctly. Redundancy requires more cues per basic element of interest than the absolute minimum. Redundancy has a cost in that it requires that the length of the signal be increased,[2] which in turn will increase the burden on such memory that is needed for holding the signal until the information is extracted. Its benefit is that it enhances the survivability of the message in conditions of noise, cross talk, attention loss etc. Efficient error correcting codes are those that maximize redundancy while not greatly lengthening the signal. We will return shortly to the application of the concept of error correcting codes to experimental phonetics. For the moment, syntactic examples will serve to illustrate its relevance to language.

Substitutes such as pronouns allow shortening of the signal while they serve primarily as checks on `given´ information. Those grammatical categories that are highly variable from one language to another are most frequently used to carry redundant information. Examples include categories which usually occur near nouns, such as number, gender, case (at least where word order is also used) and determiners; as well as categories which occur near verbs, such as tense, aspect, and mood. In the flow of information, these categories bear low information conten´ for the hearer. However, their exact information load is not fixed. For example, the modal `may´ in the sentence, ´I may come.´, acts in part as an error check on the verb, but it also is the primary carrier of the information indicating doubt or uncertainty. In the sentence `I may possibly come´, that informtion is carried more directly by the adverb `possibly´ and ´may´ serves primarily as an error check on the syntax of the verb and on the semantics of the adverb. Thus, the informtion bearing capacity of any given element is relative to other elements in the discourse. This appears to be unlike error correctors in formal coding theory where the information functions of error correctors are fixed.

Synchronous coding

Synchronous coding allows the listener to organize the incoming signal and extract information from it before the whole message is completed. Such a code may serve to highlight certain elements carrying a greater information load, or to mark higher level boundaries. In electronic communication, synchronous codes are used in systems with variable message-unit lengths where a special sync pulse is added to indicate where the unit begins or ends. The basic concept of synchronous coding was recognized by the linguists of the Prague school. Much of their early work consisted in the specification of the types of phonological oppositions and indices of sequential organization of the phonological string. The latter were the organizational functions, which they subdivided into the delimitative, culminative and continuative functions. The delimitative function serves to mark word boundaries by stress or allophonic variants. The culminative function indicates the number of major information bearing elements in a sentence and the continuative function assists the hearer in grouping elements into a larger unit.

Examples of synchronous coding are readily found in language. Changes in intonation act as `sync pulses´ marking major syntactic boundaries. Vowel harmony serves a `continuative function` in languages such as Finnish and Turkish. The switching of vowel harmony classes, then may serve as a sync pulse indicating that a word boundary has occured between the last two vowels received. Within stretches of signal, stress or accent functions as a sync pulse in that it indicates an element of high information is to be processed.

Many instances of synchronous coding involve levels of represenation that reach from syntax and semantics all the way to phonetics. For example, A.W.F. Huggins' (1975) study on isochrony and syntax indicates that vowel duration may play an important role in marking the subject-predicate break in syntax. He noted that when more unstressed morphological elements occur after a stressed vowel, even between word boundaries, the stressed vowel becomes successively shorter in duration. However, if there is a major syntactic break after the stressed vowel, and unstressed syllables are added after this break, these syllables cease to have a shortening effect on the duration of the stressed vowel before the break. In principle, then it seems that relatively narrow phonetic variation may serve in part to mark syntactic boundaries. This factor must be considered in evaluating the role of vowel duration in signalling other, e.g. phonological, oppositions.

Communicative function of `sub-phonemic` phonetic variation

The notion of redundancy in phonology is widely recognized. For a phonological system to be non redundant, all phonological segments should have an equal chance of occuring in a morpheme of some specified length. Similarly, all combinations of features should occur in the segment inventory. Restrictions on possible combinations of features and on possible sequences imply redundancy. It is in this area where Jakobson, Fant, and Halle (1963) made the distinction between distinctive features that keep messages apart and redundant features that do not. However, in our view, it is a fundamental property of language that it is not generally possible to state in advance what information is redundant. In the case of digital communication, there are usually specific portions of the message that are reserved as specific error checking mechanisms, e.g., the parity bit on a teletype tape. In the case of speech, characteristics which can reasonably be called `redundant` in citation forms of isolated words may serve other functions, especially synchronous coding functions, in other situations. Consider first the case of sequential redundancies, i.e. restrictions of sequences of segments within morphemes. Within morphemes such redundancy may serve in an error-correcting capacity. However, <u>violations</u> of such sequential constraints signal that a morpheme boundary has occured between elements of the sequence. Consider for example the word `backfire´, a boundary of some kind is indicated between /k/ and /f/ because /kf/ is not a possible within-morpheme sequence in English (unless proper names such as Blackford are to be considered monomorphemic).

Segmental redundancies, which cover much of the same ground as post-Bloomfieldian allophonic variations, can also serve to generate sync pulses. Thus for example, in English, the appearance of an aspirated stop following an /s/ indicates that a boundary of some kind has occurred. Consider for example the sentences: `He said it´s Pat´ versus `He said it spat´ and also `He said it´s Bat´.[3] This is the type of sync pulse that was dealt with by Bloomfieldian phonologists under the title `juncture´. The failure to provide such synchronous cues is the basis of the idea behind a popular children´s song of several decades ago: `Mares eat oats and does eat oats and little lambs eat ivy...´.

Such phenomena indicate the perceptual saliency of relatively narrow segmental phonetic differences in a' role of synchronous coding. Phonetic information more detailed than the segmental phoneme is available to the listener. This is perhaps the best argument for the insistance on the distinction between the phonetic and phonological levels in speech research. We will see below that the failure to keep this distinction in mind may in some cases result in misleading complications in the interpretation of phonetic data.

Experimental investigation of a multivariate phonetic distinction

We will conclude this section with an illustration of the relevance of some of the ideas discussed above to experimental phonetic research. The notion of error correcting coding may also be seen to extend to the mapping of phonological distinctions to (ultimately) physical events. For example, duration and diphthongization (changing spectral patterns) are commonly held to map the distintion between English vowel pairs such as /e-ε/ and /u-U/. However, hypotheses concerning which cues are sufficient for the perceptual and linguistic distinction are most frequently carried out through the use of synthetic speech in which only single parameters or multiple co-varying parameters are varied. An experiment was conducted by two of the authors (JTH and AJR) in which multiple signal parameters

were analysed to test their significance in the perception
of the voiced-voiceless distinction in English final consonants. The parameters of interest were chosen on the basis of previous experiments (Raphael 1972; Denes 1960) and
measurement studies (Peterson & Lehiste 1960). They are:
preceding vowel duration, silent interval duration, voice
bar duration, burst or fricative duration, silent interval
duration, duration of F2 and F3 transitions. Twenty four
words were recorded ending in six selected consonants and
preceded by the four vowels /i,I,u,U/. The vowels were
gated to produce five equal step changes in duration. The
total of 120 stimuli were presented twice to 14 subjects to
create 3620 data points. A multiple regression (of
listener's judgments with the signal parameters) was performed to evaluate the relative importance of each cue.
All the variables may have prior correlations with each
other, but in the process of calculating the regression,
the intercorrelations among the variables are taken out
making them effectively independent of each other. While
the contribution of each of the variables was statistically
significant, vowel duration and voicebar duration contributed roughly 40 percent each to the total explained variance. Fricative durations contributed about two percent.
This indicates that there are two primary signal parameters
serving as cues[4] to the perception of word final consonant
voicing in English. Note that this suggests the possibility of a kind of variable error correction such that one cue
may be more prominent in one context, e.g. vowel duration
in final position (cf. Klatt 1976) and voice bar duration
in other contexts.

In most experiments designed to test for the importance of signal parameters as speech cues, the stimuli have
been presented in absolute isolation. In one sense, such
experiments, including the one outlined above, present some
methodological oversimplification when viewed in the light
of the 'functional redundancies' for error-correcting and
synchronous coding. For example, it is known that vowel
duration is a cue for final consonant voicing, for vowel
differences (Peterson & Lehiste) and for stress (Fry 1958).
Strictly speaking, controlled signal parameter experiments
ought to be carried out in all these contexts. Possibilities for various linguistic functions of various cues are
numerous. For example, vowel duration may be the primary
cue for voicing of word final consonants in some contexts,
but in others voice bar may be more salient and vowel duration may be free to take on other signalling functions, for
example vowel distinctions. Similarly, voice onset time
(VOT: the time interval between the burst of a syllable initial stop and the onset of phonation for a following

vowel) may serve different signalling functions in different contexts. Within the VOT interval, aspiration, the
frequency value for the onset of Fl, the duration of Fl and
perhaps F2 serve as cues for the perception of word initial
voicing. However, the same physical variables, especially
the aspiration, in 'content versus con'tent may play a role
as a synchronizing cue. Such considerations pose difficulties for feature-detector theories in that a more complex
hierarchical structure may be implicated for speech perception. A detector may detect VOT, but it also seems worth
considering to what linguistic end is VOT being used and to
what extent are listeners sensitive to such differences in
function.

In summary, it appears that the consideration of functionally important redundancies (including the multivariate
nature of certain phonetic distinctions), the influence of
higher levels of information on phonetic parameters and the
relevance of allophonic variation to linguistic processing
are all factors to be considered in the design and interpretation of phonetic experiments.

3. Levels of Represention and the Invariance Problem in
Phonetics. Perhaps the single most important theoretical
concern in experimental phonetics centers around the 'invariance problem'. Broadly speaking, this involves situations in which there are variable physical manifestations
of an invariant linguisitic element. But for the correct
interpretation of the nature of this invariance problem, it
is important to analyse the locus of the linguistic element
involved: in particular, whether it is a phonetic or
phonemic unit. Discussion in the previous section indicated the relevance of sub-phonemic phonetic variation to
signalling functions in speech. While this variation was
generally limited to 'conditioned allophony', other types
of phonetic variation are also relevant to phonetic theory.

How the difference between phonological and phonetic
levels of invariance impinges on experimental phonetic research may be illustrated by the lack of control for dialect variation evident in several studies of vowel formant
frequencies. Thus, it is reasonable to speak of a phonological opposition between /a/ and /ɔ/ in many dialects of
North American English. However, the phonetic realizations
of this opposition are known to vary widely. For exa le
in one of the author's dialects (TMN, central New Jersey)
the phonetic values are near [ɑ] and [ɔ]. Certain Chicago
metropolitan dialects show something approaching [a] and
[uə]. It would not be surprising to find spectral differences between the phonologically equivalent vowels of

speakers from these two areas. But is this an invariance problem for experimental phonetics? We are inclined to say no. Although such problems do have to be solved for a general theory of speech understanding in humans, since humans are able to communicate in spite of dialect differences, we think that it is advisable to keep such cases, which in traditional terms involve a phonological rather than a phonetic invariance, in a separate category. For such salient differences in pronunciations are clearly noticeable to naive listeners as such.

Dialect variation in vowels

The Peterson and Barney (1952) study of American English vowels is one of the most important data samples in the field. Yet, the existence of dialect variation in the speaker sample used has caused difficulty in the interpretation of the results of analysis of this data. Thus, for example, Nearey (1977) presents the results of a two-way analysis of variance on log transformed F1 and F2 measurements on the original Peterson and Barney data.[5] This analysis was designed as a test of the 'constant ratio hypothesis' for speaker differences which says that the formant frequencies of the vowels of any given speaker may be related to those of any other given speaker by a single speaker dependent scale factor. In data that met this assumption perfectly, we would expect to find purely additive main effects for speaker and vowel on, for example, log(F1). Substantial deviation from this hypothesis would lead to significant vowel by subject interaction effects. However, we would also find interaction effects if the vowels of the different speakers were not phonetically equivalent. If some speakers, for example, pronounce /ɔ/ as [ɔ] and others as [uᵊ]. Nearey's findings are that main effects account for more than 92% of the total variance in both F1 and F2, with both main effects (vowels and speakers) highly significant. For both F1 and F2, there are significant interaction effects, but it is impossible to determine what portion of these interactions are due to lack of fit of the hypothesis and what due to dialect variations among the speakers.[6]

A closely related problem with dialect variation arises in the case of perceptual experiments with vowels. Thus, for example, the very high rates of confusions of the vowels /a/ - /ɔ/ in the recent experiments of Verbrugge, Strange, and Shankweiler (1976) are difficult to interpret since the listeners and talkers consisted largely of persons from the upper Midwest of the U.S, where, as in most of Canada, there is a phonological merger of these categories.

Methodological issues in vowel perception theory

Experiments by the above authors raise other methodological and theoretical problems which can be clarified,
though not solved, by a consideration of the levels of linguistic representation involved. Briefly, Verbrugge and
his colleagues have reported that speaker differences
(which are known to cause large variations in the absolute
values of formant frequency values of the same vowel) were
a relatively minor factor in the intelligibility of vowels
while the presence or absence of consonantal context was a
major factor. Isolated vowels were extremely poorly recognized even when listeners were allowed to hear the whole
set of vowels from a single speaker in a block, while /pVp/
words were recognized well even when the voices of a large
number of speakers were randomized.

Recent experiments by Kahn at U.C.L.A. (1978) have
questioned the extremely low recognition rates of isolated
vowel stimuli. In an experiment with trained listeners
listening to randomized isolated vowels spoken by 20 speakers, Kahn found less than a three percent error rate. A
recent experiment by Peter Assman (forthcoming) may shed
some light on this subject. A key problem which leaps to
the mind of anyone who has ever taught an introductory linguistics course to monolingual English speaking students is
that of orthographic interference. How do you get naive
listeners to tell you what vowel sound they have heard? In
the case of CVC syllables, there are frequently two
choices: 1) the listeners may give a spelling response, if
the syllable is an English word; 2) the listeners may give
a 'keyword' response, responding with a word from a fixed
list that is different form the syllable heard, but contains the same vowels. In the case of isolated vowels,
practically speaking, only the keyword response is applicable.

There is also a third possibility that is more direct.
That is simply to have the listener repeat what he hears
and have trained listeners do the transcription of the repetition. Assman's experiment combined a written keyword
response with a transcription of repetition response in the
following way: isolated vowels and /pVp/ syllables spoken
by three speakers were presented to 25 high school students
in an Edmonton high school's language laboratory.[7] Listeners
were asked to repeat the syllable or vowel that they heard
into the language lab microphones. The listeners' repetitions were recorded on individual tapes for later

transcription. After repeating what they heard, they were to indicate on their answer sheet the /hVd/ word that contained the same vowel as the stimulus. The results of the analyses of the data from listeners who were long term Edmonton residents indicated the following. First, in the written responses, only slight differences in the overall error rate for /pVp/ words (15.7%) versus isolated vowels (17.2%). Because of the amount of material involved, it was decided to have trained listeners transcribe only those items for each subject that were erroneously recorded on the written responses. Three trained listeners who were also long term Edmontonians (and hence familiar with the dialect of the area) were asked to transcribe dubbings of the original response tapes which were edited to contain only items with incorrect written response. The transcriptions of the errors indicated that 71% of the written error responses were actually correctly repeated and thus, in effect, were correctly perceived but incorrectly transcribed. The overall error rate for /pVp/ words and isolated vowels were nearly identical (4.9% and 4.6%, respectively).

The robustness of vowel information

The magnitude of certain problems in speech research may sometimes be overestimated. The problem of the importance of speaker dependent variation on the perception of vowels still remains. Kahn's results and Assman's research have indicated that error rates for both CVC's and isolated vowels are very low. Yet it has been repeatedly shown that natural formant frequency variation in the F1-F2 plane causes overlap in vowel categories across speakers. How then are even isolated vowels recognized so well even in speaker randomized conditions? There are several possible answers to this. First, we should examine the question of the degree of overlap in the F1-F2 plane. Linear discriminant function analysis of the raw Peterson and Barney data (transformed to log measurements) indicates that identification rates of about 81% can be expected on the first two formants alone. If log(F3) and log(f0) are included in the analysis, overlap is effectively reduced and identification rates rise to 86%.[8] The extent to which F3 and f0 are relevant in vowel perception is not fully clear, but the point to be emphasized here is that the actual overlap of the physical steady state signals is a limited problem to begin with.

But we suspect that of even greater importance than this is the multidimensional nature of the contrasts that exist among the English vowel phonemes. The broader implications of the multidimensional character of certain

phonological elements was discussed in terms of coding
theory in the previous section. Impressionistic phonetic
analyses of English vowel phonemes have indicated that they
do not differ on the basis of instantaneous steady state
quality features alone. Rather, the so called `tense´ and
`lax´ vowel sets are distinguished also on the basis of
`length´ or `intrinsic duration´ as well as on the basis of
diphthongization which may be viewed as an inherent dynamic
spectral property. The diphthongal character of English
/e/ and /o/ is almost universally recognized. In many dialects /u/ and less frequently /i/ are diphthongized at
least optionally. In our experience, it is also true that
in many North American dialects the lax vowels, especially
/I/ and /U/ show diphthongization towards schwa.[9] It is interesting to note that these off-glides are perhaps most
evident when vowels are produced in isolation.

     The important point to be made here with respect to
speaker variation is that the most serious overlap in the
F1-F2 plane may be expected between vowels in adjacent
tense/lax pairs, where additional cues are available to
sort out some of the limited ambiguity. It is our belief
that these additional cues are not confined to vowels in
CVC contexts, but rather are part of the inherent phonetic
specification of English vowels. Preliminary investigation
of the identification of vowels which have been gated to
eliminate diphthongal and durational differences indicate
that there is a greatly enhanced effect of speaker differences on identification. Natural data indicate that
there are relational properties within the vowels of a single speaker´s system that can readily be exploited in a
vowel recognition scheme. While it now appears that at
least under certain experimental conditions, it is possible
for human listeners to utilize similar `normalizing´ infor-
mation, even isolated vowels in careful speech carry enough
information to render such a process unnecessary. Further
work is needed to sort out these issues but it is our tentative conclusion that vowels are in general more robust
stimuli than is sometimes thought, and furthermore, the
reasons for this do not lie in subtle and unexplained coarticulation effects with adjacent consonants, but rather in
inherent characteristics of vowels which have been largely
anticipated in impressionistic descriptions.

Relationships of acoustic variation to phonetic distinc-
tions

     There are other issues in the study of variability in
vowel data that may be clarified in some degree by a careful consideration of the locus of linguistic invariance. A

crucial question is the relation of acoustic variation to phonetic variation. In terms of our four levels of signal description, this involves the question of how various aspects of level 1, the acoustic segments level, relate to phonetic identity. It will be useful to describe a simple typology of the relationship between variation in acoustic signals and variation in phonetic category membership. Basically three types of acoustic variation may be distinguished from this point of view.

(1) Phone indifferent variation. Such acoustic variation has no effect on the phonetic identity of the signals in question. One important sub-type of phone indifferent variation is subthreshold variation. This is variation that is not detectable by human listeners. This might be viewed as an invariance problem for level 2, the speech cue level, rather than the phonetic level.

(2) Phone differentiating variation. This type of variation causes no conceptual difficulty. It is simply a acoustic difference that is a sufficient condition for a change in phonetic category. For example, referring to Figure 1, the change in the center frequency of a noise burst from 2500 to 3800 Hz preceding the vowel /ɛ/ is sufficient to cause a change from /kɛ/ to /tɛ/.

(3) Phone-preserving co-variation. This is the most interesting case of the three and has in fact received most attention by speech researchers. It may be defined as a variation in a certain acoustic characteristic of a speech signal required to preserve the phonetic identity of a segment in the presence of a change in another characteristic of the signal. A famous example of this is again illustrated in Figure 1. The center frequency of a noise burst to produce the /k/ must be in the neighborhood of 2500 Hz in the environment of a synthetic /e/ but must be near 900 Hz in the /u/ environment. This variation in burst center frequency is thus phone preserving co-variation with respect to the change of vowel formants.

As will be discussed below, the nature of acoustic variation from the point of view of the above typology becomes very important in the interpretation of experimental results.[10]

Two experiments that have been widely cited in connection with the influence of consonantal context of vowel formant frequencies are those of Stevens and House (1963) and Lindblom (1963). The Stevens and House study involved the measurement of the formant frequency values of English

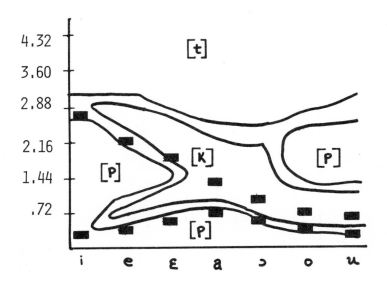

Figure 1

Categorization of stop consonants as a function of
noise burst frequency and frequencies of following
vowels (vertical axis is center frequency of noise
burst in kHz; after Cooper et al. 1951)

vowels of one speaker in various CVC contexts.   In this
study it was found that the formant frequencies of the
center portions of the vowels, and in particular F2, showed
systematic covariation with the consonantal context involved.   The phenomenon may be broadly described as an assimilation process in that the spectral properties of the
vowels were partly assimilated to spectral properties of
surrounding consonants.   Lindblom's main experiment consisted of the repetition of selected CVC syllables by a
single Swedish speaker in different prosodic contexts, i.e.
varying position and stress on the syllables in sentential
context.   Lindblom's data also generally showed an assimilation of F2 frequencies to the consonantal context.   Furthermore, the degree of assimilation increased as the

duration of the utterance decreased. Lindblom and Studdert-Kennedy (1967) obtained results in a perceptual experiment involving synthetic /jVj/ and /wVw/ stimuli that indicated that perceptual boundaries between vowels were shifted in a manner that would at least qualitatively tend to compensate for the contextual assimilation effects noted in natural data. The results of the Stevens and House and Lindblom. analyses together with the Lindblom and Studdert-Kennedy perceptual data are often cited together to indicate that the perceptual process in human listeners must be compensating in some way for the co-articulation/reduction effects in running speech which are presumed to be due to the neuro-mechanical sluggishness in the production process. In terms of present typology, it has been suggested in effect that the variation in the vowel formant frequencies in these circumstances consitute `phone preserving´ covariation that must take place to pre-serve vowel identity in various consonantal and prosodic environments. However, there are reasons for doubting the degree to which this is the case. There is good evidence that a substantial part of the contextual covariation noted by Stevens and House is simply sub-threshold, and hence `phone indifferent´ variation. The standard deviations for vowel formant frequencies across different consonantal con-texts are generally on the order of 5% of the mean frequen-cy value. Flanagan (1957) estimates the difference limens of formant values in steady state vowels at 3 to 5%. More to the point, Mermelstein (1978) has shown that DL´s for formant variation is even larger in CVC contexts and he ex-plicitly questions the perceptual relevance of the varia-tion noted by Stevens and House.

The degree of variation noted by Lindblom under dif-ferent sentence stress conditions is considerably larger than that found in the Stevens and House study and seems certainly to exceed threshold values. But a question that remains in this case is whether the variation is in fact phone preserving rather than phone differentiating. Tradi-tional phonetic analyses of stress reduction effects in languages like English and Swedish indicate that perceptu-ally different allophones of a `more schwa like´ quality are used in these environments. In fact, the very term `reduction´ is used in traditional phonetics to indicate a `reduction´ in the degree of phonetic contrast among a set of vowels. While some cases of covariation are information preserving, we question whether there is not simply infor-mation loss in the case of phonetically reduced vowels. The locus of invariance in the case of vowel reduction may then be at a phonological level, where a set of less dis-tinct allophones is used to carry, less reliably than in the case of unreduced vowels, the phonological oppositions in question. It is interesting to speculate whether this very loss of phonetic vowel quality distinctiveness may not itself be a cue to prosodic characteristics.[11]

While we do not pretend that all problems of coarticulation and reduction have been answered satisfactorily, it is clear that if any of the above suggestions about the locus of invariance is correct, then it will not do to treat all aspects of acoustic variation, even though they be systematic and uniform in direction, with the same theoretical apparatus. At the very least, an attempt to treat the variation in vowel formant frequencies in different consonantal contexts as a totally parallel problem to the variation in k-burst frequency in different vowel contexts seems to require skeptical re-examination. Presently, experimentation involving variations of the Lindblom and Studdert-Kennedy paradigm are underway in our laboratories. The major findings have been replicated, but variations indicate that an undershoot model is not adequate to account for all the results. Experiments designed to test whether the effects may be general psychophysical phenomena not limited to speech sounds are currently being planned.

4. Acoustic Variation and Speech Cues: Phonetically Oriented Psychoacoustics. An area that has received far too little attention, particularly in North America, is the question of which aspects of acoustic signals can ever be associated with phonetic variation, or in other words, which aspects of the signal are always 'sub-threshold'. In the framework presented above, this involves the question of which aspects of physical variation in signals can be limited to the 'signal parameter' to 'speech cue' mapping. The current state of instrumentation and computer technology provides a wide variety of ways to analyze and describe the speech signal in its acoustical form. Results of such analysis may suggest which are the salient signal features contributing to discrimination and recognition of various speech sounds. But as noted below, instrumental analysis of natural speech cannot in itself suffice to provide the 'correct' solution to the speech code.

Baker and Rozsypal (1978) developed an objective basis for perceptual distinction among vowels by principal factors factor analysis of the spectra of nine English vowels in the neutral /hVd/ consonantal context. The analysed stimuli were produced by eight speakers, four females and four males. The analysis resulted in a five factor solution. Two factors were related to speaker distinctions. All the three vowel discriminating factor profiles,

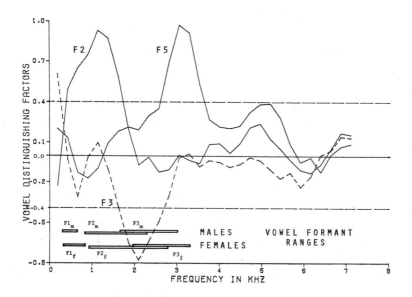

Figure 2

illustrated by Figure 2, show single pronounced peaks, mutually shifted in frequency. The peaks are at 1000, 2100,
and 3100 Hz. Frequency ranges of the first three vowel
formants cover the lower frequency slopes of the three corresponding factor peaks. This configuration resembles, for
each formant, a frequency discriminator of the single tuned
circuit type as used in demodulation of frequency modulated
signals. It can be speculated that analogies of three such
circuits tuned to fixed frequencies can account for vowel
discrimination in the perception of speech. In this case a
radically different technique has produced an analysis that
bears strong resemblance to the peak picking formant analysis traditionally performed from sonagrams. Excellent ca-
tegorizations of vowels result from either type of analysis.

    Problems arise as soon as we try to make the descrip-
tion of the speech signal compatible with the signal resolving power of human hearing. In another words, when we
try to determine which of the potential information

carrying elements of the speech signal become actual information carrying elements which serve to convey information
to the higher levels after information preprocessing at the
hearing level. Structuring the time-frequency-intensity
information field of the acoustical signal to conform to
the duration-pitch-loudness resolution of hearing is not
straightforward. Such psychoacoustical phenomena as frequency range of hearing and intensity threshold of hearing
delimit the frequency and amplitude range of the so-called
auditory field for stationary acoustic signals. Within
this field stronger signal components can mask weaker components of close frequency. The frequency spread of the
masking effect depends on the intensity of the masking signal.

The task becomes even more complicated when the acoustic signal in question is not stationary, but displays some
temporal structure. This is the case of speech signals,
which can be considered as consisting of a sequence of segments of varying duration. Typically, bursts of noise of
duration about 10 ms for stops are the shortest speech segments. Noise segments for fricatives and complex harmonic
segments for vowels and liquids represent the longest
quasi-stationary speech elements with durations up to 300
ms. With such a broad range of acoustic segment durations
we must necessarily take into consideration the unique
dynamic resolution properties of hearing.

In usual laboratory spectral analyzers the frequency
resolution Δf and the corresponding temporal resolution Δt
are constant. Their product is bound by the uncertainty
principle of observation $\Delta f \cdot \Delta t = 1/2$. Such instruments have
either good temporal resolution accompanied by poor fre-
quency resolution, as noticed, for instance, on wideband
sonagrams. In the opposite case, for good frequency resolution, we have to pay by poor temporal resolution, like in
the case of narrowband sonagrams.

In hearing the situation is quite different. Temporal
resolution of hearing adapts to the temporal structure of
the signal. From a minimum value of the order of 10 ms,
given by the mechanical properties of the basilar membrane,
the temporal resolution interval increases up to a value
about 300 ms, provided the stimulus is stationary over this
interval. The minimal temporal resolution is strongly dependent on the frequency of the received signal. The pro-
duct $\Delta f \cdot \Delta t$ in the case of hearing is not constant either,
but increases slightly with the signal duration.

This unique adaptability of hearing to the temporal

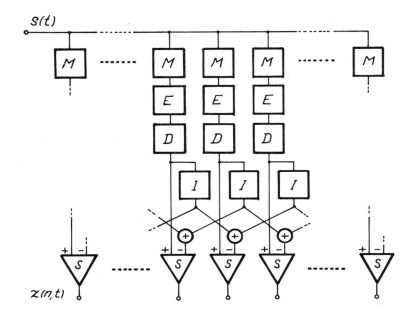

Figure 3

structure of the incoming acoustic signal gives us an analyzer with good temporal resolution for signals consisting
of short segments and with good frequency resolution for
stationary signals.

Observing responses of an analyzer modelling the
dynamical resolution properties of hearing would give us a
clearer idea which potential information bearing elements
in the speech signal are lost at the information preprocessing stage of hearing. Such components which are transmitted or even enhanced by the preprocessing become the actual
information carrying elements for the higher levels of
speech processing. Only the components preserved by the
preprocessing stage could affect the stimulus mapping in
the perceptual space of the listener.

Figure 3 shows a lateral inhibition model of the
dynamical resolution properties of hearing designed by Rozsypal (1974). In this model the speech signal s(t) is input to a bank of bandpass filters M simulating the

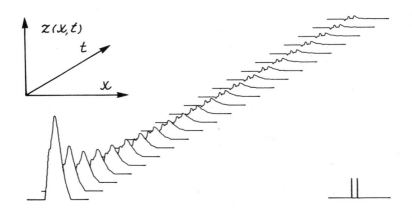

· Figure 4

frequency-to-place transformation of the basilar membrane.
Blocks E represent envelope detectors. The short-term adaptation is simulated by differentiators D in the direct
pathways of the auditory neural network. The time evolution of the lateral inhibition was simulated by integrators
I in the lateral inhibitory branches. The response z(n,t)
of the neural network is obtained at the outputs of the
differential amplifiers S. Figure 4 presents a response of
this computer model to an abruptly switched-on pure tone.
The individual frames represent neural excitation patterns
z(x,t) at 3 ms intervals. Coordinate x represents place on
the basilar membrane and is thus related to the signal frequency. It can be seen that the model responds instantly
to the stimulus onset, which indicates a good temporal resolution. The response is initially wide in frequency,
suggesting poor frequency resolution. With increased stimulus duration the frequency selectivity improves. Figure 5
shows two simultaneously switched-on pure tones whose frequency difference is smaller than one critical band of
hearing. Such tones can be resolved only after certain
signal duration, depending on the frequency separation of
the two components. As can be seen, the initially unimodal
output curve of the model becomes bimodal, each of the two
peaks corresponding to one of the input signal components.

It is interesting to speculate whether the output of

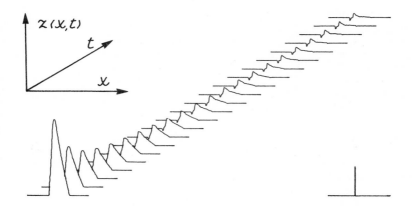

Figure 5

such a process applied to steady state vowel stimuli might
not yield 'perceptual formants' which would correspond
almost one to one to spectral peaks in cases where formants
were well separated, but which could differ substantially
in cases of close formant spacing. In any event, a number
of remarkably different analytic techniques have shown
themselves to do reasonably well at parametrically representing information necessary to separate vowels. The only
way to decide among these alternatives as potential perceptual mechanisms is to design and run perceptual experiments that have different consequences for the different
models. This entails the building of more detailed models
for some of the procedures. In our view detailed and possibly massive research is needed on at least three fronts:
(1) natural data analysis (2) perceptual experimentation
(3) mathematical modeling of hypothetical perceptual mechanisms. Only in the case of a good fit between the model
and both natural and perceptual data can we claim to have
an explanation worthy of the name.

NOTES

1. Coding theory has not received much attention by psycholinguists and phoneticians. Although there was a flurry of interest by psychologists and linguists with information theory, which is intimately related to coding theory, in the, 1950's, the interest rapidly subsided. This is perhaps due to a premature application of the theory and the use of concepts that were not well suited to the disciplines.

2. This assumes a constant channel capacity. Redundancy could also be increased by adding a new feature. This presumably would involve an additional cost in the complexity of processing rather than length of the signal.

3. A pilot study using gated natural speech indicates that it is quite possible to distinguish ` it's bat ` from `it spat' and `it's Pat' on the basis of the stop consonant information alone, provided the /Its/ portion of `it spat' is used in the context (though not if that of either of the other two sentences are used) and also provided the /b/ in bat is noticeably pre-voiced. Measurements of a few tokens of natural speech indicate that the duration of the /s/ and the vowel of `it's' may be more salient in ordinary speech, since the stops in the first two tokens do not ordinarily show marked differences in VOT in casual pronunciation.

4. This raises the question as to whether these two parameters are combined below the level of phonetic features, or are extracted separately in the perceptual processes of the listener as noticeable allophonic variation that is used by a further level of processing for a phonological decision. The error-correcting framework given here would seem to favor the latter interpretation, since if information is to have value as in an error correcting process, it must be independently recoverable by the receiving system. The present experiment, however, does not distinguish between these two interpretations.

5. The data included measurements of two repetitions of ten vowels by 76 speakers. The vowel /ɝ/ which can be almost perfectly distinguished from the other vowels by its low F3 position is not included in any of the analyses discussed here.

6. Nordstrom and Lindblom (1975) have also lamented the lack of dialect control in assessing the constant scale

factor problem with a number of data samples from various
languages.

7. Vowels were randomized, but speakers were presented se-
quentially (i.e. the experiment was blocked for speakers).
CVC syllable lists were presented before isolated vowels
for all speakers.

8. Interestingly, if log(F1) and log(F2) measurements are
normalized by subtracting the mean log(F1) and mean log(F2)
values of a single speaker from all his log(F1) and log(F2)
measurements, respectively, about 92% correct identification results (without any F3 or f0 information, cf. Nearey
1977).

9. This may be related to what Lehiste and Peterson (1961)
refer to as the long off-glide of lax vowels in consonantal
contexts.

10. We should also note that to a large degree, the analysis of a particular case of acoustic variation and its relation to the phonetic message depends in large measure on
our initial parametrization of the acoustic differences in
question. Perhaps the correct choice of original parameters would cause a problematic case to become trivial. But
this does not present any real theoretical difficulty in
itself. In general, the discovery of an apparent case of
phone-preserving covariation is a call to arms for a new
parametrization. The reaction of early motor theorists to
such a case as that in Figure 1 was to assume that the `b-
asic' parametric representation of the physical world relevant to phonetic perception was articulatory rather than
acoustic in nature. In general, we do not agree with the
particular change made by the motor theorists, since it has
not seemed to have 'panned out' in any detailed way to explain further phenomena fruitfully.

11. Fry (1965) has shown that in the case of lexical
stress (within a word, as opposed to sentence stress),
changes in formant frequency values leading to less extreme
vowel qualities, influenced stress judgments in the expected manner, though the degree of such influence was not
great. It should also be noted that the original undershoot model of Lindblom (1963) does not appear to adequately characterize the behavior of actual human speakers, as
indicated by data gathered since its publication (Harris
1974). It is perhaps a classic example of the ability of a
good hypothesis to spawn interesting research even when it
turns out to be incorrect. Gay's (1978) variations on
Lindblom's experiment have cast extreme doubt on the

general validity of Lindblom's time dependent exponential model of formant variation. Houde (1967) provides direct cinefluorographic evidence that at least some contextual variation associated with stress differences in English vowels is the result of distinctly programmed target positions rather than undershoot of stressed counterparts. This last finding strengthens the case for a component of deliberately controlled allophonic variation for reduced vowels.

12. This problem has been raised in a series of articles appearing in the same volume by Plomp (1975), Pols (1975), Karnickaya, Mushnikov, Slepokurova, and Zhukov (1975) and Carlson, Fant, and Granstrom (1975). Karnickaya et al. and Weston (1975) explicitly include lateral inhibition components in their formant extraction models. Pilot research conducted here has shown that in certain circumstances, a spectral gap can have the same kinds of phonetic effects as a spectral peak in a manner generally consistant with lateral inhibition models.

DIRECTIONS IN AMBIGUITY THEORY AND RESEARCH

JOSEPH F. KESS and RONALD A. HOPPE
University of Victoria

1. <u>Introduction</u>. The study of ambiguity has thus far presented us with somewhat conflicting results, and this over-
view attempts to set off what seem to be the major issues
at hand as well as the historical development of psycholinguistic experimentation in ambiguity. Ultimately, all inquiry is germane to the general nature of sentence processing and specifically deals with whether or not ambiguous
sentences (henceforth AS) differ from unambiguous sentences
(henceforth US) when being processed. It is, in part, a
continuation of the investigational paradigm which inquired
into whether the processing strategies employed for certain
sentence types differ in any specific way from their un-
marked counterparts. While this type of inquiry is sugges-
tive of the largely disowned derivational theory of complexity, it need not be and indeed is not intended by contemporary investigators to reflect this theoretical bias.
It is simply an inquiry into whether certain structures
like passives, negatives and inherent negatives, and ambiguities exhibit differences in their processing, storage,
or recall, and in which specific ways. It has also been
justified in that understanding the processing of these
linguistic structures may lead us to a fuller understanding
of the processes by which normal sentences are dealt with.

The question may be stated somewhat as follows. Is it
the case that at some level of performance all possible
readings of an AS are processed, one of which is finally
selected at some point in the overall comprehension process. Or is it that AS are treated exactly like US, and
only one reading is computed for any given AS. This might

lead one to expect that in some fashion, as yet unspecified, the contextual circumstances would so severely constrain the possible readings of the sentence that only one is possible. If only one reading is entertained, there should be no differences in the treatment of AS as opposed to US. However, the experimental results reported to date are not completely clear in allowing for a choice between these two simple polar opposites. The results themselves have been ambiguous on this score, supporting now the single reading hypothesis and then the multiple reading hypothesis. Other more recent investigations attempt to particularize the role of specific contributory features like context fixing or, at least, narrowing the selection process.

The study of ambiguity in linguistics, of course, is tied to its being a key consideration in the establishment of a deep structure level of the language. Attention to surface structure considerations alone simply did not provide sufficient explanatory scope to provide separate parsing procedures for sentences like "Visiting relatives can be a nuisance." It has been pointed out repeatedly (Katz & Fodor 1963; Katz & Postal 1964; Chomsky 1965) that the ability to disambiguate sentences is an important part of native speakers' linguistic competence, and thus should be included in the list of native abilities that a competence grammar of the language should attempt to be responsive to. It has been suggested that ambiguities at three distinct linguistic levels (lexical, surface structure, and deep structure) are implicit in Chomsky's (1965) analysis, and contemporaneous psycholinguistic research has included these, as well as pointing out the possibility of multiple as opposed to single ambiguity types (see MacKay 1966; MacKay & Bever 1967).

2. _Experimental Studies of Ambiguity_. The actual flurry of research activity into ambiguity dates from just over a decade ago. Early studies by MacKay (1966) and MacKay and Bever (1967) set the framework for many of the studies which followed. Their adoption of a linguistic framework provided for three types of ambiguity, supposedly at three distinct levels of lingusitic structure. Sentences which are lexically ambiguous contain a word or sequence of words with two distinct meanings: e.g., "He read the paper." Surface structure ambiguities involve the possibility of two distinct groupings of adjacent words; e.g., "Old men and women were given first chance at the lifeboats." Underlying or deep structure ambiguities involve a change in the logical relationships between words; e.g., "Visiting relatives can be a nuisance." It may be noted that much

subsequent research has been devoted to lexical ambiguity, while syntactic ambiguity has seen somewhat less emphasis, especially of late.

The earliest study dealing with ambiguity did just the opposite of what one of the readings of its title implied; rather than 'to end ambiguous sentences,' MacKay's (1966) study seems to have been at the beginning of an entire paradigm of experimentation in ambiguity. Mackay's results were extremely straightforward, as was his task. The basic results, namely, that subjects take more time to complete AS than US, and that the difficulty in completion is directly related to the linguistic level at which the ambiguity takes place, have been supported by other kinds of tasks in many subsequent studies. Though the task has come under fire, Olson and MacKay (1974) more recently report findings which exhibit 'completely consistent' results for completion and verification tasks. Mistler-Lachman (1972) similarly reports research results which indicate longer reaction times in the production of a sentence appropriate to the continuation of a hypothetical story when the preceding context is an AS as opposed to an US.

Though some work was done in these initial studies on the problem of multiple ambiguity, little has been done to incorporate multiple ambiguity into the larger scheme of things, and subsequent studies have largely avoided the problem, except to raise some questions as to its effect (Kess & Hoppe in press; Garcia 1976).

Another issue briefly raised by the initial studies is the notion of linguistic levels and the order of directionality in processing tasks. Contrary to what contemporaneous linguistic descriptions postulated as the order of rule output in the grammar, their results showed that psychological ordering went from lexical to surface structure to deep structure, the direct opposite of the logical ordering of rules in the grammar. Ordering as related to linguistic theory seems to have largely disappeared as an issue, perhaps together with the evaporation of the derivational theory of complexity, but the general notion of ordering has been investigated by others. For example, Hoppe and Kess (1977) have noted that the ordering of levels postulated by Mackay and Bever does not hold for the detection of AS in Japanese. Here there were in fact four levels which were tested; two types of lexical ambiguity are possible because of the writing system arrangements in Japanese. The ordering obtained from Japanese subjects showed surface structure the easiest, lexical-different next, then underlying or deep structure, and lexical-same the most difficult to detect.

Mistler-Lachman (1972) also found that surface structural ambiguity is resovled first, then lexical and underlying at the same time. Prideaux and Baker (1976) also
found no significant difference in error scores between the
two types of structural ambiguity, although both were more
difficult than lexical ambiguity. Obviously, there is a
certain amount of variety in the results reported, and we
are not looking at universal levels of processing.

Some later rejoinders (Carey, Mehler, & Bever 1970 a,
b) suggest that ambiguity detection studies are hampered by
the fact that detection is an unnatural process. Yet if so
many research results indicate that listeners compute both
meanings of AS, then at some unconscious processing level
listeners are metalinguistically aware of multiple readings. Secondly, what makes it an unnatural process to begin with? What makes awareness of and attention to ambiguous vocabulary words and ambiguous syntactic structures any
more unnatural than parsing sentences, writing poems that
rhyme or prose that doesn't? How human beings direct their
attention to the intended message out of the many possible
ones that could be projected for a given sequence is of
considerable interest and switching ambiguity on and off
may be a part of this process. Thirdly, Olson and Mackay
(1974) present findings that suggest that completion, verification, and detection tasks all tap the same basic mechanisms of sentence processing, and that results forthcoming from any one of the three tasks provide much the same
information and should be reliable.

Some of the strongest support for the multiple-reading
hypothesis comes from a dichotic listening study by Lackner
and Garrett (1972). They argue that the effective input of
the bias context depends in some crucial fashion upon a
linguistic analysis of the sentence being listened to in
both its meanings. Student subjects were presented with an
AS like "The spy put out the torch as our signal to attack"
in one ear, while a disambiguating sentence like "The spy
extinguished the torch in the window" was presented to the
unattended channel of the other ear at a level 5 to 10 db
less intense. Subjects were then instructed to immediately
paraprhase the sentence presented in the channel they were
instructed to attend. Interestingly, the bias significantly affected the readings of the sentences provided, while
subjects at the same time appeared unable to provide any
paraphrase abilities about the unattended channel. If both
readings are not being accessed, how could a bias lead to
the choice of one reading over the other? Lackner and

Garrett conclude that both interpretations of an AS appear
to be immediately available during the processing stage.

However, it might be noted that Harvard summer school
students initially requested to deal with the task were unable to, and the experiment had to be recast once again
during the academic year using regular MIT undergraduate
students. Even these students, however, experienced difficulty with the experimental task, and Lackner and Garret's
commentary on the particular task strategies initiated by
the student subjects to deal with their request makes interesting reading in the light of some experimental tasks
being cast as unnatural.

Another source of supporting evidence that lexical
ambiguities in a sentence increase perceptual complexity
comes from the phoneme monitoring paradigm of experiments
(Foss 1970; Foss & Jenkins 1973; Cairns & Kamerman 1975).
Foss (1970), for example, noted that reaction discrimination time in a phoneme monitoring task is slower after
ambiguous lexical items than after unambiguous lexical
items, and this finding has been replicated in each of the
above studies.

Recent work appears to disconfirm the value of the
phoneme monitoring task in assessing ambiguity processing.
Mehler, Segui, and Carey (1978) have called attention to
the fact that length and frequency of the word preceding
the phoneme to be monitored should be controlled, and if
they are, a lexically ambiguous word preceding the target
phoneme shows no discernible response time difference. In
fact, with the appropriate controls, longer French ambiguous words actually led to faster reaction times than sentences with short ones. Newman and Dell (1977) report similar findings in respect to the length of the word preceding the target phoneme, and another feature, that of phonological similarity of its initial phoneme to the target
phoneme. Their results also indicate that the presence of
such properties confound the ambiguity findings.

Little has been done on the topic of storage and recall, but Mistler-Lachman's results (1972, 1975) indicate
that sentence processing is deeper when both readings of
the AS are considered than when only one reading of an AS
is considered. Similarly, Bock (1978) has noted that AS
are better recalled when their ambiguity had been noticed.
Of course, this may reflect instead a special strategy
which employs the repetition present from a single sentence
presented twice, at least in its formal shape, or the fact
of its distinctiveness, and consequent attention being

called to it, enhances its recall. It should be noted, however, that when the ambiguity went unnoticed, there was no superiority of recall of AS over US in Bock's findings. In a study using a colour-naming task, Conrad (1974) found that both meanings of a word that has two distinct meanings are processed in memory at the time the word is heard in a sentence. These data support the multiple-meaning hypothesis of AS processing.

On the other hand, experimental results which show no differences between processing of AS and US are not lacking either. These experiments usually employ sentence set or contextual restrictions as part of the task. For example, in a complex task using pictures and sentence sets, Carey, Mehler, and Bever (1970 a, b) found no differences between reaction times for AS and US. However, if the subjects reported that the ambiguity had been noticed, only then were reaction times affected. Foss, Bever, and Silver (1968) tested the possible differences between the more frequent and less frequent readings of AS. Subjects presented with pictures after the presentation of an AS took longer to respond when the picture presented the less frequent interpretation of the AS than when it represented the more frequent one. The implication would seem to be that hearer-readers normally assign only one immediate reading to the sentence, despite the possibility of its having multiple readings. This seems intuitively to answer one's reaction to the oft-quoted Lashley (1951) sentence "Rapid /rajtin/ with his uninjured hand saved from loss the contents of the capsized canoe," and our reactions as to why we posed the immediate interpretation we did and the manner in which it was corrected.

Hogaboam and Perfetti (1975) also suggest that access to multiple meanings occurs in fixed canonical order regardless of context; thus, one or more meanings will be accessed according to whether the first biased reading fits the context which does appear. Their experimental results led them to suggest that many studies which claim to support an increase in processing difficulty in dealing with AS do so because these studies have largely failed to separate out primary and secondary senses of lexical items, thus confounding the issue. Hogoboam and Perfetti instead suggest that lexical ambiguity as such may instead increase such processing difficulty only when the secondary meaning of the lexical item is required by the context given. This view is somewhat countered by the findings of Holmes, Arwas, and Garrett (1977) whose findings suggest that prior biasing context does not have a significant effect, and in fact, that both meanings of a lexically ambiguous item must be considered even if context does make one reading more likely than the other.

It should also be noted that ambiguity need not necessarily complicate all processing tasks. Mistler-Lachman (1972) tested levels of comprehension for normal and AS and found that of three tasks -- judging meaningfulness of sentences, judging whether a sentence followed from context, and making up a sentence to follow another -- only context integration and production tasks required ambiguity resolution (with slower processing times), while the meaningfulness judgement task did not. Furthermore, Bock (1978) found that the comprehension time for AS was no longer than for US, thus supporting the one-meaning hypothesis.

Some attempts at explaining the disparities among experimental results has been offered by Bever, Garrett, and Hurtig (1973). They argue that the ambiguous results are the outcome of the actual temporal location of the experimental task posed. Their claim is that "during an ambiguous clause, both meanings are processed, but immediately after the clause is over, it is recoded with only one meaning retained (277)." Thus, in complete clauses, the presence of ambiguity does not increase comprehension or processing time, and no differences are exhibited between AS and US. On the other hand, if the experimental task interrupts the clause, differences will be shown, since up to this point both readings are presumably being processed. This is apparently in line with a more general theory of speech perception, whereby hearers project various possible interpretations for the clauses they are exposed to, but upon completion of the clause, a reading is assigned to it, it is stored in memory, and its actual phonetic manifestation is dropped from immediate memory. Since processing these various possible alternatives takes time or imposes its own specific restrictions, experimental results show differences between AS and US when the task is imposed before clause closure. On the other hand, once the projected interpretations are made, and a single one has been chosen from among the possible ones, all other projections are dropped from the working memory, and no differences are to be found. By this point, the potentially AS would be expected to have only one reading.

One problem with this approach is the counter-intuitive appeal to the problem of lexical ambiguity. Polysemy is so pervasive in language that one would expect some degree of contextual narrowing from both pragmatic and syntactico-semantic settings. The Bever, Garrett, and Hurtig argument may hold true in the case of surface and deep structure ambiguities, but its application to the problem of lexical ambiguity seems uneconomical. Here we are faced with varying degrees and ranges of ambiguity or vagueness instead. This is a feature which characterizes all sentences, and we may be considering more general processing strategies and the role that contextual information plays in these.

One of the problems separating lexical ambiguity from structural ambiguity is the continuum between vagueness and polysemous ambiguity. So many words have more than one meaning, and the relations between these multiple semantic values for vocabulary items are not all the same as they appear to be for variants of structural ambiguity. Some studies seem to take this into account, at least by admitting it, as for example, Foss and Jenkins (1973:580), in saying that "it is very difficult to find completely unambiguous control words . . . and not all of the control words were completely unambiguous." This is fair enough, but not admitting this problem at the outset leaves control sentences open to the kind of criticisms levelled by Garcia (1976).

This is complicated by the fact of vagueness in assigning many lexical items in utterances to their actual referent; even if the referent is correctly specified and identified, one still may not have the same exact image in mind that the speaker had intended. Nor is the line of demarcation between vagueness and ambiguity always easily drawn. Take, for example, the AS "The chicken is ready to eat." The two deep structure readings involving chicken as eater or eaten provide one kind of ambiguity, but what of the characterization of the chicken as ready to eat, piping hot, straight from the frying pan, or plumply strutting in the barnyard, all evoking visions of "ready to eat." Is this lexical ambiguity or just vagueness?

One interesting consequence of Bever, Garrett, and Hurtig's study is its calling attention to the insufficiency of the structural definition of ambiguity type as the main variable per se. They suggest that ambiguities are better classified in respect to the independence of the perceptual mapping rules used in the comprehension of the several readings. If we understand this correctly, we would agree that a profitable path to follow is to assess just which types of ambiguities at each of the three levels pose processing problems, and to what degree. This kind of information would be most helpful is assessing relative scales of difficulty for various AS types, and if true, might have positive practical applications, as for example, in pedagogy.

Bever, Garrett, and Hurtig's study is in fact comple-
mented by Cairns and Kamerman's (1975) results for lexical
information processing during sentence comprehension.
These results are supportive in claiming that all meanings
are retrieved in the case of ambiguous lexical items, but
once a decision stage is reached, only one meaning is
transferred to the working memory. They also receive some
support from Carmazza, Grober, and Garvey's (1977) investigation of the comprehension of anaphoric pronouns. Their
results suggest that not only is implicit causality in verb
roots an important determinant of possibly ambiguous pro-
noun assignment but that such ambiguities are normally resolved at clause boundaries.

In contrast, Garcia (1976) has recently levelled harsh
criticism at Bever, Garrett, and Hurtig's attempt to recon-
cile conflicting results. Bever, Garrett, and Hurtig, it
might be added, reply in kind and quality in the same issues of the journal. One type of criticism concerns the
nature of the linguistic theory underlying their work, and
much similarly initiated research, claiming that the classification of ambiguities into lexical, surface, and underlying structure types corresponds more to Chomsky's (1957)
Syntactic structures format than to Aspects or post-Aspects
models. Garcia claims (1976:202) that "BGH's study lacks
support from any generative-transformational model" and "it
cannot, therefore, provide support for generative grammar
as a theory of language structure." Be that as it may, we
have witnessed the divergence of linguistics and psychology
at their interface in the field of psycholinguists. It is
not crucial to psycholinguistic investigation that linguistic theory serve as input and the psycholinguistic results
serve as validation of theoretical positions espoused in
linguistics; it is enough that the relationship be sugges-
tive of research problems worthy of attention and suggest
novel approaches to traditional problems. In this respect,
the tripartite classification is not sacrosanct, but simply
as a touchstone for further research activity.

One criticism that is pertinent, however, strikes at
the heart of ambiguity research. Are the sentences posed
as experimental models truly AS and are they exemplars of
the specific type of ambiguity postulated? For example,
Garcia (205) notes that "in a number of cases, the test
sentence allows a third interpretation besides the two
tested for". Garcia also provides a detailed checklist of
potential faults in such AS followed by specific commentary
on possible defects in the stimulus sentences used by

Bever, Garrett, and Hurtig. Commentary has also been offered by Kess and Hoppe (in press) as to the status of some
of the sentences in earlier experiments by MacKay (1966)
and MacKay and Bever (1967). Several of the sentences
therein reported would be expected to have disambiguating
shapes according to the basic canons of written style; the
majority of ambiguity experiments have dealt with the
printed word, but here too operate certain stylistic canons
which might in fact serve to eliminate certain readings of
visually presented sentences. Kess and Hoppe also noted a
similar shortcoming for multiple ambiguities, where the actual ambiguity was far more multiple than imagined. For
example, the fragment "While lecturing on their stand in
Leningrad, Stalin . . ." allows at least twelve sensible
readings without stretching the imagination. While it is
difficult to say what these extra possible interpretations
contribute to the processing difference, they certainly
cloud the issue of difference between AS and US.

Not all potential ambiguities, of course, actually see
the light of day as ambiguities. This, of course, has been
the claim of some in respect to spoken language, and some
research (Lehiste (1973); Stageberg (1971); Scholes
(1971)). For example, Lehiste (1973) has investigated how
speakers actually do disambuate grammatically ambiguous
sentences and by which phonetic mechanisms. Not surprisingly, the results are mixed, but there does appear to be
a correlation between surface constituent structure and
success in disambiguation, but mainly by manipulation of
the time dimension, with intonation playing only a subordinate part. This stands in distinction to pedagogical
TESL-oriented claims by some (see Stageberg 1971) that such
tasks are both predictable and amenable to pedagogical presentation. Lehiste reports that this is not an all-or-none
proposition, but rather that some speakers were able to
disambiguate certain structures for their listeners and
some could not; similarly, some listeners were able to perceive the intended meaning over and above chance, and some
could not. The matter does not seem to be as entirely
clear-cut as some might have expected, and some sentences,
of course, were disambiguated successfully by neither
speakers nor hearers. This raises the issue of individual
differences in processing and producing ambiguities. Do
some of us follow the single-meaning hypothesis and others
a multiple-meaning hypothesis?

Recent research has concentrated on whether context
itself can provide some basis for choosing between the
single-reading and multiple-reading approaches. This line
of inquiry may also lead to a fuller understanding of just

how it is that context contributes to an appropiate set of
interpretations for any sentence or passage. While most of
this work has been limited to lexical ambiguity, some recent work has also directed its attention to structural
ambiguity of the surface or deep structure kinds.

Here too, however, the role of context has itself produced conflicting results, depending upon the nature of the
context given and the task posed. For example, Foss and
Jenkins (1973) tested for reaction time in a phoneme monitoring task when ambiguous sentence has a biased context,
and found that the single-reading model patterned after
common sense was best discarded. However, context is variable, and their sentence `The farmer put his straw beside
the machine´ might be better constrained contextually by
even more specific preceding context. Then, too, such context as Foss and Jenkins provided is largely a matter of
degree, and their biased sentence "The child put his straw
beside the machine" might be better biased by saying "The
soda jerk put his straw beside the machine."

In real discourse settings, contexts are usually more
extended, and a highly biased sentence like Garrett´s
(1970) "John´s uncle showed him a whole roomful of walking
sticks" can be easily interpreted in the Pinnochio setting
the second interpretation demands. It would suggest that
further research on context provide more extended contextual settings to make the processing task more realistic, as
well as to make up for the obvious lack of pragmatic context which also contributes its share. Part of this problem, of course, relates to the study of the isolated sentence which characterizes so much of early psycholinguistic
rsearch dependent upon linguistic theory for its theoretical input. One can expect the current interest in speech
acts and conversational analysis to be matched by similar
constraints in making psycholinguistic experimentation more
responsive in experimental design and data interpretation.

Secondly, the notion of context can obviously be taken
in varying degrees of constraint of the intended meaning.
For example, Perfetti and Goodman (1970) found that the semantic effect of a sentence is quite powerful in providing
defining context, but that single words, even when presented immediately preceding, are not sufficient and have
little or no effect. Some inplications for single sentence
contexts must also profit from this set of results, for
even when the experimental task makes use of single-word
preceding context housed within a sentence (see for example, Foss & Jenkins 1973), it may be that the structure is
completely neutral, and we are left with a single word

context; hence the controls may not really be controls.

A plausible explanation for the role of context, pragmatic as well as semantic, has been offered by Oden (1978:26), whose experimental results support the hypothesis that the judged preference for interpretations of AS is a direct function of the relative sensibleness of the interpretations. Moreover, semantic constraints determine the degree of sensibleness of each interpretation, and such constraints are both continuous and reflect world knowledge of all kinds. They are independent of each other and stable from sentence to sentence, since they characterize one's operational knowledge of the world. Oden's work seems to hold the most promise for fruitful resolution of bias determination, and the most plausible in terms of potential explanations and applications.

Similar concerns are partly reflected by several researchers (Foss & Jenkins 1973; Hogaboam & Perfetti 1975) in the notion that there may be a canonical order in which processing and integration processes work before the final synthesis of the information is transferred to the working memory. Many ambiguities are in fact biased, and the initial step would first take account of these expectations before switching to other plausible readings, given the absence of other constraining contextual information. It is not surprising that proponents of artificial intelligence programs provide their computers with exactly this kind of contextual setting before expecting successful responses. This kind of approach is both intuitively satisfying and also fits well with reported results like that of Foss, Bever, and Silver (1968:304) who note that "when Ss are presented with an ambiguous sentence, they tend to interpret it in only one way," but "if later events warrant, Ss can recover the other meaning ... ."

Recent work by Schvaneveldt, Meyer, & Becker (1976) also favors the selective access hypothesis and the role of context in biasing access to a single meaning for lexically ambiguous items. Lexical items were presented in three-word sets, with the ambiguous lexical item in the middle position, and the results clearly point in the direction of bias in one direction. In a sense, the results are the inverse of findings reported by Suls and Weisberg (1970) for processing syntactically ambiguous sentences. In a sentence like "The doctor saw the old Indian dance," bias for one reading was set by providing a preceding paragraph of context. When a word association task was then posed, the pattern of intrasentence word associations conformed almost unanimously to the structural interpretation

called for by the context. Lexical items appear to operate
in a network-like relationship; a particular sub-network
can be stimulated, and lexical items which are related to
the reading in question are given higher access priority.
Both studies appear to tap the same organizational schema,
but from slightly different points of view.

Swinney and Hakes (1976) also present strong evidence
for the disambiguating effect of prior context, both immediate and distant, on the processing of lexical ambiguities
in sentences. Interestingly, in the neutral context condition, reaction times after ambiguous words were longer. As
Swinney and Hakes (1976:682) observe, the fact of prior
context biasing the interpretive process before the ambiguity is even encounterd "appears to correspond to the general notion of expectancy which has appeared in many
theories of perception." Their work also focuses upon the
problem of the context bearing a strong predictive relationship to one reading of the ambiguity; thus, their experiment was designed to evaluate the effects of prior disambiguating contexts under conditions as favorable and selective of one reading as possible, something previous experiments have either failed to do or have provided only in
very weak fashion. They conclude that previous experiments
have failed to obtain the effect because only certain of
the possible types of disambiguating prior contexts will
produce a prior effect. This provides a commentary on the
possible reading of the results which arise from research
on ambiguity in sentences which occur in isolation, as well
as single-word context conditions like Foss and Jenkins
(1973) and those experiments which have made use of sentence set (Carey, Mehler, and Bever, 1970, a, b). While it
is true that many of the single-word contexts in the Swinney and Hakes experiment yielded much the same result as
multi-word contexts, it is important to note that these
must be highly predictive, not neutral or even merely selective of contextual effect.

Work by Tyler and Marlen-Wilson (1977) on the effects
of semantic context on syntactic processing supports this
view. Decisions regarding sentence fragments containing
syntactically ambiguous phrases can be influenced by prior
semantic context well before clause boundaries. These
findings also point up the interaction of syntactic and semantic information in continuous two-way interactional
fashion, and indicate that interpretational projectional
decisions need not await the final clause boundary, as Bever, Garrett, and Hurtig (1973) have suggested. Although
the experiment tests this in a roundabout fashion and does
not   directly   demonstrate   that   only   the

compatible-to-context syntactic structure is computed, it does point persuasively in that direction.

A recurring secondary theme in many studies is that of sentence bias in favor of a particular reading. Carey, Mehler, and Bever (1970:245) suggest "ordinarily, an ambiguous sentence has one interpretation that is computed with higher probability than the other," but the question is whether this is always the case in some structured fashion, or is the result of knowledge-related expectations, as Oden suggests (1978). It would seem that here is an area of possible fruitful research, namely, discovering whether a given ambiguity type on one of the two structural levels always has a preferred reading. For example, given a concatenational surface structure ambiguity, is the preferred bias always one way as opposed to the other; if so, which way? Is this true for all languages, for most seem to admit this type of concatenational ambiguity? What are the basic reasons for bias towards one interpretation for an AS? Is the bias caused solely by the surrounding informational context or is it a function of the structure itself, so that bias is always associated with certain ambiguous structures?

Finally, novel attempts to link ambiguity studies with other types of perceptual processes and cognitive strategies have been seen recently. For example, Lefever and Ehri (1976) have investigated the relationship between the personality characteristic of field independence and ability to disambiguate sentences. Interestingly, the results show a modest positive correlation between field independence and the ability to disambiguate sentences, suggesting that sentence disambiguation is not just a function of linguistic competence but is related to the personality or cognitive ability of the sentence processor. This of course, fits in with current thought about the relationship of linguistic development with the development of other motor and cognitive abilities, rather than just considering it in isolation as a rather unique capacity. The results are also interesting in that they relate to a possible concept of cognitive style. Leferer and Ehri suggest that the ability to restructure or overcome a previously organized field might be thought of as the ability to change mental verbal set and the quotient of field independence may vary among subjects.

3. _Conclusion_. In conclusion, we would agree with Garrett's early comments on taking ambiguity as a serious problem because of the absolute ubiquity of ambiguity and the importance of context in narrowing the selection of an

interpretation for sentences. The simple fact is that
there is simply too much vagueness and ambiguity for us not
to have some special set of strategies for coping with it
in normal discourse. Elucidation of the specific strategies by which we manage to deal with this kind of linguistic dilemma presents exciting prospects for future research
and awaits our concerted efforts.

The issue of the single-meaning versus the
multiple-meaning explanation of processing ambiguity is
still unresolved. While some of the earlier support for
the multiple meaning hypothesis from the phoneme monitoring
and the dichotic listening studies no longer seems firm,
other work still remains unchallenged in its support of the
multiple-meaning hypothesis or at least an ordered-meaning
hypothesis.

PSYCHOLINGUISTIC EVIDENCE AND LINGUISTIC THEORY

BRUCE L. DERWING
University of Alberta

1. <u>Introduction</u>. The problem of the relationship between psycholinguistic (or experimental) evidence and linguistic theory has numerous facets, not a few of which seem to have gone unrecognized by a substantial proportion of the contemporary linguistic community. The first aspect of the problem, of course, is the recognition that a problem in fact exists. Judging from the published literature, even this initial hurdle has yet to be crossed by linguistic practitioners in some of the more influential circles, especially in North America.

I can see three main reasons for this surprisingly widespread failure to recognize the nature of the problem. One, happily the rarest, is pure sloth and accompanying ignorance, often combined with the kind of arrogance that is characteristic of the narrow and inflexible mind. Linguists of this ilk do what they do simply because that's what they've always done, and they pointedly eschew anything which smacks of "self-indulgent methodological agonizing" about the foundations of their discipline (see Pullum 1978:399 for a recent example of this kind of thoroughly anti-scientific attitude[1]). Quite beyond such disreputable isolated cases, however, there is a long tradition in modern linguistic inquiry which has had the quite natural effect of misdirecting many a perfectly open-minded scholar on the question of the relevance of psycholinguistic evidence to linguistic theorizing. Under the influence of ideas which developed originally in comparative philology, the prevailing linguistic philosophy from at least Saussure's time to the present has been one of autonomy: a

language was viewed as a kind of isolated `natural object´
which could be investigated independently of the psychology
of its speakers and hearers. That is to say, the `under-
lying´ properties of the linguistic `system´ were thought
to be ascertainable from the study of observable linguistic
data (e.g., from the distributional properties manifested
in transcribed utterances or texts), in much the same way
that the essential properties of the natural world could be
discovered by the study of physical objects. In recent
years, this misapprehension has led to a concept of linguistic `competence´ (Chomsky 1965) which consists of noth-
ing more than an arbitrary set of "coding principles"
(Straight 1976) abstracted by linguists from linguistic
data. These principles are codified in the form of descriptive `grammars´ which are conceived of as `neutral´
with respect to the actual processes of language production
and comprehension by speakers. There is increasing reason
to believe, however, that `neutral´ may in fact mean `irre-
levant´ in this context. Straight summarizes the situation, for example, as follows:

> Frankly, there is reason to question the usefulness
> of a notion of `coding principles´ separate from
> mechanisms of listening and speaking. Language us-
> ers´ `judgments´ of such analytical properties as
> grammaticality, acceptability, synonymy, redundan-
> cy, ambiguity, and appropriateness appear to be a
> hopelessly diverse collection of context-dependent
> and non-natural reactions to verbal stimuli. De-
> scriptions of coding principles based on such data
> may thus be descriptive of nothing but an epi-
> phenomenon, a relatively incoherent by-product of
> perceptual and productive language abilities
> (1976:526).[2]

In short, linguists (and some psychologists heavily influenced by linguists) have profoundly confused the distinction between language as a product (i.e., a set of utterances) and language as a process (the activity of producing and comprehending utterances): a grammar which describes utterance forms can no more `explain´ them than can
a description of a painting tell how the painting came
about - or a `grammar of a cake´[3] tell how to make a cake.
The explanation of utterance forms, as well as their use
and their interpretation, all lies within the language user
who produces or comprehends these forms, and only a model
of linguistic performance (appropriately idealized[4]) can
serve this function, even in principle (see Derwing, in
press for a full discussion of this issue).

In some of his more recent work, Chomsky himself has shown some signs of recognizing the nature of this problem, as in the following citation:

> There is no guarantee that the best theory con-
> structed on the basis [of structural data]...will
> be correct; consideration of broader data (in this
> case, data of performance) might indicate that what
> appeared to be genuine explanatory principles are
> spurious and that generalizations discovered are
> accidental. Investigation of the theory of perfor-
> mance might thus lead to different theories of com-
> petence (1975:248).

But even this statement still suffers from a serious misapprehension, namely, the suggestion that there exists some non-arbitrary way for an autonomous `structural' linguistics ever to arrive at a `best theory' of competence. For, as pointed out in Derwing (1974), all of modern structural [5] linguistics suffers from an insoluble non-uniqueness problem: any set of language forms can be correctly (i.e., accurately) described in many different ways, as even the simple example of the English plural inflection clearly shows. This implies that pure `linguistic' or `internal' evidence (i.e., evidence about `static' language forms of the kind traditionally employed in linguistics) is quite inadequate to distinguish a wide range of theoretical alternatives. (See Derwing 1973, in press for arguments that this generalization still holds true even when these `primary' data are supplemented with such `secondary' data as native speaker judgments of the kind mentioned by Straight in the citation above.) The only apparent solution to this problem (apart, of course, from the adoption of arbitrary principles for grammar `evaluation' - or choosing on the basis of equally arbitrary pragmatic considerations) is to redefine the nature of the discipline: to say that the goal of linguistics is not merely to describe utterance forms, but rather to describe the knowledge and abilities which speakers have to produce these forms and which hearers have to comprehend them. Such a decision entails the potential advantage of subjecting linguistic claims to the test of truth: whereas the forms will admit to numerous possible descriptions, there are many psychological claims about the language user's knowledge and abilities which can be shown to be either wrong or at least inadequate on the basis of experimental data (see Derwing & Baker 1977). So an expanded domain of `psycholinguistic' evidence can help to sort out alternatives which the traditional kinds of `linguistic' data could not.

Moreover, as already implied above, the decision-step
to 'psychologize' linguistics is also called for on independent conceptual grounds, for it is clear that the onto-
logical status of a purely 'autonomous' linguistic
grammar-description is extremely murky, at best. Where
does one go to find 'the English language,' for example, in
order to test claims about its supposed properties as a
'natural,' 'sociological,' or otherwise non-psychological
'system'? (In practice, the analyst must always resort
ultimately to the analytical judgments or other behaviors
of living speakers or hearers.) In what kind of empirical
space reside the 'real-world' analogues of the fundamental
linguistic concepts (units, rules, conventions, etc.), if
these concepts are taken to represent something which exists outside of the minds of real language users? It is
quite possible, on the other hand, that many of the concepts which have evolved in linguistic theory, though con-
ceived in a period when psychological issues were not
thought to be relevant, much less paramount, might nonethe-
less turn out to have certain analogues in some of the various aspects of the typical real language process. That is
to say, it is not at all inconceivable that at least some
of the ideas which developed in formal descriptive linguistics might be reasonably descriptive of psychologically
real entities which actually play a role in the production
and comprehension of utterances (cf. Schlesinger 1977 for
an extensive theoretical effort in this direction). In
fact, if linguistic concepts are to have any coherent
empirical status at all, this is in general about the only
sensible direction in which to look. Physically, the language product can be studied in the form of speech articu-
lations (i.e., neuro-muscular activity), as acoustic waves
(molecular movements or pressure changes), or as auditory
events (peripheral auditory stimuli), but in none of these
three observable, physical states can we find anything
which smacks of linguistic structure (not even 'phones,'
which already involve considerable processing by the human
perceptual apparatus). Linguistic 'structure,' therefore,
is not something which utterances 'have' as an intrinsic
property, but is rather something (if the terms refers to
anything real at all) related to the representations, interpretations or levels of analysis imposed upon the speech
signal by language users, normally as part and parcel of
the communication event or language process itself (cf.
Derwing 1973:302-307). What Thorndike said about meaning,
in sum, over three decades ago, must also hold true for
virtually every other linguistic concept which has any le-
gitimate status beyond that of a purely descriptive artifact:

Meanings are in persons' minds, not in words, and
when we say that a word has or possesses such and
such meanings, we are really saying that it has
evoked, or caused, those meanings. Until it gets
into a mind, a word is only puffs or air or streaks
of ink. What a word, sentence or other expression
means to hearer or reader is mainly what it makes
him think or feel or do as a fairly direct consequence of hearing it or seeing it, and, more nar-
rowly, what it makes him think of as the direct and
almost immediate consequence of hearing or seeing
it (1946:613).

In short, psychological reality is the <u>sine qua non</u> for any
empirically valid linguistic construct, and hence for any
linguistic theory which can reasonably claim to go beyond
the bounds of an arbitrary taxonomic system.

2. <u>The Interpretation Problem.</u> To recognize the need to
psychologize linguistics is one thing, but the actual practice is something else again. As Eliasson points out,
Chomsky himself declared linguistics to be a branch of human psychology a full decade ago, yet

> the <u>central</u> core of linguistic. theory as it deve-
> loped in structuralism and generativism remains re-
> latively untouched and unaffected by cognitive psy-
> chology. Like structuralism, Chomskyan TG theory
> is still to a considerable extent an offshoot of
> the idea of an <u>autonomous linguistics</u> as opposed to
> some kind of cognitive or cognition-oriented lin-
> guistics (Eliasson 1977:61; see also Hymes & Fought
> 1975:1144).

In other words, though the so-called 'Chomskyan revolution'
may well have entailed a <u>terminological</u> re-orientation in
the direction of the psychologization of linguistic jargon
and the supposed domain of its interest and claims, no corresponding <u>methodological</u> revolution accompanied these
changes, with the result that Chomsky and his followers
"continued to practice linguistics as it has always been
standardly practiced" (Sanders 1977:165; see also Derwing
1973, in press; Linell 1978). Indeed, even at a time when
'psychological reality' has become a respectable term for
many formal grammarians of generative and other persua-
sions, Greenbaum still seems quite justified in expressing
the doubt "whether linguists will abandon a particular linguistic formulation on the basis of psycholinguistic evidence, though they might flaunt the evidence to discomfort
an opponent" (1977:127). In other words, even among

linguists who do accept the idea that psychological reality
is is an important, perhaps even indispensable, aspect of
linguistic formulations, there still exist a large and influential group of True Believers for whom, in the words of
Fodor & Garrett, "the internal evidence in favor of the
structural descriptions modern grammars generate is so
strong that it is difficult to imagine their succumbing to
any purely experimental disconfirmation" (1966:152).

While I personally find extraordinary difficulty in
coming to grips with this particular mode of thinking, I
can offer one conjecture which might plausibly explain it.
Perhaps such people simply do not understand the full ramifications of the term, `psychological reality.´ For them,
this term (like many others which appear in the linguistic
literature, such as productivity, language acquisition, in-
nateness, the ideal speaker-hearer, etc.) is just another
purely formal notion appended to linguistic theory and defined therein. Thus linguistic concepts can be said to
acquire psychological reality "by definition" (cf. Valian
1976:66), following the same logic by which a rule may be
said to `be´ productive simply by virtue of the fact that
it can be formalized as a rule, hence part of the
make-believe competence of an `ideal speaker-hearer,´ which
is in turn the end product of an imaginary process of `la-
nguage acquisition´ guided by made-up `innate´ linguistic
principles (see Derwing 1973, in press for a full discussion). The trouble with all this, of course, is that there
is nothing substantive here to connect any of these
theoretical ideas with whatever real rules are really
acquired by real speakers and hearers and really used by
them in the actual production and comprehension of speech.
The Chomskyan approach is a mere ruse which attempts to
give the arbitrary evaluation principles of the linguist
some appearance of psychological respectability;[6] it thus
circumvents the problem of psychological reality rather
than facing it. Its only advantage is the practical,
therapeutic one (at least for those who are willing to accept it) of allowing linguistic practice to proceed essentially as it always has, free of any of the aforementioned
`agonizing´ about fundamental foundational issues or meth-
odological doubts.

Thankfully, there is increasing evidence that the proportion of naive True Believers (of all three types) is already on the wane within the general population of professional linguists. But as I have already said, the awareness problem is only the first of many aspects of the more
general task of establishing the psychological reality of
linguistic constructs. Thus, alongside this dwindling

group of True Believers, we also find a substantial number
of less radical linguists whom we might conveniently refer
to as the Eternal Optimists. At least this group is considerably easier to understand: they, too, believe that linguistics has undoubtedly hit upon a good thing, yet also
recognize the need to 'expand the data base' in order to
put these beliefs to any kind of meaningfully stringent
empirical test. Thus we find many well-meaning appeals in
the recent linguistic literature admonishing one's fellows
to look longer and harder through the "window" which language change provides onto linguistic theory, for example
(cf. Kiparsky 1968), or to recognize the importance of
such things as borrowings (Hyman 1970), speech errors
(Fromkin 1971), language variation and other "sociolinguistic" data (Labov 1971; Hymes 1972), and even, perhaps, to
take a look at various "language games" (Sherzer 1970).
Yet none of these efforts have produced any substantial effects on linguistic thinking. Part of the reason for this,
of course, is that the data obtained from these new sources
have been equivocal (cf. Goyvaerts 1976 on Fromkin's work,
for example) and sometimes even contradictory (cf. Botha
1973:141). More fundamentally, however, this very laudable
tendency to seek empirical grounds for the resolution of
theoretical indeterminacies has foundered, I believe, for
lack of any coherent conceptual basis on which to connect
such a heterogeneous body of observation to any particular
brand of linguistic theory. Somehow, in the mad scramble
to find the ultimate 'key' to psychological reality, the
'lock' has been virtually ignored. Do the data _fit_ the
available theories (or, better, vice versa)? Are they even
relevant (See Botha 1973:130-172, for an excellent discussion of "questions of external evidence" in contemporary
linguistics.) What has been almost completely neglected in
latter-day 'mentalistic' linguistic theorizing is the question of _what, precisely, does a linguistic description mean_
under a psychological interpretation? If linguistic descriptions are intended to describe _mind_ and not just
forms, what particular aspects of mind are involved? Or,
at the very least, what critical _psychological_ claims are
intended to be associated with any particular _linguistic_
analysis? Obviously, before we can ever hope to make use
of new kinds of empirical evidence to test or evaluate psychological claims, we must first know what the particular
claims are that we are required to evaluate.

        This is the crux of what I have called the "interpre-
tation problem" for grammars (Derwing 1974). If grammars
merely describe utterance forms, then evidence about such
forms is the only evidence relevant to the evaluation of
grammars, and a selection from among competing grammars can

only be made on the basis of criteria which are ultimately
arbitrary. But if grammars describe psychological events
or states, then we need to _interpret_ grammars psychologically so as to make it clear what the new empirical implications of these grammars are. In other words, a formal
grammar requires a psychological interpretation before it
can become a part of a psychological theory.

Now the problem of interpretation is not nearly so se-
vere with respect to some of the older, more concrete linguistic notions than in the case of many of the more recent, abstract developments. Consider the following four
ways of describing the regular English plural forms, for
example (taken from Derwing 1974):

Analysis 1:   List all plural forms in the lexicon.

Analysis 2:   Describe the three regular 'allomorphs' of
                the plural as conditioned by the final vowel
                plus (optional) consonant or consonant clus-
                ter.

Analysis 3:   Describe these same morpheme variants as con-
                ditioned instead by the final segment of the
                stem, ignoring any non-final vowels or con-
                sonants (cf. Gleason 1958:61).

Analysis 4:   Describe these variants as conditioned merely
                by certain phonetic _features_ of the final seg-
                ment of the stem (cf. Halle, 1964:328).

It is a quite straightforward, almost trivial matter to
conceive of psychological theories of English pluralization
which correspond to these four (formal) descriptive alternatives:

Theory 1:   Learning to pluralize in English involves
                merely the item-by-item memorization of those
                plural forms to which the learner has been ex-
                posed.

Theory 2:   Learning to pluralize in English involves the
                identification of three distinct plural mark-
                ers (suffixes), as well as the rule that
                these suffixes are selected on the basis of a

rhyming analogy (i.e., stems which rhyme take
the same suffix.)

Theory 3:   The same three suffixes are identified, but
                 the more general selection principle is
                 learned which states that all stems ending in
                 the same final segment take the same suffix.

Theory 4:   Again, the same three suffixes are learned,
                 but this time the basis for selection is ta-
                 ken to be the presence or absence of certain
                 phonetic features in connection with the fin-
                 al segment of the stem.

    At this point, now that differential psychological
claims have been identified for each of the theoretical
alternatives, experimental tests can reasonably be proposed
which are designed to test the critical features which
serve to distinguish the four theories:

Test 1:   Is there evidence for rule-learning of any
                 kind as far as the production of the English
                 plural forms is concerned? (cf. Berko 1958,
                 who found such evidence by means of a produ-
                 ctivity task involving the pluralization of
                 novel, nonsense stems, i.e., the production
                 of plural forms which her subjects could not
                 have known had Theory 1 been fully correct.)

Test 2:   Can speakers pluralize novel forms which do
                 not rhyme with familiar plurals? Is there
                 evidence that non-final vowels are irrelevant
                 to English pluralization behavior? (See Der-
                 wing & Baker 1977 for a discussion of experi-
                 ments which have shown that the answers to
                 both of these questions are in the affirma-
                 tive, hence that Theory 2 is also inadequate
                 to explain the pluralization behavior of the
                 subjects tested.)

Test 3:   Does the capacity to pluralize novel noun
                 stems develop on an individual stem-class ba-
                 sis (r-stems, then l-stems, then n-stems,
                 then t-stems, etc., with the order perhaps
                 predictable from the relative frequencies of
                 real plural forms in each of these

sub-classes), or are entire classes of
stem-types mastered more or less simultaneously (e.g., all vocalic stems, all obstruent
stems, all fricative stems, all non-sibilant
stems, etc.), regardless of the frequencies
of the various sub-types? [7](See Derwing & Baker 1977 for evidence that only the second of
these expectations is in accord with the
facts, hence that Theory 3 must yield to
Theory 4.)

Of all the four theories outlined, therefore, only the
fourth survives this particular series of experimental
tests (whereas all four of the original descriptive analyses, we recall, were in full accord with the purely linguistic facts.) This is scientific progress.

There are, of course, many other possible linguistic
approaches to the descriptive problem of the (regular)
English plural forms, but many of these do not lend themselves so readily to a psychological interpretation, with
the result that the nature of a suitable kind of experimental test is much less clear.[8] One such example is the analysis preferred by Anderson (1974:54-61), which can be sum-
marized as follows:

Analysis 5:   The plural suffix is assigned the single 'b-
asic' or 'underlying' representation /z/ in
the lexicon, which is supplemented by two general phonological rules to account for any (r-
egular) deviation from this norm. The two
rules predict (1) vowel insertion if a word
ends in a sequence of two sibilants (e.g., if
an underlying stem ends in a sibilant before
the word-final sibilant suffix /z/) and (2)
voicing assimilation within obstruent clusters (e.g., devoicing of the /z/ to /s/ if the
stem ends in a voiceless obstruent.) Further, the first of these rules must 'apply before' the second in order to 'generate' the
correct output.

Even ignoring the problem of what psychological interpretation to place upon the general notion of the grammatical 'generation' of forms,[9] what psychological sense are we
to make, first of all, of the concept of the 'extrinsically
ordered phonological rule' (i.e., a rule which arbitrarily
'applies before' another rule in the grammar of a particular language, yet for which no claim of sequencing in 'real

time' is made.) To my knowledge, no one has ever even proposed a sensible real-world interpretation for this idea
(though some proposals have been made with respect to certain so-called `intrinsically ordered' rules; cf. Derwing
& Baker 1977), and without an interpretation, of course, it
is impossible to tell what kind of experimental test is
even relevant. Fortunately, in this instance, at least,
the concept is one that linguistic theory seems to be able
to get along very well without, merely by reformulating all
rules (e.g., Anderson's first rule in this illustration) in
such a way that no arbitrary ordering relations are required between them. The result in this case is a pair of
rules both of which can be sensibly interpreted as formali-
zations of phonetic or articulatory habits, acquired as the
result of frequent practice (cf. Derwing 1973, 1974, 1975;
Braine 1974). Under this interpretation therefore, speakers who have learned such rules would be expected to make
use of them in any situation which presented the requisite
kind of phonological circumstances (e.g., two sibilants occuring together at the end of a word, in which situation
the speaker should `automatically' and `unconsciously' in-
sert the vowel.) This suggests one quite obvious type of
test for such a `phonotactic' theory of English pluraliza-
tion which might in principle be tried using Berko-type
novel stimuli.[10]

Another, less artifical test is also suggested by the
interpretation in question. For the theory also entails
the expectation that, since both all but the /z/ allomorphs
of the regular English plural result from the acquisition
of one or another articulatory habit, either of these habits ought to be manifested just as strongly in one appropriate morphological configuration as in another. Thus, in
the acquisition of the language, once a given class of
stem-types is properly pluralized (say with the voiceless
suffix /-s/, by virtue of the general voicing assimilation
rule), the same subject would be expected to use the appropriate (voiceless) variant for the possessive, present
tense and past tense suffixes, as well (see Derwing 1974
for further discussion and details). Thus a very high correlation should be expected throughout the acquisition period for all stem-types among the response types (suffixes)
used by subjects in each of these four morphological categories (i.e., plural, possessive, present and past tenses).
In one small, early study, Baird (1973) did not find this
kind of covariance, but a preliminary analysis of the much
larger Derwing & Baker (1974, 1976) corpus indicates a
quite respectable level of correlation, at least across
subjects. For the moment, therefore, the `phonotactic'
theory (based on linguistic Analysis 5 above) cannot be

said to have been decisively falsified, though the same
also holds true for the more concrete `feature' version of
the `allomorph' theories (i.e., the one based on Analysis
4). This leaves us to explore the one remaining difference
between the two linguistic formulations: should the plural
morpheme have multiple representations in the lexicon (Analysis 4), or a single `underlying' representation (Analysis
5)?

What psychological sense, then, if any, are we to make
out of the linguist's notion of the `underlying' or `base'
form in phonology? Linell (1974) grapples at length with
this problem, but no clear suggestions emerge, much less
answers. One hint of a suggestion can be found in a few
studies on child language, where the term is used in the
sense of the (child's) "perceived" (Ingram 1976) or "remembered" (Priestly forthcoming) form. Such hypothetical
"child's underlying forms", however, are described as being
no more abstract than the "adult's surface forms" (cf. also
Kiparksy & Menn 1977), which are affected only by various
"organizational" and "production" factors within the child.
We cannot be talking here, therefore, about the same kind
of `underlying form' which appears, for example, in
Anderson's analysis of the English plural, for the latter
involves a level of abstraction which subsumes variation in
the adult's surface forms, as well (e.g., the variation
among the three regular `allomorphs' of the plural).

In a more recent paper, Linell (in press) considers
the possibility of viewing the (adult's) `underlying form'
as a kind of `target pronunciation,' which may be descrip-
tion of what the speaker `thinks' he is saying, as opposed
to what he actually says (cf. also Birnbaum 1975:137, on
`ideal sounds' or `sound images'). Now it is, of course,
quite conceivable that various kinds of experimental tests
could be devised to test the concept of `underlying form'
under this interpretation (for example, a `same-
versus-different' test for the three regular allomorphs of
the plural),[11] but since there is nothing particularly compelling about Linell's proposal here, there may be just as
much reason to reject the interpretation as the concept, in
the event of disconfirmatory experimental evidence.[12]

There is, however, a more compelling indirect test of
at least some linguistic analyses which treat (adult) morpheme alternants as derived from a single, `underlying'
lexical representation. The basic rationale for this test
is outlined in Derwing (1976), which was the first published report of my on-going research into the question of
`morpheme recognition' by ordinary (i.e., linguistically

untrained) speakers of English. The keystone argument is
that there is no basis for positing a single `underlying´
representation for any set of supposed `morpheme alter-
nants´ unless the alternants in question can indeed be said
to represent the same `meaning unit´ (i.e., morpheme). For
example, the decision to derive the words <u>decisive</u> and <u>de-
cision</u> from the root represented by the word <u>decide</u> involves the assumption that all three words share a common
morpheme, namely, the unit meaning `decide.´ Thus a test
which assesses a speaker's ability to `recognize morphemes´
can indirectly provide evidence relevant to the question of
the extent to which psychological theories might plausibly
be constructed which seek to build upon the linguistic notion of the `underlying form´ in phonology. For example,
on the basis of `morpheme recogniton´ data collected by
means of the `comes from´ and `recall´ tests described in
Derwing (1976), there are data which indicate that
word-pairs are judged to contain a common morpheme by a majority of speakers only if the semantic similarity of the
word-pair (as assessed by independent tests) is 50% or
higher <u>and</u> if the phonetic similarity (also independently
measured) is at least 33%. In other words, this research
suggests that only a small minority of ordinary adult
English speakers see any clear morphological connection between such word-pairs as <u>fable</u> and <u>fabulous,</u> for example,
which lie outside of this `critical region,´ and whose
likelihood of being morphologically related is judged, in
fact, to be about on a par with the word-pair <u>hide</u> and <u>hi-
deous</u> (cf. Derwing 1976:65). Thus any linguistic analysis
(such as Chomsky & Halle 1968) which attempts to derive
such forms from a single `basic´ lexical representation is
not even psychologically feasible for any but this small
minority of speakers. This line of research is only beginning, however, and most efforts to date have been expended
in developing and validating a variety of alternative experimental tests. Considerable work remains to be done,
therefore, in applying such tests to the empirical evaluation of a broad range of theoretical alternatives.

     Regardless of the outcome of any particular line of
research, however, the point has been made, I trust, that
it is quite misleading to describe experimental (psycho-)
linguistics as "a new linguistic subdiscipline...primarily
characterized by methodology and research tools rather than
by linguistic content or theory" (Greenbaum 1977:125). For
without associated theoretical analysis and development,
there is no basis for even guessing what type of `method-
ological tool´ might possibly be called for in any particular case (see also section 4 below).

3. Some Typical Methodological Problems. While the recognition and solution of the interpretation problem represents the main barrier to the establishment of the psychological reality of linguistic constucts, there are still quite a number of smaller obstacles which also have to be faced and overcome before genuine progress can be expected. For one thing, we must learn to resist the temptation to be Bathtub Experimentalists ("Eureka, I have found it"). I use this label to describe those investigators who (laudably) recognize the need both to interpret and to test linguistic theories on psychological territory, but (for lack of laboratory experience, for example) can fail to anticipate many of the problems which can arise out of the very activity of constructing, carrying out, and finally evaluating experiments. The most insidious of these difficulties, no doubt, is the one associated with the phenomenon of the experimental artifact, for just as (autonomous) linguistic theorizing can yield concepts which have no real-life analogues in the knowledge or skills of language users, a particular experimental technique can also yield data which are more representative of the technique than of the experimental subjects' control of the phenomenon of real theoretical interest. A particular experiment does not always test in practice what the experimenter thinks it is testing in theory. I have encountered this phenomenon at least twice so far in my own research on the psychological reality of morphological analyses, as briefly described above. The first instance occurred in connection with an attempted test of `morpheme recogniton' itself (see Derwing 1976:46-50) and the second in connection with a supposed test for the productivity of one proposed rule of English derivational morphology (43). It has also been alleged that certain of the best-known experimental attempts to evaluate various implicit psychological claims of `classical' generative phonology (e.g., as characterized in Chomsky & Halle 1968) are likewise invalidated by considerations of this kind (cf. Fromkin 1976; Kiparsky & Menn 1977). Fromkin's criticisms focus largely on suspicious defects in the design and interpretation of some of Ohala's work (1972), but Kiparsky and Menn go even further in citing positive data which were obtained by means of a new experimental procedure (cf. Myerson 1976, since corroborated by Cena 1977, 1978) and which conflict with earlier, negative findings (cf. Steinberg & Krohn 1975).[13] Since we cannot take time here to delve into the respective merits of all of these specific studies, suffice it to say that there is only one sure way to dispel doubts about the `experimental artifact' and to clarify disputes of this kind, and that is via the painstaking route of cross- methodological verification: each evaluation problem must be

approached by means of a variety of alternative experimental routes, in order to insure that the results obtained are independent of any particular experimental procedure.[14] I therefore consider it vital to the long-range endurance of the psychological claims which have resulted from my own research on the question of `morpheme recognition,´ for example, to cross-validate the results by means of a variety of experimental techniques. By this time, therefore, I am already working on my fourth experimental approach to the study of this skill, and a fifth is waiting in the wings. By the same token, it is also crucial (particularly in view of Myerson´s and Cena´s findings) to attempt to cross-validate the results of the Berko-type test and to discover why it seems so readily to yield clear evidence for the psychlogical productivity of rules which are descriptive of some of the more widely attested alternations of English inflectional and derivational morphology, but fails to do so in the case of certain `less regular´ surface alternations, such as those associated with the so-called `vowel shift.´[15]

There are, of course, other methodological problems to be mentioned, as well. There is always, for example, the possibility of `the just plain goof´ whenever experimental data are collected, interpreted and evaluated, a danger which springs from causes as trivial as the mispunching of data cards to others as abstruse as failure to attend to assumptions which underlie a particular statistical model. Yet the one kind of mistake can prove to be just as serious as the other, if it is not caught in time. The most common type of error to sneak through a data analysis unattended, perhaps, is the one which results from a failure to take due cognizance of the effects of unanticipated confounding variables (see Derwing & Baker 1977 for an example of this kind which might easily have led to rather embarrassing consequences had the variables in question not been spotted when they were.) But there is in the end no sure or simple formula to guarantee safe passage through such ever-changing and unpredictable waters as these; one can only take the utmost care possible in evaluating his own work, then hope that his readers and critics will pick out whatever errors and oversights remain. (This, to my mind, is the main value of theoretical controversy and disagreement: we are no doubt all much more inclined to be carefully critical of work which challenges our pet views that of work we agree with. This is only natural and is defense enough for the idea of theoretical pluralism.)

Finally, there is also the problem of extraneous or `nuisance´ variables, so-called, no doubt, because they are often so very hard to eliminate from the experimental situation, even when the investigator may fully realize that they are present. In my 'morpheme recognition' research again, for example, the interpretation of the data is continually complicated by the factor of possible orthographic interference. Can judgments of the 'phonetic similarity' of common words ever be completely free of interference from spelling for literate subjects? How much are judgments of 'morpheme recogniton' conditioned by the academic task of learning to read (cf. hand and handkerchief, for example), thereby complicating our efforts to understand the 'natural' course of language acquisition through mere exposure to spoken language forms under normal circumstances of use? Answers to such questions can only be partially and very tentatively answered so long as one is forced to deal exclusively with literate experimental subjects. For this reason, I am very happy to see that some aspects of my work are soon to be replicated and extended to the study of Lapp morphology by R. Endresen of the University of Oslo, for included in his population samples will be many speakers who are at least illiterate in their own language, thereby making it possible to investigate systematically at least some of the effects of the orthographic variable. Unfortunately, not all 'nuisance' factors can always be dealt with in such a satisfactory way, and these others will continue to constitute one of the more troubling aspects of trying to advance our knowledge by means of controlled experimental research. But since this is the way of science and the only secure route we know of for establishing knowledge about the world and its inhabitants, we have little real choice.

4. Theoretical Advance through Experimentation. So far in this paper we have looked upon psycholinguistic experiments exclusively as means appropriate for the testing or evaluation of antecent theoretical positions. This is far too narrow a view and one which must be amended, if only in token fashion here. For the role of experimentation in science is not merely to test prior theories, but also to contribute to the development of new or revised theories which can be submitted to a whole new round of experimental tests (cf. Cattell 1966:14-16, on the inductive-hypothetico-deductive "spiral").

The first clear illustration of this kind of influence in my own work came as the result of my attempt to understand the results obtained for a sample of real, irregular English plural forms, which was one small part of the large-scale inflections study already mentioned (Derwing & Baker 1974, 1976). As anticipated, I learned that some of

these irregular plural forms were consistently acquired at
a much earlier age than others, and (especially in the case
of forms which illustrated completely unique alternations,
such as child versus children) I expected that the results
should be explained by the relative frequency of these
forms (i.e., that the first irregular plurals to be learned
should be the most common ones, the last to be learned the
least common, etc.). Taking my frequency information from
the available word counts for English (e.g., Rinsland
1945), I discovered that this prediction fared quite well
for most of the items studied (see Table 1A). There were a
few disturbing exceptions to this, however, as shown in
Table 1B: overall performance on men and teeth was almost
identical over my full sample of 112 children (aged 3-9
years), but the word counts indicated that (even ignoring
compounds) the first of these items was several times more
frequent than the second. It was also observed, however,
that the typical erroneous response to all of the irregular
stems in the study was an 'overgeneralized' response, i.e.,
a response which suggested treatment as a regular stem
(such as the response *mans in place of men, *tooths for
teeth, etc.). Our data also indicated clearly that this
regular pattern for a resonant-stem word (e.g., for n-stem
words such as pans, beans, guns, etc.) was both much more
frequent and performatively much stronger than was the regular pattern for a fricative-stem word (e.g., a word ending in /θ/, such as deaths, myths, faiths, etc.). Thus
while frequency considerations indicated that the particular irregular form men ought to be much easier to learn
than the other irregular form teeth, these same considerations also suggested that the competing 'regular' pattern
on which the response *mans is modeled ought also to be
stronger than the corresponding regular pattern leading to
the response *tooths. The end result of this conflict was
thus a virtual tie in overall performance on these two
items.

This discovery suggested that we should introduce into
language acquisition theory a multivariate notion of 'rule
strength,' which was the result of this kind of 'competition' among alternative or conflicting patterns in the primary linguistic data to which the child was exposed.[16] That
such a notion might be of quite general explanatory value
was soon seen from the fact that it could also serve to account for a number of other, seemingly unrelated experimental results. One such example was the radical difference
in both adults' and children's performance with the derivational -er construction in the 'agentive' sense (e.g.,
teacher, or 'a person who teaches') as opposed to its 'instrumental' sense (e.g., eraser, or 'an instrument that is

		PERFORMANCE MEANS (%)	TOKEN FREQUENCY	REGULAR STEM-CLASS FREQUENCY	
				T	t
A.	feet	50	2617		
	teeth	45	847		
	mice	40	298		
	geese	21	139		
	oxen	0	105		
	cacti	0	0		
B.	men	46	5061	269	15,148 (/n/)
	teeth	45	847	13	304 (/θ/)
C.	geese	21	139	30	910 (/s/)
	women	20	770	269	15,148 (/n/)
D.	men	46	5061	269	15,148 (/n/)
	women	20	770	269	15,148 (/n/)

Table 1
Competition Between Conflicting Formal Patterns

used to erase with'): though the same 'formal pattern' was
ostensibly represented in both cases (i.e., the addition of
the -er suffix to a verb stem), performance with Berko-type
nonsense stems has proved to be consistently and significantly better in the first case than in the second (Derwing
1976:44). This can also be explained by evoking the notion
of competing surface patterns, since the latter,
slower-learned construction is actually faced with a strong
formal competitor, namely, in null (no suffix), while the
former is not (cf. bat, ski, skate, lift, hammer, as opposed to batter, skier, skater, lifter, hammerer, etc.). [17]
Similarly, in syntax, Prideaux (1976, 1978) has argued that
the comparatively rapid acquisition of the rule for WH-word
placement in WH-questions, as compared to the rule for the
proper placement of the auxiliary, which is learned much
slower, can be explained by the fact that the latter is in
competition with a conflicting rule which holds for relative clauses. (Compare the positions of the auxiliary relative to the subject noun phrase in the two sentences
"Where is the man going?" and "I don't know where the man

is going.")

Such findings have also led to a general notion of (learnable) syntactic rules which represent "functionally based surface generalizations...about the relative ordering of constituents in various types of sentences" (Prideaux 1976:419), a natural extension of the notion of a rule as a "true surface generalization" (cf. Derwing 1973:188-218). And by the present time, in fact, on the basis of a great deal of other groundwork psycholinguistic experimentation (much of which is described in Prideaux, Derwing & Baker in press), this notion of rule has been incorporated into a broad theoretical framework appropriate for the study of the entire language process - and it is this new "inform-ation structure" or "information communication" theory which is now being invoked in the conception and design of an entire new generation of psycholinguistic experiments (cf. Baker 1976; Derwing & Baker 1978; Prideaux 1975, 1976, 1978; Schutz & Derwing 1978; Smyth, Prideaux, & Hogan 1979).

Though I have been able to sketch here only a few brief (and tentative) illustrations of the role that exper-imental psycholinguistic investigation might eventually play not merely in the evaluation but also the future deve-lopment of linguistic theory, the main point to be made from these examples is a very important one insofar as its ultimate ramifications are concerned. This point is that although experimental psycholinguistics is today in its in-fancy, and may for the moment be reasonably viewed as that (sub-) discipline which seeks to assess the possible psy-chological utility of linguistic concepts, this (temporary) division of labor has largely resulted from a historical accident: due to strong anti-mentalist influences which vastly inhibited theoretical development in cognitive psy-chology generally, it just so happens that most of the theoretical raw material we currently find available for building our language user (or process) models has come to us via the linguistic tradition which focused on the study of the language product. The result has been the develop-ment of quite a body of linguistic concepts which may have little or no psychological utility (such as extrinsically ordered rules and perhaps underlying forms, as discussed above), or which may find their place in a fully integrated psychological theory only after much alteration or modifi-cation. So long as linguistics persists in its very narrow conception of the nature of the problem, therefore, it is quite likely that the kinds of theories which develop as the result of experimental psycholinguistic research will eventually supplant those to be found in linguistics proper, with the result that psycholinguistics will come to rely more and more upon its own resources and less and less upon those of the linguists. If and when that day arrives, the (autonomous) linguist will find himself in the unfortunate position of solving puzzles and weaving theories of a kind which are of no interest whatsoever to anyone but himself. This would be a sad fate indeed for a discipline which once promised so much.

NOTES

1. Another strange aspect of Pullum's position is his apparent attempt to make something of the observation that "the linguists who have the most to say about the the supposedly impending methodological catastrophe seem to be precisely those who do the least [formal] linguistics" (399). Yet who but a fool or hypocrite would voluntarily participate massively, if at all, in an activity which he had strong reasons to believe was a waste of time? By their very nature, the doing of X and the criticizing of X are almost mutually exclusive activities. (How many critics of the foundations of tagmemics or of stratificational grammar, to take two familiar examples, are themselves active practitioners of Pikean or Lambian doctrines, respectively?)

2. Cf. McCawley's more detailed discussion of the "four pernicious ideas" which "have held linguistics back from developing into what Chomsky (1968) has described it as: `a branch of cognitive psychology`," and which "all constitute excuses for the linguist to confine himself to `linguistic data` even when questions arise that can only be answered on the basis of details about how language is used, perceived and acquired" (McCawley 1976:163).

3. The following is offered as a first approximation of such a grammar, which describes (but scarcely `explains`) the basic `constituent structure` of one kind of cake:

Given: ##CAKE##

PS1.   CAKE -> BODY (+CANDLE)

PS2.   BODY -> LAYER (+LAYER)(+LAYER)

PS3.   LAYER -> BATTER + FROSTING*

PS4.   CANDLE -> WAX + WICK

PS5.   BATTER -> FLOUR + SUGAR + EGGS + MILK
                 + BUTTER + B.P.** (+ NUTS)

PS6.   FROSTING -> SUGAR + BUTTER

$$PS7. \quad SUGAR \rightarrow \left\{ \begin{array}{l} GRANULATED \: / \: FLOUR \: -- \\ \\ CONFECTIONERS' *** \end{array} \right\}$$

* Replace by "ICING" in some dialect areas.

** B.P. = BAKING POWDER or SODA

*** Replace by "POWDERED" in some dialect areas.

Two important points can be noted from this seemingly trivial example. First, although this `cake grammar,´ not unlike a generative `sentence grammar,´ is cast in an algorithmic or `process´ form, it is not at all descripitive of any kind of real-life processes (such as those a baker might go through in making or baking a cake, for example), but is merely descriptive of the output of the baker's efforts (i.e., the cake itself). The model, in short, shows one way to analyze or `break down´ a cake into its component parts, but not how to synthesize or `build one up.´ The `dynamic´ aspects of such a model are thus completely uninterpreted empirically and hence are illusory, just as in the case of sentence grammars. And second, though such a `cake grammar´ may seem to suffer in comparison with its linguistic analogue in that only its hierarchical (i.e., non-linear) structure is empirically interpretable, it also has a compensating advantage in that its own `constituents´ are far more easily verified that are the corresponding units for sentences. (See section 1 above for indications that many linguists have not thought very deeply about such questions as the real, empirical status of sentence constituents, or of any other kind of linguistic unit, for that matter).

4. The familiar and straightforward kind of idealization implied here (see Hymes 1972:280) is to be sharply contrasted with the novel and totally bizarre kind represented by a generative model of "competence" (cf. Derwing 1973:251-258 and n. 3 above).

5. See Hymes & Fought (1975) and Derwing (1973, in press) for detailed arguments in support of the thesis that transformational-generative grammar must be regarded as a perfectly natural extension of the `structural´ or `autonomous´ linguistic tradition, rather than a departure

from it that is in any significant sense `revolutionary.´

6. There is another possible, somewhat more generous interpretation of this, namely, that linguists who accept
Chomsky´s ideas on matters of `grammar evaluation´ honestly
believe that he (and they) have fortuitously hit upon the
secret of divining psychological reality. It is a mystery
to identify any substantial basis for such belief, yet un-
shaking faith in such a `serendipity principle´ is not un-
precedented in social science, as evidenced, for example,
by those `artificial intelligence´ types who seem to be-
lieve that they are `modeling the mind´ with their computer
programs. My belief is, in contrast, that we must look
into the mind (i.e., by way of controlled experiments) in
order to find out what is actually going on inside it
(i.e., the methodological appeal is ultimately to Galileo,
rather than to Chomsky, Freud, or Plato).

7. Halle (1978:301) proposes a sensible alternative test,
but one which was rejected by Derwing (1974) because of anticipated problems of practical implementation. It is interesting, therefore, that Halle does not actually carry
his proposed experiment out, but simply `knows the answer
in advance´ by way of armchair speculation. If Halle were
more experienced in the testing of ordinary (i.e., linguistically naive) subjects, he would perhaps better realize that it is far less than `perfectly obvious´ that
/baxs/ would be "the response that the majority of English
speakers would make" (301-302), if they were asked to
pluralize the name of the German name <u>Bach.</u> My experience
would suggest that the (relatively uninformative) response
/baks/ would be a much more reasonable expectation, although, of course, the experiment would actually have to be
carried out to know for sure.

8. See Derwing (1974) for a discussion of still other
alternative linguistic analyses of the English plural and
of problems related to their interpretation and experimental evaluation.

9. `Generate´ cannot, of course, mean `produce´ (i.e., by
real speakers in real time), for reasons which are discussed at length in Derwing (1973), especially Chapter 7.
See also Cook (1974) and n. 3 above.

10. T.M. Nearey and I are, in fact, currently working on
an experiment of this kind, but there are no results as yet
to report.

11. The `expected´ results of such an experiment, based on

the informal observation of numerous beginning linguistics students, are discussed in Derwing (1975), but no carefully controlled study of the kind described has yet, to my knowledge, been carried out.

12.   This is not an unreasonable approach in the situation at hand, since there are no strong extrinsic considerations which motivate the particular interpretation described. As a _general_ methodological strategy, however, to exploit the ever-available loophole to `reject the interpretation´ in order to `save the (formal) theory´ is untenable (though by no means unprecedented in actual practice; cf. Derwing & Harris 1975:309-310), since it forces a return to the kind of of `linguistic evidence´ already seen to be inherently equivocal. Though some of Fromkin´s criticisms of early experimental linguistic research are well taken, therefore, her proposed `solution´ to let unanswered questions "be decided by linguistic evidence" (Fromkin 1976:59) is, of course, no solution at all: an unanswered question is still an unanswered question. Thus, while it it is quite correct to say that "lack of evidence does not negate an hypothesis" (54), neither, of course, does it show that the hypothesis is correct! Linguists may _claim_ that such-and-such generalizations "are available to be abstracted by speakers" (47) or may believe that such-and-such constraints "would limit grammars in such a way as to prevent them from being psychologically real" (49), but without any means of testing such claims and beliefs, these, too, represent mere "a priori opinion" (50). Only when supplemented by some non-empirical `meta- principle´ (such as a formal simplicity criterion, for example) are the linguistic facts ever "strong enough" (53) to decide in favor of any particular linguistic analysis or general linguistic theory; yet, as Steinberg clearly points out, the _crucial_ question in grammar evaluation is the question of the psychological _validity_ of a linguistic formulation, a question which is quite _independent_ of formal simplicity (_pace_ Fromkin:56):

> Such formal criteria as simplicity or elegance alone are inadequate to provide psychological support for a theory.... Two known invalid theories for example, could be evaluated according to a simplicity criterion. The selection of the simplest theory hardly establishes its validity. A criterion of simplicity is meaningful only if it is applied to theories not already considered invalid.
>
> Thus, that Chomsky´s grammar may be simpler than some other grammar could not provide support for the _validity_ of his grammar. A determination

of simplicity for the theory is insufficient to over-ride any independent conclusion concerning its psychological validity. When psychological phenomena are being considered, psychological evidence take[s] precedence over formal evidence (Steinberg 1976:385-386, emphasis added).

In sum, since a linguistic formulation must be psychologically interpreted in order to be psychologically tested, almost <u>any</u> interpretation is preferable to no interpretation at all. Sooner or later the theory must be forced to go out on a limb and make <u>some</u> kind of (testable) psychological claim. Otherwise it is simply not worth talking about as anything other than an arbitrary scheme for describing language forms.

13. As Cena points out, however, these experimental results clarify questions of the "content," but not the "form," of the phonological rules involved. That is to say, while both Myerson and Cena seem to have found evidence that morphophonemic alternations such as /e/∿/æ/ and /t/∿/š/ can indeed be psychologically productive for at least some speakers, their data are not sufficient to justify any particular <u>formulation</u> of the rules (say the Chomsky-Halle formulation) to the exclusion of other, more concrete formulations (such as any of quite a number of alternatives which would be consistent with the set of constraints outlined and defended in Derwing 1973:188-218).

14. Plans for a thorough cross-methodological check of data obtained using the Berko-type 'Wug Test' were laid some time ago, and it is only limitations of time and manpower which have so far prevented these from being carried out. Kiparsky & Menn's claim that such results are invalidated <u>prima facie</u> by a "strangeness effect" (1977:64) is not, in itself, very convincing, since only a minority of adults seem to be susceptible to it--in both Haber's (1975) study and my own, more extensive replication (Derwing 1977) and there is no evidence that children are bothered by it to any significant extent at all (Derwing & Baker 1976, 1977).

15. One reasonable surmise is simply the one that the particular alternation patterns involved in this latter situation are of such marginal formal productivity (see the discussion of 'rule strength' above) that a much more sensitive experimental test is required to demonstrate their psychological productivity for those few speakers who have managed to extract the regularities involved. (See Derwing

& Baker 1977 for a discussion of the distinction between `formal´ and `psychological´ productivity.) This is at least as reasonable a suggestion, at any rate, as Myerson´s, which is to interpret her findings as crucial evidence in favor of the abstract Chomsky & Halle analysis (1968). `Wishful thinking´ can muddle the interpretation of positive as well as negative evidence, and the tendency to `jump·to conclusions´ should be resisted at least until a modicum of readily available theoretical alternatives can be experimentally explored. In this business, patience is, indeed, a virtue.

16. Brown (1973) took no principle of this kind into account in his own analysis of the role of frequency in language acquisition (see especially 361-368), and so his very pessimistic conclusions may eventually have to be modified somewhat (see also Clark & Clark 1977:346).

17. J. Gray has kindly researched the class of derived `agentives in null´ for me and has managed to come up with some three dozen examples, the actual total being subject to some dialectal variation. While a few of the words on this list are common enough (e.g., _cook_, _guide_, _judge_, _spy_, _tease_, etc.), the majority are either of a kind that we would not expect the typical young child to use or even know (e.g., _advocate_, _counsel_, _escort_, _chaperone_, _emcee_, etc.) or else they are nouns whose verbal counterparts are quite unusual or highly marked (e.g., _father_, _mother_, _police_, _clown_, _pirate_, etc.). In short, there is little here to suggest that these data might feasibly conjoin to yield a viable `competing alternative´ to the -_er_ suffix. The same is also true, of course, of the -_ent_ suffix (e.g., _correspondent_, _student_, _regent_, etc.), a relatively rare historical remnant which seems to be completely non-productive for speakers.

EPILOGUE

ON DRAINING THE CONCEPTUAL SWAMP
AN EPILOGUE

WILLIAM J. BAKER
University of Alberta

It is not my intention to try to recapitulate the primary topics and critical comments which this conference has evoked. The speakers themselves did an effective job on their own. Rather, I would like to try to highlight a few underlying themes which emerged here and which seem to recur with a frequency sufficient to suggest that they need some clarification.

Initially, I would like to clarify the position of this linguistics department with respect to its emphasis on experimental linguistics both as a focal point for the department and as the theme for this conference. This emphasis is made in order to distinguish our viewpoint from, but not to place it in opposition to, formal linguistics as this is pursued in more traditional departments. We are neither anti-rationalist nor anti-theoretical. That would be absurd. What we do see is a critical need, if linguistics is to be taken seriously as a science, for strong empirical constraints on what can be theoretically postulated about human language, just as we recognize the requirement for clear theoretical guidelines for sensibly directing empirical research on it. We are trying to make explicit how theory and data must interact, and how they may best be integrated. You simply can't have one without the other if you want a viable science.

If we have an argument with current views in linguistics, as Dr. Derwing's paper would suggest, it would be with respect to the priviledged position adopted by a number of theorists for select kinds of evidence, and the arbitrary exclusion of a great deal more. Hymes and Fought

(1975:1144) characterized it this way:

> Now, for Chomsky, what language is to its users,
> and how it performs its role in human life, are
> held to depend, so far as linguistic theory is con-
> cerned, exactly on what linguists are concerned
> with in any case: linguistic structure. Enlarged
> terms, such as `competence', and appeal to the im-
> age of language-acquiring children, do not, in
> fact, represent any enlargement of linguistics
> itself. Linguistics may be defined as a branch of
> cognitive psychology, but cognitive psychology is
> not allowed to affect it. Linguistics may stimul-
> ate new developments in psycholinguistics, but lin-
> guistic theory is not to be changed as a result of
> psychological experiment. Linguistics remains en-
> tirely autonomous, a challenge to psychology, but
> able to pursue its theoretical goals on the basis
> of logic and introspection, independent of research
> of other kinds.

We are concerned with opening up this one-way street, with
trading linguistic autonomy for linguistic reality -- language in the context of the behaving organism that uses
language as a tool. Much of the conceptual confusion which
I will comment on here has been engendered by a failure to
study language in its proper context.

First, let's consider the conceptual morass in which
two once useful terms, competence and performance, seem ho-
pelessly mired. If these terms are to mean anything at
all, they must minimally refer to `what you know' and `what
you do with what you know'. In general, only performance
is directly observable. We infer from observing successful
performance that a subject must, in some sense, possess the
knowledge required for that performance and the ability to
use that knowledge effectively. We attempt to infer, then,
both factual knowledge and procedural knowledge. This latter distinction seems almost completely unappreciated in
the linguistics literature and this, in turn, leads to no
end of conceptual obfuscation between so-called competence
grammars and performance grammars. Frankly, what the latter would be, as a grammar, has always been a mystery to
me. In the first place, it should be an `ability grammar',
but simply saying that should make it obvious how vacuous
the notion of grammar must become if this idea is to be entertained.

To attempt to formulate a grammar to describe a linguistic system or what users know about a linguistic system

makes eminent sense, linguistically and psycholinguistical-
ly. In addition, psycholinguistics will require a process
(or user) <u>model</u> to account for how speakers and hearers use
this grammar, but it helps not at all, conceptually, to
call this model a grammar too. Both linguists and psychologists have been guilty of this kind of loose usage.
Dr. Kess seems to slip into this type of error when he suggests that `the ability to disambiguate sentences ...
should be included in the list of native abilities that a
competence grammar ... should attempt to `e responsive to'.
Again, the grammar ought to describe the .ind of linguistic
knowledge the user must possess in order to exercise such
an ability, but why (or how) should it describe the ability
per se? Are grammars to become general models of human behavior? Note too, in this context, that while some ambiguities can be handled clearly at the level of the linguistic system, others, just as clearly, can not. These latter
ran be dealt with only by an extra-linguistic, cognitive
system.

     This problem is quite similar to the confusion gener-
ated by case grammarians when they attempt to incorporate
into a grammar distinctions such as agent vs. instrument
when these are not formally marked within the linguistic
system. Recourse must be made to ad hoc `interpretive' ar-
guments which are dependent upon non-linguistic, cognitive
functions such as knowledge of the world, etc. These latter factors ought to be outside the purview of the grammar
as such and it ought to be clearly recognized that the linguistic system, while obviously important in the communication of meaning, cannot and does not do the whole job. The
linguistic system can do the fascinating things it does
only because it is embedded in an even more fascinating
cognitive system. I've developed a detailed view of the
place of the linguistic system in the communicative situation in a paper entitled `An Information Structure View of
Language' (Baker 1976). In any event, though, no one, as
Dr. Lieberman observed, has a `pipe line to revelation' so
that the form or content of the underlying factual or procedural knowledge is anything but obvious from performance
data.

     In dealing with explicitly acquired knowledge, i.e.,
the consequences of specific instruction, we can distinguish knowledge of the factual kind from a user's abilities
because, a priori, we know the exact content of the input.
We could test both good and bad chess players, e.g., and we
might show that both groups knew all of the specific per-
missable moves for each piece in the game. We could then
assert that they differ only in their ability to make

effective use of that knowledge to play good chess. Linguistically, this would correspond to `knowing the grammar´
as opposed to ´communicating effectively´, but here we are
not at all clear about what it is we are attributing to the
subject when we say he `knows the grammar´. The `rules´,
which, a priori, we do not know, were not explicitly tagged
on input so that we know neither their number nor kind.
They are acquired as a consequence of psychological processes we know little about, which operate at a preconsci-
ous, effectively unremembered level on an unspecified data
base. They are not even a consequence of deliberate,
directed learning. They are more akin to products of incidental learning, taking place simply as a by-product of
trying to learn to communicate, a goal which is only partly
dependent upon mastering the linguistic system, and which
is not necessarily predicated upon perfect use of the `per-
missable rules´.

As long as we remain ignorant of the nature of the
specific input to the subject, and the nature of the knowledge resulting from his psychological processing of that
data, we will be unable, as we logically might have in the
chess example, to equate good and bad communicators on the
basis of factual knowledge and then infer, from variations
in performance, information about differences in ability to
use that knowledge. These must remain inextricably confounded until we develop our understanding of what, precisely, is acquired and how it is retained. This is tantamount to saying, at the present time, that competence cannot be differentiated from ability by observing performance.

Notice too, that this confounding holds even for the
much vaunted `intuitions of the native speaker´. Intuiting
(really, making judgments about utterances) is performing
and that performing is a function of the factual knowledge
and abilities of the performer which are further confounded
with judgments at the level of communicative effectiveness.
This latter aspect alone brings in a host of additional
variables and suggests the utter futility of debates on
variations at the intuitive level or the more bizarre
claims for the priviledged status of intuitive judgments.

Dr. Watt´s paper evoked some discussion of the `si-
mplicity metric´ whose track record has been anything but
impressive as a device for settling arguments about competing formal descriptions. In spite of this, it still
emerges in linguistic debates. It fails for what ought to
be two quite obvious reasons. It is an intrinsic rather
than an extrinsic principle, and it fails to specify the

goal or purpose of the simplification. The first point
fails to recognize the role of language as a tool, a device
for accomplishing a goal external to itself. One evaluates
a tool in terms of how well it does its job, and the structural properties of the tool in terms of how these contribute to that accomplishment. In this sense, the criteria
for evaluation are necessarily extrinsic. For the second
point, once a goal for simplification is introduced, it becomes obvious that simplification for the speaker's task is
in opposition to simplification for the hearer's task. A
number of points in Dr. Watt's paper illustrate this and it
should be clear that linguistic systems are <u>optimized</u> with
respect to their dual roles in production and comprehension
rather than being maximally simple for either side. But
again, this is only obvious when you step outside of the
system and seriously consider what it is used for. Surely
by this time we can at least concede that language is not
produced as an end in itself.

Dr. Marschark unintentionally triggered discussion of
an old issue which, though tangential to his paper, still
evokes considerable conceptual confusion. This is with respect to the real or even logical separability of syntax
and semantics (and, ultimately, to the possible autonomy of
linguistics). Their apparent separability seems to have
been crystalized by Morris' (1946) unfortunate tripartite
distinctions among semantics, syntactics, and pragmatics.
Since then, a number of theorists have attempted the development of syntactic descriptions free of semantic considerations (most notably, Chomsky's 1957 position). Si-
mplistically, Morris could be construed as having said:

Language = Semantics + Syntactics + Pragmatics

as if these were three co-equal and relatively independent
pieces. More precisely, it should imply that the conveying
of meaning through language is dependent upon these three
components. In any case, none of the attempts at separating syntax from semantics have been at all satisfactory for
the simple reason that syntactic devices exist only for semantic reasons. They are, in that sense, inseparable. If
we consider the more global problem of meaning, or the communication of meaning, it might better be formulated as:

Semantics = f(Lexicon, Syntax, Pragmatics)

where semantics characterizes the general field of inquiry
whose properties are realized through a speaker's utiliza-
tion of his available lexicon, store of syntactic devices,
and knowledge of the situation in which communication is

occurring. These latter three are used to evoke a specific
semantic interpretation in the hearer which, hopefully,
conveys the speaker's intended meaning. Again, the inter-
play of these various components is dealt with at greater
length in my 'Information Structure' paper (Baker 1976).

Dr. Kess, in characterizing the analysis of ambiguous
sentences in terms of surface as opposed to deep structures
raises an issue which, I believe, is quite obscure within
linguistics and which is also consistently misunderstood in
the interchange between linguistics and psychology. In
formal linguistics, deep structures (which appear to be
sometimes referred to as underlying or base structures)
were initially meant to be underlying syntactic representations. Their 'existence' was presumed to be necessary if
the syntatic structure was to provide a sufficient basis
for disambiguation to the so-called (but, quite generally,
completely unexplained) interpretive component of the grammar. In effect, this placed the cognitive system within
the linguistic system rather than the other way around.
This is one of the more unfortunate consequences of assuming the primacy of syntax, and it is a classic illustration
of the quixotic attempts in modern linguistics to make individual sentence forms, in and of themselves, capable of
providing all of the information necessary for their complete interpretation. This is a burden which the linguistic system, by itself, cannot be made to bear. It simply
doesn't work, as the rise and fall of the theory of transformational generative grammar so amply demonstrates.

Quite apart from the linguistic issues, psychologists
have generally recognized a distinction between the surface
form of an utterance and its meaning. Since the meaning
was presumed to 'underlie' the surface form, it was an
easy, though blatant, error to equate this to what linguists were calling 'deep structure'. The error was rein-
forced by the gradual encroachment of more cognitive or interpretive components into the grammar as a consequence of
the failure of syntactic considerations alone to solve what
are really broader semantic problems. As formal linguistics moved from early transformational grammar into generative or interpretive semantics, almost all of the vital
distinctions between specifically linguistic and cognitive
concepts have been incredibly muddled. This, in turn, is
what has led to the postulation, as noted earlier, of grammars as general models of human behavior attempting to incorporate, not just the linguistic system but, everything a
human can do with the linguistic system.

The ensuing conceptual chaos in linguistics, and the

failure of linguistic theories to provide viable frames of
reference for psycholinguistic experimentation, have begun
to engender a negative reaction within psychology toward
linguistics. Psychologists are in danger of rejecting the
whole discipline, as if it had nothing to contribute.
That, of course, would be extremely unfortunate since language and the structure of language must occupy a central
role in modern theories of information processing, artificial intelligence, and cognitive psychology in general.
Historically, psychologists have acted as if surface forms
functioned as completely unbiased filters through which
they could immediately grasp the 'underlying propositional
structure' or the intended meaning. Their all-too-quick
acceptance of what transformational generative theory
seemed to offer in the early 60's clearly showed that this
disregard of language was more a function of having no dis-
ciplined way in which to treat the phenomenon. Given the
promise of a solution, psychologists jumped on the band wa-
gon with the same enthusiasm as the linguists of that period. It would be very unfortunate if the essential links
that were formed between psychology and linguistics are se-
vered merely because of the failure of one theoretical position.

The papers presented by Dr. Lieberman and Dr. Nearey
both touched on two points which seem to be perennial conceptual problems not so much for what they say, which seems
obvious enough, as for our failure to keep what they say in
mind in dealing with research on speech production and perception. These are the important distinctions between
structural complexity and task complexity for the first
case, and the distinction between the physical stimulus and
the effective stimulus for the other. Both of these confusions stem from the need for a conceptual differentiation
between the physical or physiological event on the one
side, and the psychological event on the other. Unless you
are willing to dismiss the latter with hand-waving and labels such as 'epiphenomenological', as our erstwhile behaviorist brethren were wont to do, this distinction must be
seen as being theoretically critical.

In describing the mechanisms required for speech production, one is, quite properly, impressed by the incredible complexity of the physiological mechanisms involved.
If a child had to learn to direct all of the parts of such
a complex mechanism explicitly, speech would probably be
impossible. But such, of course, is not the child's task.
The child approaches the task holistically. He has a voca-
lizing apparatus which he guides, rather loosely, toward
some target noise. His attention would appear to be

focused much more on the goal of the activity than on the route to that goal. This all makes it quite difficult to pin down the relationship between the actual task demands and the complexity of the structures through which those demands are met. This, in turn, makes it difficult to move with any clarity from structural descriptions to statements about task complexity in producing various sounds. There is a tendency to forget this distinction and to conclude, following a complex anatomical or physiological description, that the task of using such a mechanism is, ipso facto, a complex task. That, of course, does not necessarily follow.

The 'stimulus error' was made explicit for us by Titchener around the turn of the century, but his distinction between the stimulus as a physical event and as a psychological event was dismissed by later behaviorists as mere sophistry. Gradually, though, its significance has become generally, albeit somewhat grudgingly, accepted. Modern views on information processing (which, incidentally, are completely unrelated to earlier information theory) emphasize the active role of the organism in determining those components of the physical array which become effective or salient in relation to the organism's response to that stimulus. In addition to differential sensitivity to various components of the physical array as a function of the physiological states and properties of the receptor mechanisms - which determine the potentially effective stimulus - we must also contend with the differential salience or significance which the organism learns to attach to the various signal components it can detect. Only after this latter stage can we begin to talk about the actually effective stimulus.

As a consequence of the organism's critical role in determining the nature of the effective stimulus, our ability to measure the acoustic signal in exquisite detail is something of a mixed blessing. Signal measurement per se is not the problem. What we need to be able to do is to represent numerically just those properties of the signal which are potentially effective for the organism in a manner which is consistent with the organism's response so that we may effectively study what the organism does with that information in developing its skills in speech production and perception. All of our discussions with respect to signals, features, and cues must be placed in the context of the critical organismic variables if the use of the potential information in speech production and perception is to be understood.

Few of the conceptual issues I have alluded to in the preceding comments are particularly new. Their persistence as conceptual problems in attempted explanations of human language and language behavior serves primarily to illustrate how lax we are in taking our theoretical responsibilities seriously. We tend to operate too close to our particular sets of data or areas of interest and we fail to back off from time to time to see where our particular efforts fit into the more general scheme of things. Hopefully, a conference such as this will cause us to do that. Certainly it has led me in that direction. Now if, in addition to bringing these conceptual issues to our attention, it will also lead us to some solutions for some of them, we might even begin to feel successful.

MASTER LIST OF
REFERENCES

MASTER LIST OF REFERENCES

Aaronson, Doris. 1976. "Performance Theories for Sentence Coding: Some Qualitative Evidence". *Journal of Experimental Psychology: Human Perception and Performance* 2.42-55.

Aaronson, Doris, and H. Scarborough. 1976. "Performance Theories for Sentence Coding: Some Quantative Evidence". *Journal of Experimental Psychology: Human Perception and Performance* 2.56-70.

Abrams, K., and T. Bever. 1969. "Syntactic Structure Modifies Attention During Speech Perception and Recognition". *Quarterly Journal of Experimental Psychology* 21.280-90.

Anderson, John. 1976. *Language, Memory and Thought*. Hillsdale, N.J.: Lawrence Erlbaum.

Anderson, John, and Gordon Bower. 1973. *Human Associative Memory*. Washington: V.H. Winston.

Anderson, N., J. Sawyers, and B. Farkas. 1972. "President Paragraphs". *Behavioral Research Methods and Instrumentation* 4.177-92.

Anderson, Richard C., and Janet Hidde. 1971. "Imagery and Sentence Learning". *Journal of Educational Psychology* 62.526-30.

Anderson, Richard C., and Andrew Ortony. 1975. "On Putting Apples into Bottles - A Problem of Polysemy". *Cognitive Psychology* 7.167-80.

Anderson, Stephen R. 1974. *The Organization of Phonology* New York: Academic Press.

Anglin, Jeremy, and George Miller. 1968. "The Role of Phrase Structure in the Recall of Meaningful Verbal Material". *Psychonomic Science* 10.343-44.

Atal, B.S., and S.L. Hanauer. 1971. "Speech Analysis and Synthesis by Linear Prediction of the Speech Wave". *Journal of the Acoustical Society of America* 50.637-55.

Baird, Raymond. 1973. "Children's Phonological Rules: A Failure to Replicate". *Language Learning* 23.223-30.

Baker, Wm. J. 1976. "An 'Information Structure' View of Language". *Canadian Journal of Linguistics* 21.1-16.

Baker, Wm. J, and A. J. Roszypal. 1978. "An Empirical Basis for Perceptual Distinctions Among Vowels and Speakers". Paper read to the Annual Meeting, Canadian Psychological Association, Ottawa.

Barclay, J.R., John Bransford, Jeffrey Franks, Nancy
McCarrell, and Kathy Nitsch. 1974. "Comprehension and
Semantic Flexibility". *Journal of Verbal Learning and
Verbal Behavior* 13.471-81.
Barclay, J. Richard. 1973. "The Role of Comprehension in
Remembering Sentences". *Cognitive Psychology* 4.229-54.
Bates, Reed R. 1969. *A Study in the Acquisition of Language*.
Ph.D. diss., Univ. of Texas at Austin, Texas. Unpub.
Begg, Ian. 1969. "Recall of Meaningful Phrases". *Journal of
Verbal Learning and Verbal Behavior* 4.431-49.
Begg, Ian, and Allan Paivio. 1969. "Concreteness and Imagery
in Sentence Learning". *Journal of Verbal Learning and
Verbal Behavior* 8.821-27.
Bell, Alexander Melville. 1867. *Visible speech or self-inter-
preting physiological letters for the writings of all lan-
guages in one alphabet*. London: Simpkin & Marshall.
Bell, C.G., H. Fujisaki, J.M. Heinz, K.N. Stevens, 'and A.S.
House. 1961. "Reduction of Speech Spectra by Analysis-by-
Synthesis Techniques". *Journal of Acoustical Society of
America*   33.1725-36.
Berko, Jean. 1958. "The Child's Learning of English Morpho-
logy". *Word* 14.150-77.
Birnbaum, Henrik. 1975. "Linguistic Structure, Symbolization,
and Phonological Processes". *Phonologica 1972: Akten der
zweiten Internationalen Phonologie-Tagung Wien, 5.-8.
Sept. 1972* ed. by Wolfgang U. Dressler & F.V. Mares, 131-
49. Munich: Fink.
Bever, Thomas G. 1970. "The Cognitive Basis for Linguistic
Structures". *Cognition and the Development of Language*
ed. by John R. Hayes. New York: Wiley.
Bever, Thomas G., Merril F. Garrett & Richard Hurtig. 1973.
"The Interaction of Perceptual Processes in Ambiguous Sen-
tences". *Memory and Cognition* 1.277-86.
Bever, Thomas G., Merrill F. Garrett & Richard Hurtig. 1976.
"Projection Mechanisms in Reading, or When the Journal Re-
view Process Fails". *Journal of Psycholinguistic Research*
5.215-26.
Bock, M. 1978. "Levels of Processing of Normal and Ambiguous
Sentences in Different Contexts". *Psychological Research*
40.37-51.
Bond, Zinny S. 1976. "Identification of Vowels Excerpted From
Neutral and Nasal Contexts". *Journal of the Acoustical So-
ciety of America* 59.1229-32.
Botha, Rudolf P. 1973. *The Justification of Linguistic Hypo-
theses* The Hague & Paris: Mouton.
Bower, Gordon, & F. Springston. 1970. "Pausing as Recoding
Points in Letter Series". *Journal of Experimental Psycho-
logy* 83.421-30.
Braine, Martin D.S. 1973. "On What Might Constitute Learn-
able Phonology". *Language* 50.170-299.

Bransford, John, John Barclay, and Jeffrey Franks. 1972.
"Sentence Memory: A Constructive Versus Interpretive Ap-
proach". *Cognitive Psychology*   3.193-209.
Bransford, John D., and Marcia K. Johnson. 1972. "Contextual
Prerequisites for Understanding: Some Investigations of
Comprehension and Recall". *Journal of Verbal Learning and
Verbal Behavior* 11.717-26.
Bregman, A., and R. Strasberg. 1968. "Memory for the Syntac-
tic Form of Sentences". *Journal of Verbal Learning and
Verbal Behavior* 7.496-503.
Bresnan, Joan. 1975. "Toward a Realistic Model of Transfor-
mational Grammar". Unpub. manuscript.
Brewer, William. 1975. "Memory for Ideas: Synonym Substit-
ution". *Memory and Cognition* 3.458-64.
Brown, Roger. 1973. *A First Language: The Early Stages*.
Cambridge, Mass.: Harvard University Press.
Cairns, Helen. 1973. "Effects of Bias on Processing and Re-
processing of Lexically Ambiguous Sentences". *Journal of
Experimental Psychology* 97.337-43.
Cairns, Helen, and Charles Cairns. 1976. *Psycholinguistics*
New York, Rinehart & Winston.
Cairns, Helen S., and Joan Kamerman. 1975. "Lexical Infor-
mation Processing During Sentence Comprehension". *Journal
of Verbal Learning and Verbal Behavior* 14.170-79.
Campbell, R., and Roger Wales. 1970. "The Study of Language
Acquisition". *New Horizons in Linguistics* ed. by John
Lyons, Harmondsworth.
Canale, Michael. 1978. *Word Order Change in Old English:
Base Reanalysis in Generative Grammar*.   Ph.D. diss.,
McGill University.
Carey, Peter W., Jacques Mehler, and Thomas G. Bever. 1970a.
"Judging the Veracity of Ambiguous Sentences". *Journal of
Verbal Learning and Verbal Behavior* 9.243-54.
Carey, Peter W., Jacques Mehler, and Thomas G. Bever. 1970b.
"When do we Compute All the Interpretations of an Ambig-
uous Sentence?". *Advances in Psycholinguistics* ed. by G.B.
Flores d'Arcais & W.J.M. Levelt, Amsterdam: North-Holland
Publishing Co.
Carmazza, Alfonso, Ellen Grober, and Catherine Garvey. 1977.
"Comprehension of Anaphoric Pronouns". *Journal of Verbal
Learning and Verbal Behavior* 16.601-09.
Carpenter, Patricia and Marcel Just. 1977. "Integrative Pro-
cesses in Comprehension". *Perception and Comprehension*
ed. by D. LaBerge, and S. Samuels. Potomac, Maryland: Law-
rence Erlbaum.
Catlin, Jack, and Jane-Carol Catlin. 1972. "Intentionality:
A Source of Ambiguity in English?". *Linguistic Inquiry*
3.504-08.
Cattell, R. B., ed. 1966. *Handbook of Multivariate Exper-
imental Psychology.* Chicago: Rand McNally.

Cena, Restituto M. 1976. *An Experimental Investigation of Vowel Alternation in English*. Unpublished doctoral dissertation, The University of Alberta, Edmonton.

Cena, Restituto M. 1978. "When is a Phonological Generalization Psychologically Real?". Bloomington, Indiana: I.U. Linguistics Club.

Chiba, T. and J. Kajiyama. 1941. *The Vowel: Its Nature and Structure*. Tokyo: Tokyo-Kaiseikan.

Chomsky, Noam. 1957. *Syntactic Structures*. The Hague: Mouton and Co.

Chomsky, Noam. 1959. Review of *Verbal Behavior* by B.F. Skinner. *Language* 35.26-58.

Chomsky, Noam. 1965. *Aspects of the Theory of Syntax*. Cambridge, Mass.: The M.I.T. Press.

Chomsky, Noam. 1973. "Conditions on Transformations". *A Festschrift for Morris Halle* ed. by Stephen Anderson and Paul Kiparsky. New York:Holt, Rinehart & Winston.

Chomsky, Noam. 1975. *Reflections on Language*. New York: Pantheon.

Chomsky, Noam. 1976. "On the Biological Basis of Language Capacities". *The Neuropsychology of Language* ed. by R.W. Rieber. New York:Plenum.

Chomsky, Noam and Morris Halle. 1968. *The Sound Pattern of English*. New York: Harper & Row.

Chomsky, Noam and Howard Lasnik. 1977. "Filters and Controls". *Linguistic Inquiry* 8.425-504.

Clark, Herbert H. and Eve V. Clark. 1977. *Psychology and Language: An Introduction to Psycholinguistics* New York: Harcourt Brace Jovanovich.

Coker, C.H. and N. Umeda. 1975. "Speech as an Error Correcting Process". *Proceedings of the Speech Communications Seminar* ed. by G. Fant. Stockholm: Almquist & Wiksell.

Conrad, Carol. 1974. "Context Effects in Sentence Comprehension: A Study of the Subjective Lexicon". *Memory and Cognition* 2.130-38.

Cook, Vivian J. 1974. "Is Explanatory Adequacy Adequate?". *Linguistics* 133.(August)21-31.

Cooper, William E. 1974. "Adaptation of Phonetic Feature Analyzers for Place of Articulation". *Journal of the Acoustical Society of America* 56.617-27.

Cooper, F.S., A.M. Delattre, A.M. Liberman, J.M. Borst, and L.J. Gerstman. 1952. "Some Experiments on the Perception of Synthetic Speech Sounds". *Journal of the Acoustical Society of America* 24.597-606.

Craik, Fergus I.M. and Robert S. Lockhart. 1972. "Levels of Processing: A Frame-work for Memory Research". *Journal of Verbal Learning and Verbal Behavior* 11.671-84.

Denes, Peter. 1960. "Effect of Duration on the Perception of Voicing". *Journal of Acoustical Society of America* 32.693-703.

Derwing, Bruce L. 1973. *Transformational Grammar as a Theory of Language Acquisition* London: Cambridge University Press.

Derwing, Bruce L. and Wm. J. Baker. 1974. "Rule-learning and the English Inflections". *Final report to the Canada Council,* File No. *S72-0332.*

Derwing, Bruce L. and Wm. J. Baker. 1977. "The Psychological Basis for Morphological Rules". *Language Learning and Thought.* ed. by John Macnamara New York: Academic Press.

Derwing, Bruce L. and Peter R. Harris. 1975. "What is a Generative Grammar? *The transformational-generative paradigm and modern linguistic theory* ed. by E.F.K. Koerner, 297-314. Amsterdam: John Benjamins, B.V.

Derwing, Bruce L. 1976. "Linguistic Rules and Language Acquisition". *Cahiers Linguistique d'Ottawa* 4.13-41. Reprinted ed. by W. Von Raffler-Engel and Y. Lebrun. *Baby Talk and Infant Speech* Atlantic Highlands, N.J.: Humanities Press.

Derwing, Bruce L. 1976. "Morpheme Recognition and the Learning of Rules for Derivational Morphology". *The Canadian Journal of Linguistics* 21.38-66.

Derwing, Bruce L. 1977. "The Acquisition of English Morphology". *Final report to the Canada Council,* Leave Fellowship No. *45L-77502.*

Derwing, Bruce L. "Against Autonomous Linguistics" *Evidence and Argumentation in Linguistics* ed. by T. Perry, Berlin & New York: de Gruyter, in press.

Derwing, Bruce L. "English Pluralization: A Testing Ground for Rule Evaluation". *Experimental linguistics: Integration of theories and applications* ed. by Gary D. Prideaux, Bruce L. Derwing and Wm. J. Baker. Ghent: E. Story-Scientia, in press.

Derwing, Bruce L. and Wm. J. Baker. 1976. "On the Learning of English Morphological Rules". *Final Report to the Canada Council,* File No. *S73-0387.*

Derwing, Bruce L. and Wm. J. Baker. 1977. "The Psychological Basis for Morphological Rules". *Language Learning and Thought.* ed. by John Macnamara, New York:Academic Press.

Derwing, Bruce L. and Wm J. Baker. 1978. "On the Re-integration of Linguistics and Psychology". *Recent Advances in the Psychology of Language. Part B: Formal and Experimental Approaches* ed. by R.N. Campbell & P.T. Smith. New York: & London: Plenum Press.

Derwing, Bruce L. and Wm. J. Baker. "Rule Learning and the English Inflections (with special emphasis on the plural)". *Experimental Linguistics: Integration of Theories and Applications* ed. by Gary D. Prideaux, Bruce L. Derwing and Wm. J. Baker. Ghent:E. Story-Scientia, in press.

Dooling, D. and R. Lackman. 1971. "Effects of Comprehension on Retention of Prose". *Journal of Experimental Psychology* 88.216-22.

Dooling, D. and R. Mullet. 1973. "Locus of Thematic Effects in Retention of Prose". *Journal of Experimental Psychology* 3.404-06.

Dooling, D. and R. Christiaansen. 1975. "Thematic Intrusions in Memory for Prose: Storage or Retrieval?". Paper presented at Midwestern Psychological Association Meetings.

Dooling, D. and R. Christiaansen. 1977. "Episode and Semantic Aspects of Memory for Prose". *Journal of Experimental Psychology: Human Learning and Memory* 3.428-36.

Dunn-Rankin, P. 1968. "The Similarity of Lower-Case Letters of the English Alphabet". *Journal of Verbal Learning and Verbal Behavior* 7.990-95.

Eimas, P.D., E.R. Siqueland, P. Jusczyk, and J. Vigorito. 1971. "Speech Perception in Infants". *Science* 171.303-06.

Eliasson, Stig. 1977. "Cognitive Processes and Models of Language". *CC 77: International Workshop on the Cognitive Viewpoint* ed. by M. deMey, R. Pinxton, M. Poriau and F. Vandamme. Ghent:University of Ghent.

Fant, G. 1956. "On the Predictability of Formant Levels and Spectrum Envelopes From Formant Frequencies". *For Roman Jakobson* ed. by M. Halle, H. Lund, and D.C. Maclean. The Hague:Mouton.

Fant, G. 1975. "Non-uniform Vowel Normalization". (Quarterly Progress and Status Report 2-3, 1-19). Stockholm: Royal Institute of Technology: Speech Transmission Laboratory.

Faris, J.C. 1972. *Nuba Personal Art* Toronto: University of Toronto Press.

Fillenbaum, Samuel. 1966. "Memory for Gist: Some Relevant Variables". *Language and Speech* 9.217-77.

Fillmore, Charles M. 1977. "The Case for Case Reopened". *Syntax and Semantics 8* ed. by P. Cole and J. Saddock. New York: Academic Press.

Flanagan, J. L. 1957. "Difference Limen for Formant Amplitude". *Journal of Speech and Hearing Disorders* 22.205-212.

Fodor, Jerry A., Thomas g. Bever, and Merrill Garrett. 1974. *The Psychology of Language* New York: McGraw-Hill.

Fodor, Jerry A., and Merrill Garrett. 1966. "Some Reflections on Competence and Performance". *Psycholinguistic Papers* ed. by J. Lyons and R.J. Wales. Edinburg: Edinburg University Press.

Foss, Donald J., Thomas G. Bever, and M. Silver. 1968. "The Comprehension and Verification of Ambiguous Sentences". *Perception and Psychophysics* 4.304-06.

Foss, Donald J. 1970. "Some Effects of Ambiguity Upon Sentence Comprehension". *Journal of Verbal Learning and Verbal Behavior* 9.699-706.

Foss, Donald J. and Charles M. Jenkins. 1973. "Some Aspects of Context on the Comprehension of Ambiguous Sentences". *Journal of Verbal Learning and Verbal Behavior* 12.577-89.

Franks, Jeffrey, and John Bransford. 1972. "The Acquisition of Abstract Ideas". *Journal of Verbal Learning and Verbal*

Behavior 11.311-15.

Frederickson, C. 1972. "Effects of Task Directed Cognitive Operations on Comprehension and Memory Processes". *In Comprehension and the Acquisition of Knowledge,* Washington, D.C.: V.H. Winston.

Fromkin, Victoria A. 1971. "The Non-anomalous Nature of Anomalous Utterances". *Language* 47.27-52.

Fromkin, Victoria A. 1975. "When Does a Test Test a Hypothesis?". *Testing Linguistic Hypotheses* ed. by David Cohen and Jessica R. Wirth. New York: Wiley.

Frommer, M.S. 1975. *The Influence of Linguistic Context on the Processing of Lexically Ambiguous Sentences by Four-, Six-, and Eight-year Old Children.* Ph.D. diss., Columbia University. Unpub.

Fry, D.B. 1958. "Experiments in the Perception of Stress". *Language and Speech* 1.126-52.

Fry, D.B. 1965. "The Dependence of Stress Judgements on Vowel Formant Structure". *Proceedings of the Sixth International Congress of Phonetic Sciences* ed. by E. Zwirner and W. Bethge. Berlin: Karger.

Garcia, Erica. 1976. "Some Remarks on Ambiguity and Perceptual Processes". *Journal of Psycholinguistic Research* 5.195-213.

Garrett, Merrill F. 1970. "Does Ambiguity Complicate the Perception of Sentences?". *Advances in Psycholinguistics* ed. by B.G. Flores d'Arcais and W.J.M. Levelt. Amsterdam: North-Holland Publishing Co.

Gay, Thomas. 1974. "A Cinefluorographic Study of Vowel Production". *Journal of Phonetics* 2.255-66.

Gay, Thomas. 1978. "Effect of Speaking Rate on Vowel Formant Movements". *Journal of Acoustical Society of America* 63.223-230.

George, S.L. 1978. *The Relationship Between Cranial Base Angle Morphology and Infant Vocalizations* Ph.D. diss., University of Connecticut, Storrs. Unpub.

Gibson, E.J. 1969. *Principles of Perceptual Learning and Development* New York: Appleton Century Crofts.

Gleason, H.A., Jr. 1961. *An Introduction to Descriptive Linguistics* New York: Holt, Rinehart, & Winston.

Goldman-Eisler, Frieda. 1958. "Speech Production and the Predictability of Words in Context". *Quarterly Journal of Experimental Psychology* 10.96-106.

Goyvaerts, D.I. 1976. Review of *Speech Errors as Linguistic Evidence* by V.A. Fromkin. *Language* 52.980-82.

Greenbaum, Sidney. 1977. "The Linguist as Experimenter". *Current Themes in Linguistics: Bilingualism, Experimental Linguistics, and Language Typologies* ed. by Fred R. Eckman New York: Wiley.

Gross, C.G. and M.H. Bornstein. 1978. "Left and Right in Science and Art". *Leonardo* 11.29-38.

Haber, Lyn. 1975. "The Muzzy Theory". *Papers from the Eleventh Regional Meeting of the Chicago Linguistic Society* Chicago: Department of Linguistics, University of Chicago.

Halle, Morris. 1964. "On the Bases of Phonology". *The Structure of Language: Readings in the Philosophy of Language* ed. by Jerry A. Fodor and Jerrold J. Katz. Englewood Cliffs, N.J.:Prentice-Hall.

Halle, Morris. 1978. "Knowledge Unlearned and Untaught: What Speakers Know About the Sounds of Their Language". *Linguistic Theory and Psychological Reality* ed. by Morris Halle, Joan Bresnan, and George A. Miller. Cambridge, Mass., M.I.T. Press.

Halle, Morris and Kenneth N. Stevens, 1959. "Analysis by Synthesis". *Proceedings of the Seminar on Speech Compression and Processing* ed. by W. Walthen-Dunn and L.E. Woods. AFCRT-TR-59-198. Vol. II, Paper D7.

Halliday, M.A.K. 1970. "Language Structure and Language Function". *New Horizons in Linguistics* ed. by John Lyons. Baltimore: Penguin.

Halliday, M.A.K. 1977. "Structure and Function in Language". Paper presented to the Symposium on Discourse and Syntax, University of California, Los Angeles, 18-20 November.

Hankamer, Jorge. 1973. "Unacceptable Ambiguity". *Linguistic Inquiry* 4.17-68.

Harris, K. 1974. "Physiological Aspects of Articulatory Behavior". *Current Trends in Linguistics, Vol. 12: Phonetics* ed. by T. Sebeok. The Hague: Mouton.

Hogaboam, Thomas W., and Charles A. Perfetti. 1975. "Lexical Ambiguity and Sentence Comprehension". *Journal of Verbal Learning and Verbal Behavior* 14.265-74.

Holmes, V.M., R. Arwars, and M.F. Garrett. 1977. "Prior Context and the Perception of Lexically Ambiguous Sentences". *Memory and Cognition* 5.103-10.

Hoppe, Ronald A., and Joseph F. Kess. 1977. "Differential Detection of Ambiguity in Japanese". Unpub. manuscript.

Houde, R. 1967. *A Study of Tongue Body Motion During Selected Speech Sounds* Ph.D. diss., University of Michigan, Unpub.

Hughes, G.W. 1961. *The Recognition of Speech by Machine* (Tech. Rep. 395). Cambridge, Mass.: M.I.T. Research Laboratory of Electronics, May.

Huggins, A.W.F. 1975. "On Isochrony and Syntax". *Auditory Analysis and Perception of Speech* ed. by G. Fant and M. Tatham. New York: Academic Press.

Hyman, Larry M. 1970. "How Concrete is Phonology?". *Language* 46.58-76.

Hymes, Dell H. 1972. "On Communicative Competence". *Sociolinguistics* ed. by J.B. Pride and J. Holmes. Harmondsworth: Penguin Books.

Hymes, Dell H. and J. Fought. 1975. "American Structuralism". *Current Trends in Linguistics* 13.903-1176. The Hague.

Ingram, David. 1976. "Phonological Analysis of a Child". *Glossa* 10.3-27.

Irwin, O.C. 1948. "Infant Speech: Development of Vowel Sounds". *Journal of Speech and Hearing Disorders* 13.31-34.

Jakobson, Roman. 1963. "Kindersprache, Aphasie, und Allegemeine Lautgesetze". *Selected Writings* ed. by R. Jakobson. The Hague: Mouton.

Jakobson, Roman, C.G. Fant and M. Halle. 1963. *Preliminaries to Speech Analysis*. Cambridge, Mass.:, The M.I.T. Press.

Jarvella, Robert. 1970. "Effects of Syntax on Running Memory Span for Connected Discourse". *Psychonomic Science* 19.235-39.

Jarvella, Robert. 1971. "Syntactic Processing of Connected Speech". *Journal of Verbal Learning and Verbal Behavior* 10.409-16.

Jarvella, Robert and S. Herman. 1972. "Clause Structure of Sentences and Speech Processing". *Perception and Psychophysics* 11.381-84.

Johnson, M., J. Bransford, S. Nyberg, and J. Cleary. 1972. "Comprehension Factors in Interpreting Memory for Concrete and Abstract Sentences". *Journal of Verbal Learning and Verbal Behavior* 11.451-54.

Jones, Danial. 1919. "X-ray Photographs of the Cardinal Vowels". *Proceedings of the Royal Institute* 22.12-13.

Just, M. and H. Brownell. 1974. "Retrieval of Concrete and Abstract Prose From Memory". *Canadian Journal of Psychology* 28.339-50.

Kahn, D. 1978. "On the Identifiability of Isolated Vowels". *U.C.L.A. Phonetics Laboratory Working Papers in Phonetics* 41.26-31.

Kaplan, R. 1975. "On Process Models for Sentence Analysis". *Explorations in Cognition* ed. by D. Norman and D. Rumelhart San Francisco: W.H. Freeman.

Katz, Jerrold J. and Jerry A. Fodor. 1963. "The Structure of a Semantic Theory". *Language* 39.170-210.

Katz, Jerrold J. and Paul M. Postal. 1964. *An Integrated Theory of Linguistic Description* Cambridge, Mass.: The M.I.T. Press.

Kess, Joseph F. and Ronald A. Hoppe. "On Psycholinguistic Experiments in Ambiguity". In press.

Kennedy, A. and A. Wilkes. 1971. "Functional Structure in Sentences: A Performance Analysis". *Quarterly Journal of Experimental Psychology* 23.214-24.

Kintsch, Walter. 1974. *The Representation of Meaning in Memory* Potomac, Md.: Lawrence Erlbaum.

Kiparsky, Paul. 1968. "Linguistic Universals and Language Change". *Universals in Linguistic Theory* ed. by E. Bach and R.T. Harms. New York: Holt, Rinehart & Winston.

Kiparsky, Paul, and Lisa Menn. 1977. "On the Acquisition of Phonology". *Language Learning and Thought* ed. by J. Macnamara. New York: Academic Press.

Kiss, G. 1975. "An Associative Thesaurus of English: Structural Analysis of a Large Relevance Network". *Studies in Long Term Memory* ed. by A. Kennedy and A. Wilkes. New York: Wiley.

Klatt, D.H. 1976. "Linguistic Uses of Segmental Duration in English: Acoustic and Perceptual Evidence". *Journal of Acoustical Society of America* 59.1208-21.

Kolers, P.A. 1968. "The Recognition of Geometrically Transformed Text". *Perception and Psychophysics* 3.57-64.

Kolers, P.A. and D.N. Perkins. 1975. "Spatial and Ordinal Components of Form Perception and Literacy". *Cognitive Psychology* 7.228-67.

Kratzenstein, C.G. 1782. "|Sur la naissance de la formation des voyelles". *Acta Academia Petrograd.* [Engl. transl. in: *Journal of Physical and Chemical History of Natural Arts* 21.358-81.]

Kuhl, P.K. and J.D. Miller. 1975. "Speech Perception by the Chinchilla: Voice-Voiceless Distinction in Alveopalatal Plosive Consonants". *Science* 190.358-81.

Kubaska, K. *Vowel Duration in Initial Phonologic Stage* In preparation.

Kuiper, N. and A. Paivio. 1977. "Incidental Recognition Memory for Concrete and Abstract Sentences Equated for Comprehensibility". *Bulletin of the Psychonomic Society* 9.247-49.

Kunnepas, T. 1966. "Visual Perception of Capital Letters". *Scandinavian Journal of Psychology* 7.189-96.

Labov, William. 1971. "Methodology". *A Survey of Linguistic Science* ed. by W.O. Dingwall. Linguistic Program, University of Maryland.

Labov, William. 1972. *Sociolinguistic Patterns* Philadelphia: University of Pennsylvania Press.

Labov, William. 1975. "Empirical Foundations of Linguistic Theory". *The Scope of American Linguistics* ed. by Robert Austerlitz. Lisse, The Netherlands: Peter de Ridder Press.

Lackner, J.R. and M.F. Garrett. 1972. "Resolving Ambiguity: Effects of Biasing Content in the Unattended Ear". *Cognition* 1.359-72.

Ladefoged, P. and D. Broadbent. 1957. "Information Conveyed by Vowels". *Journal of the Acoustical Society of America* 29.98-104.

Ladefoged, P., J. DeClerk, M. Lindau and G. Papcun. 1972. "An Auditory Motor Theory of Speech Production". *U.C.L.A. Phonetics Laboratory, Working Papers in Phonetics* 22.48-76.

Lakoff, George. 1970. "A Note on Vagueness and Ambiguity". *Linguistic Inquiry* 1.357-59.

Lakoff, George. 1977. "Linguistic Gestalts". *Papers From the Proceedings of the Thirteenth Regional Meeting, Chicago Linguistic Society.*

Lashly, K.S. 1951. "The Problem of Social Order in Behavior". *Cerebral Mechanisms in Behavior* ed. by L.A. Jeffress, 112 ff. New York: Wiley.

Lefever, M.M. & L.G. Ehri. 1976. "The Relationship Between Field Independence and Sentence Disambiguation Ability". *Journal of Psycholinguistic Research* 5.99-106.

Lehiste, Ilse. 1973. "Phonetic Disambiguation of Syntactic Ambiguity". *Glossa* 7.107-22.

Lehiste, Ilse, and G.E. Peterson. 1961. "Transitions, Glides, and Diphthongs". *Journal of the Acoustical Society of America* 33.268-77.

Lesser, H. and C. Drouin. 1975. "Training in the Use of Double-Function Terms". *Journal of Psycholinguistic Research* 4.285-303.

Lieberman, Philip. 1963. "Some Effects of Semantic and Grammatical Context on the Production and Perception of Speech". *Language and Speech* 6.172-87.

Lieberman, Philip. 1965. "On the Acoustic Basis of the Perception of Intonation by Linguists". *Word* 21.40-54.

Lieberman, Philip. 1967. *Intonation, Perception and Language* Cambridge, Mass.: The M.I.T. Press.

Lieberman, Philip. 1970. "Towards a Unified Phonetic Theory". *Linguistic Inquiry* 1.307-22.

Lieberman, Philip. 1975. *On the Origins of Language: An Introduction to the Evolution of Human Speech* New York: Macmillan.

Lieberman, Philip. 1976. "Phonetic Features and Physiology: A Reappraisal". *Journal of Phonetics* 4.91-112.

Lieberman, Philip. *Speech Physiology and Acoustic Phonetics* New York: Macmillan.

Lieberman, Philip. "On the Development of Vowel Production in Young Children". *Proceedings of NIH Conference on Speech Development, June 1978* Cambridge, Mass.: The M.I.T. Press, in press.

Lightfoot, David. *Principles of Diachronic Syntax* Cambridge: Cambridge University Press.

Lindau, M., L. Jakobson, and P. Ladefoged. 1972. "The Feature Advanced Tongue Root". *U.C.L.A. Phonetics Laboratory Working Papers in Phonetics* 22.76-94.

Lindblom, Bjorn. 1963. "Spectographic Study of Vowel Reduction". *Journal of the Acoustical Society of America* 35.1773-78.

Lindblom, Bjorn, and M. Studdert-Kennedy. 1967. "On the Role of Formant Transitions in Vowel Recognition". *Journal of the Acoustical Society of America* 42.830-43.

Linell, P. 1974. "Problems of Psychological Reality in Generative Phonology: A Critical Assessment". *Reports From*

164 PERSPECTIVES IN EXPERIMENTAL LINGUSITICS

Uppsala University Department of Linguistics No. 4.

Linell, P. 1978. "Notes on the Relation Between Linguistics and Psycholinguistics". *Salzburger Beitrage zur Linguistik* 5 ed. by G. Dracham. Salzburg: Wolfgang Neugebauer.

Linell, P. "Evidence for a Funtionally-based Typology of Phonological Rules". *Phonology in the 1970's* ed. by D.L. Goyvaerts. Ghent: E. Story-Scientia, in press.

Mackay, Donald G. 1966. "To End Ambiguous Sentences". *Perception and Psychophysics* 1.426-36.

Mackay, Donald G. 1970. "Mental Diplopia: Towards a Model of Speech Perception at the Semantic Level". *Advances in Psycholinguistics* ed. by G.B. Flores d'Arcais and W.J.M. Levelt. Amsterdam: North-Holland Publishing Co.

Mackay, Donald G., and Thomas G. Bever. 1967. "In Search of Ambiguity". *Perception and Psychophysics* 2.193-200.

Maia, E. *Nazalization in Portuguese Vowels* Ph.D. diss., Brown University, Providence, R.I., in preparation.

Marks, L. 1967. "Some Structural Factors in the Processing of Sentences". *Journal of Verbal Learning and Verbal Behavior* 6.707-13.

Marschark, Marc. 1977. *Prose Processing: A Chronometric Study of the Effects of Imagability* Ph.D. diss., University of Western Ontario. Unpub.

Marschark, Marc and Allan Paivio. 1977. "Integrative Processing of Concrete and Abstract Sentences". *Journal of Verbal Learning and Verbal Behavior* 16.217-31.

Marschark, Marc. 1978. "Analysis of Word-by-Word Processing Times for Narrative Prose". Submitted for publication.

Mehler, Jacques, Juan Segui, and Peter Carey. 1978. "Trials of Words: Monitoring Ambiguity". *Journal of Verbal Learning and Verbal Behavior* 17.29-35.

McCawley, James D. 1976. "Some Ideas Not to Live By". *Neuren Sprachen* 75.151-65.

Mermelstein, Paul. 1978. "Difference Limens for Formant Frequencies of Steady-State and Consonant-Bounded Vowels". *Journal of the Acoustical Society of America* 63.572-80.

Miller, George A., and K.E. McKean. 1978. "A Chronometric Study of Some Relations Between Sentences". *Memory and Cognition* 86.420-27.

Mistler-Lachman, J.L. 1972. "Levels of Comprehension in Processing of Normal and Ambiguous Sentences". *Journal of Verbal Learning and Verbal Behavior* 11.614-23.

Mistler-Lachman, J.L. 1975. "Queer Sentences, Ambiguity, and Levels of Processing". *Memory and Cognition* 3.395-400.

Morris, Charles W. 1946. *Sign, Language, and Behavior* Englewood Cliffs, N.J.: Prentice-Hall.

Morton, J. 1969. "The Interaction of Information in Word Recognition". *Psychological Review* 76.165-78.

Moslin, Barbara. 1978. *The Role of Phonetic Input in the Child*

Acquisition of the Voice-Voiceless Contrast in English
Ph.D. diss., Brown University, Providence, R.I. Unpub.

Moslin, Barbara, and Elizabeth Cowper. 1975. "Identification of CVC Syllables in Single and Multispeaker Ensembles". Unpub. manuscript. Department of Linguistics, Brown University, Providence, R.I.

Moulton, William G. 1960. "The Short Vowel System of Northern Switzerland". *Word* 16.155-82.

Muller, J. 1848. *The Physiology of the Senses, Voice and Muscular Motion With the Mental Facilities* (Trans. by W. Baly). London: Walton & Maberly.

Myerson, Rosemarie F. 1976. *A Study of Children's Knowledge of Certain Word Formation Rules and the Relationship of This Knowledge for Various Forms of Reading Achievement* Ph.D. diss., Harvard University. Unpub.

Nearey, Terrance M. 1977. *Phonetic Feature Systems for Vowels* Ph. D. diss., University of Conneticut, Storrs. Unpub.

Neisser, Ulrich. 1977. *Cognition and Reality* San Francisco: W.H. Freeman and Co.

Newman, J.E., and G.S. Dell. 1977. "The Phonological Nature of Phoneme Monitoring". Paper presented at the Annual Meeting of the Canadian Psychological Association, Vancouver, B.C.

Nordstrom, P., and B. Lindblom. 1975. "A Normalization Procedure for Vowel Formant Data". Paper 212, Eight International Congress of Phonetic Sciences, Leeds.

Norman, D., and D. Rumelhart. 1975. *Explorations in Cognition* San Francisco: W.H. Freeman.

Oden, G.C. 1974. *Semantic Constraint and Ambiguity Resolution*. Ph.D. diss., University of California, San Diego. Unpub.

Oden, G.C. 1978. "Semantic Constraints and Judged Preference for Interpretations of Ambiguous Sentences". *Memory and Cognition* 6.26-37.

Ohala, John J. 1972. "On the Design of Phonological Experiments". Paper presented at the winter meeting of the Linguistic Society of America, Atlanta, Georgia.

Olson, D. 1970. "Language and Thought: Aspects of a Cognitive Theory of Semantics". *Psychological Review* 77.257-73.

Olson, J.N., and D.G. MacKay. 1974. "Completion and Verification of Ambiguous Sentences". *Journal of Verbal Learning and Verbal Behavior* 12.457-70.

Paivio, Allan. 1971. *Imagery and Verbal Processes* New York: Holt, Rinehart, Winston.

Paivio, Allan, and Ian Begg. 1971. "Imagery and Comprehension Latencies as a Function of Sentence Concreteness and Structure". *Perception and Psychophysics* 10.408-12.

Patel, P.G. "What is Structural Ambiguity?". *Experimental Linguistics* ed. by G. Prideaux, B. Derwing, and Wm. Baker. Ghent: E. Storia Scientia. In press.

Perfetti, Charles A., and D. Goodman. 1970. "Semantic Con-
straints on the Decoding of Ambiguous Words". *Journal of
Experimental Psychology* 86.420-27.
Perfetti, Charles A., and Robert Lindsey. 1974. "Polysemy
and Memory". *Journal of Psycholinguistic Research* 3.75-89.
Peterson, G., and H. Barney. 1952. "Control Methods Used in
a Study of Vowels". *Journal of Acoustical Society of Amer-
ica* 42.175-84.
Peterson, G.E., and I. Lehiste. 1960. "Duration of Syllable
Nuclei in English". *Journal of the Acoustical Society of
America* 32.693.703.
Piquette, Elyse. 1976. "The Translator's Sensitivity to Syn-
tactic Ambiguity: A Psycholinguistic Experiment". *Canadian
Journal of Linguistics* 21.95-108.
Piquette, Elyse. 1976. "Réflexions sur l'ambiguïté syntaxique
à la lumière d'une expérience faisant appel à la traduction"
Psycholinguistique Experimentale et Theorique ed. by R.
Sarrasin. Montreal: Presses de l'Université du Québec.
Pompi, K., and R. Lackman. 1967. "Surrogate Processes in the
Short Term Retention of Connected Discourse". *Journal of
Experimental Psychology* 75.143-50.
Postal, Paul M. 1974. "On Certain Ambiguities". *Linguistic
Inquiry* 5.367-424.
Prideaux, Gary D. "An Information-Structure Approach to Syn-
tax". Paper presented to the University of Ottawa and Car-
leton University, March, 1975.
Prideaux, Gary D. 1976. "A Functional Analysis of English
Question Acquisition: A Response to Hurford". *Journal of
Child Language* 3.417-22.
Prideaux, Gary D. and Wm. J. Baker. 1976. "The Recognition of
Ambiguity". *Human Communication* 1.51-8.
Prideaux, Gary D. 1978. "The Acquisition of English Relative
Clauses". Paper presented at the Annual Meeting of the
Canadian Linguistic Association. London, Ontario.
Prideaux, Gary D., Bruce L. Derwing, and Wm. J. Baker (ed.
by). *Experimental Linguistics: Integration of Theories and
Applications* Ghent: E. Story-Scientia. In press.
Priestly, T.M.S. "On Homonymy in Child Phonology". Forthcoming.
Pritchard, R.M., W. Heron, and D.O. Hebb. 1960. "Visual Per-
ception Approached by the Method of Stabilized Images".
Canadian Journal of Psychology 14.67-77.
Pullum, Geoffrey K. 1978. Review of *Assessing Linguistic Ar-
guments* ed. by J.R. Wirth. *Language* 54.399-402.
Raphael, L.J. 1972. "Preceding Vowel Duration as a Cue to the
Voicing Characteristics of Word-Final Consonants in American
English". *Journal of the Acoustical Society of America*
51.1296-1303.
Richman, B. 1976. "Some Vocal Distinctive Features Used by
Gelada Monkeys". *Journal of the Acoustical Society of Amer-
ica* 6.718-24.

Rinsland, H.D. 1945. *A Basic Vocabulary of Elementary School Children* New York: Macmillan.

Rosenberg, Samuel. 1968. "Associative and Phrase Structure in Sentence Recall". *Journal of Verbal Learning and Verbal Behavior* 7.1077-81.

Rozsypal, A.J. 1974. "Functional Modeling of Auditory Analysis of Transient Signals". *Journal of the Acoustical Society of America* 55.433(A).

Russell, G.O. 1928. *The Vowel.* Columbus, Ohio: Ohio State University Press.

Sachs, Jacqueline. 1967. "Recognition Memory for Syntactic and Semantic Aspects of Connected Discourse". *Perception and Psychophysics* 2.437-42.

Sanders, Gerald A. 1977. "Some Preliminary Remarks on Simplicity and Evaluation Procedures in Linguistics". *Minnesota Working Papers in Linguistics and Philosophy of Language* No. 4. ed. by L.G. Hutchinson.

Savin, H.B., and E. Perchonock. 1965. "Grammatical Structure and the Immediate Recall of English Sentences". *Journal of Verbal Learning and Verbal Behavior* 4.348-53.

Schank, Roger. 1973. "Identification of Conceptualizations Underlying Natural Language". *Computer Models of Thought and Language* ed. by R. Schank and K. Colby. San Francisco: W.H. Freeman.

Scherzer, Joel. 1970. "Talking Backwards in Cuna: The Sociological Reality of Phonological Descriptions". *Southwestern Journal of Anthropology* 26.343-53.

Schlesinger, I.M. 1966. "The Influence of Sentence Structure on the Reading Process". U.S. Office of Naval Research Technology, Report 24. (Cited in Bever, 1966).

Schlesinger, I.M. 1977. *Production and Comprehension of Utterances* Hillsdale, N.J.: Lawrence Earlbaum.

Scholes, Robert J. 1971. "On the Spoken Disambiguation of Superficially Ambiguous Sentences". *Language and Speech* 14.1-11.

Schutz, Noel W., and Bruce L. Derwing. 1978. "A Theoretical Defense of the Pattern Drill". *1976-77 Papers in ESL: Selected Conference Papers of the ATESL.* ed. by B.W. Robinett. Washington, D.C.: NAFSA.

Schvaneveldt, R.W., D.E. Meyer, and C.A. Becker. 1976. "Lexical Ambiguity, Semantic Content and Visual Word Recognition" *Journal of Experimental Psychology: Human Perception and Performance* 2.243-56.

Smith, Neil V. 1975. Review of *Transformational Grammar as a Theory of Language Acquisition* by B.L. Derwing. *Journal of Linguistics* 11.261-70.

Smyth, Ronald H., Gary D. Prideaux, and John T. Hogan. 1979. "The Effect of Context on Dative Position". *Lingua* 47.27-42.

Stageberg, Norman C. 1971. "Structural Ambiguity and the Suprasegmentals". *English Record* 21.64-68.

Steinberg, Danny D., and Robert K. Krohn. 1975. "The Psychological Validity of Chomsky and Halle's Vowel-Shift Rule". *The Transformational-Generative Paradigm and Modern Linguistic Theory* ed. by E.F.K. Koerner. Amsterdam: John Benjamins, B.V.

Stevens, Kenneth N. 1972. "Quantal Nature of Speech". *Human Communication:A Unified View* ed. by E.E. David Jr. and P.B. Denes. New York: McGraw-Hill.

Stevens, Kenneth, and Sheila E. Blumstein. 1978. "Invarient Cues for Place of Articulation in Stop Consonants". *Journal of the Acoustical Society of America* 64.1358-69.

Stevens, K., and A. House. 1955. "Development of a Quantitative Description of Vowel Articulation". *Journal of the Acoustical Society of America* 27.484-93.

Stevens, K., and A. House. 1963. "Pertubation of Vowel Production by Consonantal Contexts: An Acoustical Study". *Journal of Speech and Hearing Research* 6.111-28.

Stevens, K., P. Lieberman, and M. Studdert-Kennedy. 1969. "Cross-language Study of Vowel Perception". *Language and Speech* 12.1-23.

Stokoe, William C. 1972. *Semiotics and Human Sign Language: Approaches to Semiotics* 12. The Hague: Mouton.

Straight, Stephen. 1976. "Comprehension Versus Production in Linguistic Theory". *Foundations of Language* 14.525-40.

Strange, W., R. Verbrugge, D. Shankweiler, and T. Edman. 1976 "Consonant Environtment Specifies Vowel Identity". *Journal of the Acoustical Society of America* 60.213-24.

Sulin, R., and James Dooling. 1974. "Intrusion of a Thematic Idea in Retention of Prose". *Journal of Experimental Psychology* 103.255-62.

Suls, J.M., and R.W. Weisberg. 1970. "Processing of Syntactically Ambiguous Sentences". *Journal of Experimental Psychology* 86.112-14.

Swinney, D.A., and D.T. Hakes. 1976. "Effects of Prior Content Upon Lexical Access Sentence Comprehension". *Journal of Verbal Learning and Verbal Behavior* 15.681-89.

Tannenbaum, P., F. Williams, and C. Hillier. 1965. "Word Predictability in the Environments of Hesitations". *Journal of Verbal Learning and Verbal Behavior* 4.134-40.

Thorndike, E.L. 1946. "The Psychology of Semantics". *American Journal of Psychology* 59.613-32.

Townsend, John T. 1971."Theoretical Analysis of an Alphabetic Confusion Matrix". *Perception and Psychophysics* 9.40-50.

Trubetzkoy, N.S. 1969. *Principles of Phonology* Translated by C.A.M. Baltaxe. Berkeley: University of California Press.

Tulving, E. 1962. "Subjective Organization in the Free Recall of Unrelated Words". *Psychological Review* 76.282-99.

Tulving, E., and S. Osler. 1968. "Effectiveness of Retrieval Cues in Memory". *Journal of Experimental Psychology* 77.593-601.

Tulving, E., and D. Thomson. 1971. "Retrieval Processes in Recognition Memory: Effects of Associative Context". *Journal of Experimental Psychology* 87.116-24.

Tyler, L.K., and W.D. Marslen-Wilson. 1977. "The On-line Effects of Semantic Content on Syntactic Processing". *Journal of Verbal Learning and Verbal Behavior* 16.683-92.

Underwood, B. 1966. *Experimental Psychology.* New York: Appleton-Century-Crofts.

Valian, Virginia. 1976. "The Relationship Between Competence and Performance: A Theoretical Review". *CUNY Forum* 1.64-101.

Verbrugge, R., W. Strange, and D.P. Shankweiler. 1976. "What Information Enables a Listener to Map a Talker's Vowel Space". *Journal of the Acoustical Society of America* 60. 198-212.

von Kempelen, Wolfgang. 1791. *Mechanismus der menschlichen Sprache nebst Beschreibung einer sprechenden Maschine.* Vienna: J. B. Degen. (Facs.-repr., Stuttgart-Bad Cannstatt, 1970.)

Watt, William C. 1970. "On Two Hypotheses Concerning Psycholinguistics". *Cognition and Development of Language* ed. by J.R. Hayes. New York: Wiley.

Watt, William C. 1973. "Late Lexicalizations". *Approaches to Natural Language* ed. by J.M.E. Moravscik and P. Suppes. Dordrecht: Reidel.

Watt, William C. 1974a. "Competing Economy Criteria". *Problèmes actuels de la psycholinguistique* ed. by F. Bresson. Paris: Centre National de la Recherche Scientifique.

Watt, William C. 1974b. "Mentalism in Linguistics, II". *Glossa* 8.3-40.

Watt, W.C., and D. Jacobs. 1975. "The Child's Conception of the Alphabet. *1975 Yearbook* Claremont Reading Conference.

White, L. 1977. "Some Proposals for a "Narrow" Theory of Language Acquisition and its Interaction With a Theory of Grammar". *Montreal Working Papers in Linguistics* 9.241-66.

Wilkes, A. 1975. "Encoding Processes and Pausing Behavior". *Studies in Long Term Memory* ed. by A. Kennedy and A. Wilkes New York: Wiley.

Wisher, R. 1976. "The Effects of Syntactic Expectations During Reading". *Journal of Educational Psychology* 68.597-602.

Yuille, J., and A. Paivio. 1969. "Abstractness and Recall of Connected Discourse". *Journal of Experimental Psychology* 82.467-71.

Zwicky, Arnold M., and Jerrold M. Saddock. 1975. "Ambiguity Tests and How to Fail Them". *Syntax and Semantics* 4.1-36.

INDEX OF AUTHORS

* * * * *

INDEX OF SUBJECTS